CONTRIBUTIONS TO MATHEMATICAL PSYCHOLOGY

The Thurstone Hall Dedication Conference

CONTRIBUTIONS TO MATHEMATICAL PSYCHOLOGY

Editors

Norman Frederiksen   *Harold Gulliksen*

with chapters by

ROBERT P. ABELSON   CLYDE H. COOMBS

J. P. GUILFORD   HAROLD GULLIKSEN

PAUL HORST   LEDYARD R TUCKER

DOROTHY C. ADKINS

HOLT, RINEHART AND WINSTON, INC.

NEW YORK · CHICAGO · SAN FRANCISCO · TORONTO · LONDON 1964

PREFACE

The Educational Testing Service, in the spring of 1962, dedicated a new building, naming it in honor of the late Louis Leon Thurstone. In the ceremonies marking the dedication of the building, Henry Chauncey, President of Educational Testing Service, said:

"Louis Leon Thurstone was a pioneer in the field of psychometrics and one of the outstanding figures in the entire history of psychology. His influence on the course of development at ETS, particularly our research program, was very great. He contributed directly by his many invaluable suggestions as a member of our Research Advisory Committee, on which he served from the time ETS was established until his death. Even more important, his students, and the students of his students, have done a major share of the research over the past fifteen years and will continue to do so for many years to come. It is with gratitude, admiration, and affection, and in a spirit of humility and dedication, that we name this building Louis Leon Thurstone Hall."

The Thurstone Hall dedication was marked by a conference on Contributions to Mathematical Psychology, at which papers were presented dealing with problems in areas where Professor Thurstone made pioneering contributions. Speakers were chosen not only because of the quality and importance of their work, but also because their contributions are quite directly traceable to

Thurstone's influence. Four of the speakers were Thurstone's students at the University of Chicago, one was a student of a student of Thurstone, and two were Thurstone's students in all but a formal sense. This volume contains the papers that were presented to an audience of about a hundred scholars at the Dedication Conference.

The first paper deals with the life and scientific contributions of L. L. Thurstone; it was printed in the form of a brochure and distributed at the time of the conference. This biographical paper was written by Dorothy C. Adkins, who also prepared the complete bibliography of Thurstone's published works that follows her chapter.

The committee appointed by Mr. Chauncey to plan the conference consisted of Anna Dragositz, John W. French, Harold Gulliksen, William B. Schrader, Catherine G. Sharp, Ledyard R Tucker, and Norman Frederiksen, who served as chairman. The tactical and logistic problems of the conference were ably handled by Frances M. Ottobre and Sara B. Matlack. Acknowledgment is also made of the careful work of Mrs. Matlack and Ann King in preparing the manuscript for publication.

March, 1964

Norman Frederiksen
Harold Gulliksen

CONTENTS

CONTRIBUTIONS TO MATHEMATICAL PSYCHOLOGY

The Thurstone Hall Dedication Conference

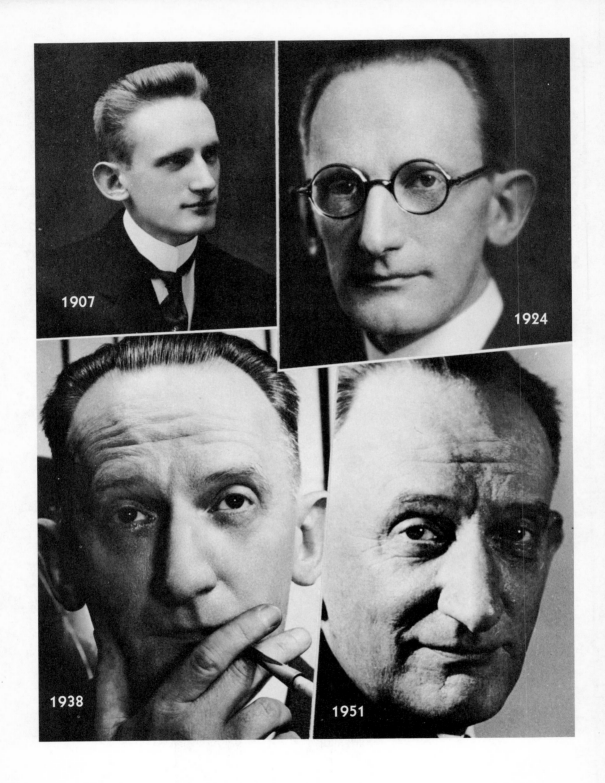

1907 — Upon high-school graduation (*Nelson Brothers*, Jamestown, N. Y.); 1924 — Upon appointment to the faculty of the University of Chicago (*Harris and Ewing*, Washington, D. C.); 1938 — Courtesy of Kenneth Heilbron of *Time* magazine; 1951 — Courtesy of Carl Davis, a personal friend of the Thurstones

1

LOUIS LEON THURSTONE: CREATIVE THINKER, DEDICATED TEACHER, EMINENT PSYCHOLOGIST

Dorothy C. Adkins
University of North Carolina

ACKNOWLEDGMENTS

In the preparation of the biographical sketch that follows, I am gratefully indebted to Louis Leon Thurstone, whose many scientific accomplishments have provided abundant subject matter from which to choose. Especially helpful was an autobiography, which has already appeared in condensed form (173).*

Professor Thurstone's wife and collaborator, Thelma Gwinn Thurstone, kindly made available to me the original manuscript. She also offered assistance in many other ways — by permitting me to use a complete file of her husband's publications, by assembling the bibliography,** and by reviewing the manuscript prior to publication.

Lyle V. Jones, formerly Professor Thurstone's collaborator at the University of Chicago and later Director of the Psychometric Laboratory at the University of North Carolina, offered numerous suggestions for clarification, for which I express my appreciation.

Finally, I wish to thank many staff members of the Educational Testing Service, notably Norman Frederiksen, Director of Research, and his colleagues, who helped me in the preparation of the manuscript for publication.

*The numbers in parentheses refer to the titles listed in Section A of the Bibliography at the end of this chapter.

**The author believes that this bibliography is complete. Section A is a serially numbered list of 188 books, monographs, and articles published by Thurstone between the years 1908 and 1957. Section B includes reports on the American Council on Education Psychological Examinations, titles of tests, Psychometric Laboratory Reports from both the University of Chicago and the University of North Carolina, and microfilms available from the library of the University of Chicago or the Library of Congress. The total number of items in both sections of the bibliography is 372.

1 LOUIS LEON THURSTONE: CREATIVE THINKER, DEDICATED TEACHER, EMINENT PSYCHOLOGIST

Louis Leon Thurstone, one of the world's creative psychologists who was to become widely acclaimed as the most eminent psychometrician of his time, was born in Chicago, Illinois, on May 29, 1887. He was the son of Conrad and Sophie Stroth Thurstone, both of whom had been born in Sweden. The family name, originally Thünström, was changed to Thurstone because it was so frequently mispronounced and misspelled.

Conrad Thurstone joined the Swedish army and acquired the educational background necessary to enable him to teach mathematics and fortifications. Later he became a Lutheran minister, a newspaper editor, and a publisher.

EARLY EDUCATION

As a youth, Leon Thurstone attended schools in Chicago and Berwyn, Illinois; Centerville, Mississippi; both a public school and a boys' school in Stockholm, Sweden; and finally an elementary and a high school in Jamestown, New York, where his family moved from Stockholm in 1901.

His mother, who had an excellent voice and a strong interest in music, saw that both the boy and his younger sister, Adele, were exposed to the piano at early ages. Adele persisted and earned a Bachelor of Music degree. Leon in his high-school years was fascinated by a course in harmony and occasionally experimented with musical composition. Although he discontinued formal study, his interest in, and fine appreciation for, classical music were retained.

When he was eight years old, the youth Thurstone was transplanted to Stockholm, where he was a foreigner among his classmates. Upon his return to the United States at the age of 14, he was again cast in this role. He later remarked that, disturbing as this sequence of experiences was to him, it nonetheless probably contributed to an attitude of objectivity. In Sweden, he had observed that all of the heroes of episodes narrated in history textbooks were Swedes, whereas upon his return to the United States he similarly noted that all of the historians' plaudits were showered upon Americans. This seeming lack of objectivity in the recital of history doubtless fostered his interest in certain areas of social psychology in which he believed a subjective approach was a deterrent to scientific progress.

Having lived in Stockholm and having attended schools where he was only occasionally exposed to spoken English — and that with a British accent — he acquired facility in the Swedish language which he retained to a remarkable degree in later life. When he returned to this country, his first ambition was to regain mastery of English. He has told how he sometimes spent an entire hour with a tutor practicing a single sentence or even a particular word. Anyone who heard him speak or who was exposed to his lucid prose could only marvel at the efficacy of his diligence in this direction.

While in high school, Leon elected a course in sketching and charcoal. He received a cash award in the Prendergast competition in geometry, using the money to purchase a bicycle and a box camera. These events were forerunners of his strong interest in photography, which was always his principal hobby and in which he displayed noteworthy skill, especially in composition. This high-school boy also had mastered three typewriter keyboards — one on an old Caligraph typewriter, one the standard keyboard on his father's Williams typewriter, and one on a Simplex typesetting machine. This feat seems quite remarkable in a day when command of a single keyboard seems to be a signal accomplishment.

At the age of 14, an impasse occurred when Leon declined to learn the catechism in the face of his father's expectations that he would be confirmed in the Lutheran church. The final compromise solution was that he would be permitted to choose three questions to which he was willing to learn the answers. Of course he had to read the entire catechism in order to be able to make his selection, so he has admitted somewhat ruefully that his seniors really won the case.

As the time for graduation from Jamestown High School approached, Leon requested private audience with the principal. Concerned with the requirement that each senior present a five-minute talk to the school assembly — a group of several hundred students — he announced that he would never attempt such an ordeal and that the principal could prevent his graduation if this were the only possible solution. Faced with such a decision, the principal allowed an exception, one that was to prove influential in the development of twentieth-century psychology.

Not until five years later, when he approached his first teaching assignment, did Leon ever address an audience. In citing this incident, he later commented, surely with tongue in cheek: "I admire especially the abilities of men who can address an audience graciously even when they have nothing definite to say, because that has always been beyond me."

His first publication was a letter to the *Scientific American*, written when he was a high-school sophomore (24). The hydroelectric power companies at Niagara Falls had been accused of diverting so much water to their power plants that the beauty of the falls was impaired. He proposed a simple solution to the conflict that he argued would provide for ample power and at the same time preserve the tourist attraction. Thurstone the engineer was beginning to emerge.

Another high-school experience may have influenced his later interests. The New York State Regents system provided uniform high-school achievement examinations throughout the entire state, and this applied to his own high school in Jamestown. Thurstone attributed his later concern with problems of large-scale educational and psychological measurement, as for example those dealt with by the Educational Testing Service, to his early exposure to that testing program.

Dorothy C. Adkins / 4

As a high-school sophomore, Leon developed a French curve that could be used with a straightedge for trisecting any angle. Later, as a college freshman, he wrote the equation for the solution (which of course was not within the restrictions of Euclidean geometry). This constituted his second publication, which also appeared in *Scientific American* (25).

ENGINEERING TRAINING

At Cornell University, which Thurstone entered in 1908, he began training in civil engineering but later changed to electrical engineering. That he did not choose physics is probably fortunate for the psychological world, for it is possible that he might have persisted in it. He did do some experimental work with one of the physics instructors and also began to work on a design for a motion-picture camera and projector. Every point on the screen was continually lighted so that there was no dark interval or flicker. The machine was built and demonstrated several years later.

Through a course in machine design, Thurstone became fascinated with the psychological aspects of visual-motor coordination. As an outgrowth of this interest, he suggested a number of improvements in early models of desk calculating machines, which were adopted. He always regarded the application of psychological considerations to machine design as an important field.

As a college student, he was sensitive to the general ineptness of many teachers. In his senior year we find him producing a sophisticated editorial for the *Sibley Engineering Journal*, of which he was editor-in-chief, concerned with the efficiency of teaching in the College of Engineering (26). Undoubtedly this interest was primarily responsible for his movement into psychology, for his early concentration in this field was related to the learning process. Even while he was still studying engineering, he was curious as to the amenability of the learning function to scientific study and attended lectures by such psychologists as Bentley and Titchener.

Shortly before his college graduation, Thurstone was able to arrange to demonstrate his model motion-picture projector, which in the meantime had been patented, in the laboratory of Thomas A. Edison in East Orange, New Jersey. Edison and his staff regarded the model with considerable favor but decided against producing it because of the necessary retooling that such a change would have required. Edison did, however, offer the young inventor an assistantship in his laboratory, an activity that Thurstone pursued after having received his degree in mechanical engineering. In daily encounters with Edison, Thurstone was impressed by his tremendous fluency of ideas, reporting that for every failure he immediately had several new ideas to be explored. This unusual opportunity for close association with genius at work probably played some part in Thurstone's later interest in the general question of creativity and, more directly, in his development of tests of ideational fluency.

FIRST ACADEMIC POST

Seeking a return to an academic setting, the young graduate engineer in the fall of 1912 began teaching descriptive geometry and drafting in the College of Engineering at the University of Minnesota. He was at once impressed by the great individual differences in the ability to visualize evidenced among his students in descriptive geometry. This observation was a precursor to his development of tests to measure differences in spatial abilities.

In the course of his teaching, Thurstone constructed some wire models to illustrate the principles of projection and rotation. He also observed wide differences in students' abilities to learn free-hand lettering and developed a formal procedure for teaching it by applying the principles of the Pahlman system of teaching handwriting, to which he had been exposed in Sweden. A lettering book that he prepared was printed by a Chicago publisher (2), but he characteristically notes that he never had any reports as to whether or not any of the books were sold.

THE SHIFT TO PSYCHOLOGY

Thurstone became more curious about the experimental study of learning while still at Minnesota and obtained some instruction in psychology from Herbert Woodrow and J. B. Miner. Two years later, in the summer of 1914, he enrolled for graduate study in psychology at the University of Chicago. Reporting on his formal induction to this field, Thurstone has written as follows (173, p. 300): "I recall one of my first impressions of graduate students of psychology. When they were asked a question, they would start to talk fluently, even when they obviously knew nothing about the subject. [Thus, just as Edison may have suggested the factor of ideational fluency to him, perhaps it was the psychology student who stimulated the idea of verbal fluency.] . . . One of my first courses was called advanced educational psychology . . . I used to wonder what the elementary course could be like if the course that I was taking was called 'advanced.' I soon became accustomed to the fact that prerequisites did not mean anything and that there was no real sequence of courses in psychology, even though they were listed by number and title to give the appearance of a sequence . . . I never had an elementary course in psychology or in statistics."

In his early work in psychology Thurstone concentrated on problems for which some kind of continuous function might be discovered to describe psychological effects. He turned to the learning function as a thesis topic and fitted a hyperbola with two parameters to the typewriter learning record of each subject (3). One parameter, the asymptote, was interpreted as the physiological limit. The other represented the rate at which the limit was approached. Thurstone has commented that the hyperbola was nothing but a simple empirical equation and that an engineering sophomore could have done as well. He had minored in education because of his strong interest in teaching and learning, but he remarked upon the trivial and dull nature of courses in education.

Applied Psychology at Carnegie Institute of Technology

Having been deferred from the draft in World War I, while still a graduate student Thurstone accepted an assistantship in Walter V. Bingham's newly established Division of Applied Psychology at the Carnegie Institute of Technology. This work, although oriented primarily toward the applications of psychology, also seemed to provide an opportunity for theoretical interests. Thurstone continued at Carnegie Institute, after receiving his doctorate from Chicago, until he became a full professor and chairman of the Department of Psychology.

The work at Carnegie Institute clearly was at the forefront of applied psychology, and especially of the intensive development of psychological tests. One important problem was to overcome irrational arguments against objective testing, such as that it was absurd for a clerk to score an examination in a subject he knew nothing about. The many varieties of tests developed at Carnegie Institute in attempts to predict scholarship and vocational success almost certainly must have influenced Thurstone's later impatience with a single over-all index of general intelligence, which he has referred to as "a hodge-podge of unknown abilities combined at unknown weights." In the early days at the Institute, tests for various cognitive functions, including visualization and word fluency, were being developed. Even then the seeds were being sown for the later development of the fruitful concept of primary mental abilities, together with the penetrating approach to the study of test performance known as multiple-factor analysis.

With the onset of World War I, the Carnegie objective tests were made available for use by the Army. Thurstone was assigned to work on oral trade tests in Newark, and initiated the "keyword" principle, whereby a response that includes any of a number of specified key words is counted as correct. This device permitted the administration and scoring of tests in various trades by persons themselves unfamiliar with the work in question. Later, during mobilization for World War II, Thurstone made available to military establishments countless tests produced in his laboratory. Throughout this period, he served as a member of the Committee on Classification of Military Personnel in the Office of the Adjutant General.

While at Carnegie Institute, Thurstone wrote *The Fundamentals of Statistics* (7), for use in self-defense, as he says, when offering a course for women in the Research Bureau for Retail Training. He purposely limited his treatment to the simple rudiments. Later he often disparaged it, because of its omissions of qualifications and reservations that had become commonplace. Nonetheless, many students for whom this little book constituted their introduction to statistics have had reason to be grateful that it made the subject seem quite easy and thus did not intimidate them. Perhaps all statistics texts should be written for women bent upon a career in retailing.

At Carnegie Institute also was written a monograph on *The Nature of Intelligence* (5), which reportedly grew out of ideas initiated by Professor Mead's lectures at Chicago in what was then known as social psychology. Thurstone himself has said that he never read a textbook summary of the ideas in this monograph that he could understand. Perhaps a fresh look may be illuminating. The author was trying to reconcile the disparities between the point of view implied in abnormal psychology and psychiatry that action begins in the person himself and the stress upon various features of the stimulus-response sequence to the neglect of the person. In a previous paper on "The Stimulus-Response Fallacy in Psychology" (54), he had argued for replacement of the sequence "stimulus — person — behavior" by the sequence "person — stimulus — behavior." In a still earlier article, "The Anticipatory Aspect of Consciousness" (39), he had developed the theme that a concept is an unfinished act which points toward a type of adjustment.

In this monograph, he advanced these ideas, his main thesis being that mental life is action in the process of being formulated and that the several cognitive categories should be interpreted as differing mainly in the degree of completion of the act. Upon pursuing to its limits the assumption that conduct originates in the person, he concluded that intelligence is the "capacity to live a trial-and-error existence with alternatives that are as yet only incomplete conduct" (5, p. xv). In reaching this point of view, Thurstone observed the overt trial and error, randomly determined, of lower forms of animals. He then analyzed, in turn, perceptual, ideational, and conceptual trial and error. "Intelligent conduct implies the inhibition of a motive at an undefined stage in order to make it focal in its incomplete form." (5, p. 122.)

This analysis still seems instructive and is appropriately regarded as a forerunner of much later discussions of implicit trial-and-error behavior. In fact, in many ways it is a more complete treatment than those that have followed.

Applied Psychological Work in Washington

Early in 1923, Thurstone left Carnegie Institute for Washington to help the foundation-supported Institute for Government Research in some inquiries into methods of selecting civil service personnel. His task was to prepare instructional manuals and specimen materials that would assist civil service agencies in learning to use the new objective examining devices. Once again this scholarly man was quite willing to work upon the application of his knowledge, skill, and ideas to very practical problems.

During his period in Washington, he discussed with friends in the Department of the Navy the possibility of investigating the problem of learning during sleep. This may well have been a novel idea as applied to adult subjects for the purpose of developing mastery of definite skills or subject matter. In any case, Thurstone was encouraged to conduct some experimentation on the learning of the Morse code. An instructor presented code associations at night while the subjects were asleep, alternating practice with no-practice periods every half-hour. The class in Washington completed the course in record time, and a more controlled experiment was begun at Hampton Roads. Unfortunately for science, however, the instructors of the control group feared that their teaching efficiency was under surveillance. Hence they apparently provided several hours of additional practice per day to the control group.

The experiment failed. The experimenter, nevertheless, learned an important lesson about the conduct of psychological experiments in government or industrial settings: The planner of an investigation must be assured that the persons who actually carry out the work and collect the raw data themselves understand explicitly the procedures to be followed and are able and willing to participate objectively. Although Thurstone never returned to any further controlled experimentation in the field of sleep learning, he continued to believe that it might be a profitable and interesting field for study.

While in Washington, he became acquainted with C. R. Mann, the Director of the American Council on Education, who proposed that he prepare a psychological test to be used in selecting or classifying college students. This assignment he undertook with the assistance of Thelma Gwinn, who also had joined the staff of the Institute for Government Research. Together they were responsible for the editing of 24 successive annual editions of the *American Council on Education Psychological Examination*, an achievement that occasionally led Mr. Thurstone to deplore his lack of business acumen.

CONTRIBUTIONS TO TEST THEORY

In the summer of 1924, Leon and his co-worker, Thelma, were married. They returned to Chicago, where he had been appointed Associate Professor of Psychology at the University of Chicago. Here he taught a course in descriptive statistics; but the principal challenge was a course in mental test theory, an area greatly in need of organization at that time. Because teaching in this field was based mainly upon test manuals and was devoted principally to details of the Stanford-Binet test, and because mental test work enjoyed very low prestige, Thurstone was strongly motivated to get to the heart of basic problems in psychological measurement.

Scrutiny of various educational scales revealed their underlying assumption that the distributions of scores for various age groups differed only with respect to the mean. In order to improve the quantitative description of general intelligence, Thurstone decided to permit two parameters to vary for different age groups, the mean and the dispersion. Thence appeared in 1925 his first paper on measurement theory, presenting a scaling method for psychological tests (66). This he regarded as one of his best articles.

Soon thereafter, he blasted the foundation from under the mental-age concept (69), a feat that has yet to come to the attention of many of our friends who worship at the altar of the I.Q. In the same year, he proposed that an appropriate test score would be the value exceeded by as many successes as there are failures below it, thus allowing for some errors due to distractibility rather than lack of ability (70).

Somewhat later, noting that the relation between mean-scaled score and standard deviation for each age group for some particular test data was linear, he extrapolated the line until it reached zero dispersion. (This may be regarded as an example of serendipity, because Thurstone had not requested his research assistant to make the plot in question.) The ingenious reasoning was that the point on a scale at which variability of test performance becomes zero can be regarded as a rational origin. For several scaled tests, this line of attack yielded an origin at a few months before birth (83). Having a method for scaling test data with a check on internal consistency and for locating a rational origin, he turned to the construction of a mental growth curve (90). His conclusion was that the growth curve is S-shaped. He entertained some doubts, however, as to the location of the inflection point, believing that it might vary with different levels of intelligence.

Through a part-time affiliation with the Institute for Juvenile Research in Chicago, Thurstone was able to place Richard Jenkins, later Director of the Institute, on a research assistantship. They collaborated on a monograph on the problem of intelligence in relation to age of parents and birth order, which was published in 1931 (10).

The lack of a textbook on mental test theory was finally met by a lithoprinted book, entitled *The Reliability and Validity of Tests*, published in the same year (9). This book clearly was much more needed elsewhere than its author had anticipated, for a demand persisted long after it had been out of print. In later years, Thurstone had planned its revision into an elementary textbook, but this project was not completed.

In 1937 appeared a paper with a fresh slant on the problem of speed versus power in the appraisal of intelligence (125). The central idea of Thurstone's 1919 work on the anticipatory aspect of consciousness (39) recurs in a speech on creative talent, which he wanted to distinguish from lesson-learning ability and scholarship. This paper, delivered at the 1950 Invitational Conference on Testing Problems, also contained some leads on experimental investigations of the problem of creative talent (175).

DEVELOPMENT OF PSYCHOPHYSICAL METHODS

Thurstone himself regarded as his best contribution to psychological theory his initial paper in the field of subjective measurement, "Psychophysical Analysis," which appeared in 1927 (73). Here he first tackled the problem of how to deal with a subjective unit of measurement and with stimuli unrelated to any ordinary physical dimensions. In presenting the older psychophysical methods to students, he had found it dull to deal with comparisons of pairs of weights. Instead, he had asked which of two nationalities was preferred or which of two offenses was the more serious, for example. The proportion of subjects who preferred stimulus j to stimulus k was tabulated for all stimuli. The problem then was to explore whether a rational theory could be developed to fit the observed proportions. Introducing the concept of the discriminal dispersion, Thurstone inventively formulated the equation of comparative judgment.

A penetrating series of additional articles dealing with subjective measurement was forthcoming in this highly productive period, six more articles being published in 1927 (71, 72, 74, 75, 76, 77). In these articles Thurstone further developed the new approach to psychological measurement, related the law of comparative judgment to previous concepts such as Weber's law and Fechner's law, and illustrated the application of the new law to the measurement of social values. In later papers, he examined the inconsistency of the phi-gamma hypothesis with Weber's law (85), some of the limitations of the method of equal-appearing intervals (89), the use of the method of rank order as a substitute for the more laborious method of paired comparisons in the collection of data (103), and the problem of the numerical evaluation of the dispersions of stimuli presented by the constant method (109).

These early papers assumed a unidimensional subjective continuum but contained tests for the adequacy of this assumption. Thurstone soon recognized that some psychological problems are concerned with a multidimensional domain. Later extensions of the experimental methodology and analytical procedures to cover this case have proved feasible, as is of course well known.

As an outgrowth of conversations with a mathematical economist, Henry Schultz, Thurstone developed an interest in the applicability of psychological measurement concepts to problems in economics. In a 1931 article on "The Indifference Function" (102), the satisfaction that the owner of a specified quantity of a commodity derives was treated as measurable in terms of the subjective unit of measurement, the discriminal error. The equation for the indifference curve was based upon the psychological postulate that motivation toward accretion of a commodity is inversely proportional to the amount already possessed. Several of his later formulations of measurement theory and methods seem to have sprung from this early venture into economics. In Chapel Hill, for example, where he went in 1952, he continued to work with his former collaborator, Lyle V. Jones, on the experimental determination of the zero point in a scale of utility and was able to demonstrate that subjective values are additive. This was accomplished by locating an origin in such a way that the sum of the scale values for two stimuli is equal to the scale value of the combination of the two stimuli (188).

In the meantime, the obverse psychophysical problem of the prediction of choice had engaged Thurstone's attention. Previously, the chief concern had been with allocating each psychological object to a point in a subjective space. Given the scale parameters for a set of objects, the obverse problem is to predict their relative popularity when subjects are presented with a choice of one among the set. The general notion was to examine the effects of the discriminal dispersion upon prediction of choice. In a 1945 paper (143), he demonstrated that the dispersion of affective values, as well as the average affective value of a proposal, is significant in the measurement of social attitudes of a group. Still later, the techniques for the prediction of choice, using the method of successive intervals, were applied to the prediction of menu selections (165, 170, 176).

Constantly seeking improved methods, Thurstone in the 1950's was still investigating several new approaches to the subjective metric. A new scaling method was derived to escape the assumption of normality of the subjective distribution for each stimulus. The less restrictive assumption that repeated judgments by the same individual will be normally distributed on the subjective continuum was explored (182, 183).

A 1954 paper, "The Measurement of Values," provides an edifying review of fundamental concepts of subjective measurement, presented with the enlightened perspective that only a lifetime of thinking and working could have developed (179).

THE MEASUREMENT OF ATTITUDES

The most widely popularized application of Thurstonian methods to the study of subjective values has been in the measurement of social attitudes, where physical stimulus measurement is irrelevant. Hence this development will be traced briefly, apart from the main stream of psychophysical research that flowed from the Psychometric Laboratory at the University of Chicago. An article appearing in 1928 with the challenging title, "Attitudes Can Be Measured" (80), gives the assumptions and an outline of the method of equal-appearing intervals for the construction of an attitude scale. In the same year another method was offered for the derivation of a rational base line for describing the distribution of opinion, such that equal intervals on the scale represent equal-appearing opinion differences (82). The unit of the scale was the discriminal dispersion of the statements. Still a third paper applied the method of paired comparisons and the law of comparative judgment to a study of nationality preferences (84). In 1929 came the monograph, *The Measurement of Attitude*, coauthored with E. J. Chave, which described in detail the application of measurement techniques to attitudes toward the church (8). Thurstone regarded the method of paired comparisons as a far more sensitive method for appraising attitudes than the statement scales, but noted that the former is not so generally applicable to social issues.

In a 1929 paper, "Theory of Attitude Measurement" (88), Thurstone also described the method of similar reactions. The degree of similarity of attributes, or the extent to which they coexist in the same individual, is measured in terms of the Φ coefficient, which permits the allocation of the attributes along a continuum. Thurstone's 1931 presidential address to the Midwestern Psychological Association soon thereafter covered developments to that date in the field of attitude measurement (107). Much of this work, which was financed by the Payne Fund, was treated in a lithoprinted monograph and later comprised a portion of a book (112).

Although it seems to have had no formal inauguration, perhaps for historical purposes Thurstone's Psychometric Laboratory at the University of Chicago may be considered to have been launched at the time he moved his office and staff to the Social Science Research Building at 1126 East 59th Street. This was in the spring of 1930, at a time when he was encountering great interest in the application of attitude scales to many issues and to all sorts of groups. He soon became disenchanted, however, with the relative lack of concern for the methodological problems which to him constituted the significant issues. With a growing realization that his laboratory might be swamped by the relatively trivial applications of attitude measurement techniques, he abandoned this field to clear the path for the development of multiple-factor analysis.

Thurstone sporadically reverted to problems that could be regarded as falling within the general area of social psychology, such as the use of obverse factor analysis to describe voting records of Supreme Court judges (171) and the application of psychophysical concepts to the study of the growth of a social group (University of Chicago Psychometric Laboratory Report No. 74). But social-psychological content did not return to dominate the Psychometric Laboratory as it had been threatening to do in the heyday of attitude scale construction.

MULTIPLE-FACTOR ANALYSIS

Although Thurstone was most pleased with his success in breathing life into psychophysics — an evaluation in which later historians may concur — probably his productive work in multiple-factor analysis was accorded more attention in his lifetime. As long ago as 1922 he had made a note on the original observation equation, but he did not return to it until seven years later. Even then, other commitments prevented his giving full attention to the problem for another year or so. Early efforts were supported by annual grants from the Social Science Research Committee at the University of Chicago and by the Carnegie Corporation. When he saw that further special grants would be needed, he approached the Carnegie Corporation with a request for funds to develop what he called multiple-factor analysis, making clear that he could provide no assurance that the big gamble he proposed would be successful. The initial award of $5000 was followed by several others, to be sure. Its size, however, might indeed give pause to the unseasoned research worker of today who glibly and confidently requests a grant of $200,000 or more for a couple of years of inquiry into some limited area.

At many points the career of Thurstone reveals the value of the cross-fertilization of ideas between different disciplines. While at lunch one day with two University of Chicago colleagues, a mathematician and an astronomer, he asked a question about some arithmetical operations that he was performing with rectangular arrays of numbers. They told him that he was extracting the root of a matrix and referred his curiosity about matrices to another mathematician. He then sought tutelage in the elements of matrix algebra. Anyone who has looked at the mathematical introduction to *The Vectors of Mind* (15) or *Multiple-Factor Analysis* (21) will attest to the success of this digression. Later, one of these same colleagues helped him to state the question he was trying to solve in developing the principal-axes solution, which turned out to be an old problem in celestial mechanics that he had previously encountered in theoretical mechanics.

Impatient with the long-standing debate on Spearman's single-factor method, the universality of a general factor, and the role of group factors, Thurstone hit upon the expedient of restructuring the basic question. Instead of asking whether a table of correlation coefficients supported a general factor, he wondered how many factors must be postulated in order to account for the observed correlations. The power of this approach was that whether or not one factor should be regarded as general could be answered factually for each study.

In view of the still widespread preoccupation with the problem of a general factor in the early thirties, he at one time set out to investigate the relation of his multiple-factor approach to Spearman's method. Having jotted down the tetrad difference equation on a piece of paper, he at once saw that it represented the expansion of a second-order minor. He related this insight to the principle that the highest order of the nonvanishing minors indicates the rank and hence the number of linearly independent factors represented in a correlation matrix. Once again it is evident that a part of Thurstone's genius lay in his ability to recast problems into a form that pointed to their solution.

His excursions into multiple-factor analysis led to several additional extensions of the earlier approach. These include the concept of communalities, the notion of rotation of the reference frame, the use of oblique reference axes, the principle of factorial invariance, and the highly significant idea of simple structure. This keen solution to the problem presented by the infinite number of possible positions of the reference axes may indeed be Thurstone's most noteworthy single contribution to factor analysis. Other methodological ideas were concerned with second-order factors and studies on the effects of selection upon factorial structure.

Among the criticisms to which the new approaches to factor analysis were subjected has been their lack of concern with such statistical niceties as the standard error of a factor loading. In his early publication on elementary statistics, Thurstone had written (7, p. 165): "Throughout the study of the probable error, and the other statistical constants that measure reliability or unreliability of statistical measures, one should bear in mind that they give us some indication of the expected degree of fluctuation in successive samples selected in the same way, and that this indication refers to the *least important*[1] of the various causes that disturb the validity of statistical findings, namely, the factor of chance fluctuation."

Consistently enough, Thurstone's interests and energies were focused upon important scientific discoveries, not upon chance fluctuations. He has noted that his emphasis had been on factor analysis as a scientific method as distinguished from the statistical condensation of data, although he regarded the latter as a legitimate problem for study.

His first paper on multiple-factor analysis was published in 1931 (105), and

[1] Author's italics.

a factorial analysis of vocational interests appeared in the same year (106). A booklet, *The Theory of Multiple Factors* (11), and his presidential address to the American Psychological Association, "The Vectors of Mind" (113), were produced in short order. A major book bearing the latter title came out in 1935 (15), and the more extensive revision, *Multiple-Factor Analysis*, was produced in 1947 (21). Several other articles listed in the bibliography also deal with methods of multiple-factor analysis.

Thurstone's developments in this area have not been without controversy, especially those intended to resolve some of the problems of factorial indeterminacy. These include the communality idea, the principle of simple structure, and the use of an oblique reference frame when it is helpful. In the main, it seems fair to say that students and others who have seen these concepts given extensive trial in Thurstone's laboratory or elsewhere, and who have observed the facilitation of interpretations of factorial results that ensues, have been favorably disposed toward their use.

In 1952, Thurstone retired from the University of Chicago and established his Psychometric Laboratory at the University of North Carolina, where he went as its director and as Research Professor of Psychology. Still at the advancing frontiers of factor analysis, he developed an analytical method of rotating the reference axes (181), at about the same time that several other persons began to work on this problem from different angles.

During a plane trip from Stockholm to Helsinki in 1954, Thurstone thought of a new method of factor analysis and proceeded to describe to the author the technique that involves solely the off-diagonal entries in the correlation matrix, thus avoiding the communality problem (184). Although this approach appeared promising, it does not seem to have been developed to any extent as yet.

Applications of Multiple-Factor Analysis

Once the basic techniques of multiple-factor analysis were available, major applications of this powerful approach became concurrent with further refinements of methodology. The first large study entailed the development of a battery of 57 tests of various cognitive functions, which were administered to 240 subjects. A brief report of this work appeared in *Psychometrika* in 1936 (120), and a more complete treatment as *Psychometric Monograph No. 1*, in 1938 (17). This experiment was followed by a number of others, often with the active assistance of Thelma Gwinn Thurstone; several sizeable studies were completed in his laboratory as student dissertations.

As results began to accrue and several factors had been identified in more than one study, an experimental battery of tests of primary mental abilities for use in schools was made available in 1938. The early forms were distributed by the American Council on Education; later, simplified and shortened forms became available from Science Research Associates. In these and many other efforts, Thurstone was fortunate in having the able collaboration of his wife, who was largely responsible for the development of appropriate tests for a factorial study of the abilities of five-year-old children. A new set of tests was based upon this study. It was followed by a series of booklets designed expressly to offer young children training in different primary mental abilities.

The Thurstones came to the opinion that the rejection of the early doctrine of formal discipline had been a mistake. They believed that extensive practice in a certain type of thinking would actually augment the overt performance, to the definite advantage of the individual. This effect could well be so important as to overshadow the appraisal of the native endowment of the individual by stable tests. That problem, they felt, could be solved by the selection of suitably novel material for test purposes.

THE FOUNDING OF PSYCHOMETRIKA

Although Thurstone always insisted upon giving credit to others for the founding of the Psychometric Society and of its journal *Psychometrika*, he was clearly close to the nucleus of 10 or 12 persons who brought them into being in 1936. This group contained several of his former students, but others as well. The psychological journals had been wont to reject manuscripts that contained mathematical notation or to insist that the mathematics be relegated to an appendix or eliminated. Started with a few small loans, the journal has been a financial success almost from its inception. Its purpose was to foster the development of psychology as a quantitative rational science, a goal to which Thurstone truly devoted his professional life. The venture always enjoyed his active support. He was the first president of the society and served for many years as Chairman of the Editorial Council. In the early days, the journal was shipped in bulk by the printer to his office. Its remailing to subscribers constituted an irksome and often harrowing experience.

EXAMINING ACHIEVEMENT AT THE UNIVERSITY OF CHICAGO

In 1931, Thurstone was appointed the first chief of the Board of Examinations of the College at the University of Chicago, a post that he held for some seven years. He initiated several important ideas in the examining procedures. He insisted that the examinations become public property once they had been given, in order to evade the problem of fraternity files. This of course meant that new questions had to be constructed repeatedly, a requirement that doubtless had desirable effects on the curriculum. The identity of the student was not known to the person who assigned the marks, which were determined by inspection of score distributions. Whenever possible, the examinations were objective. The faculty itself was responsible for developing them in collaboration with an examiner on the central examining staff. Many of the teachers became quite skillful in adapting their course content to various types of objective-test items (14).

Thurstone soon came to feel that the practice of determining a mark for a whole year's study in a field on a single comprehensive examination is a mistake. He expressed the opinion that freshmen and sophomores need the assurance and guidance of frequent appraisal of their work, and that instruction is not complete unless the student has considerable contact with an experienced teacher. Even so, he felt that lectures can be very effective when they are well done.

APPROACHES TO PERSONALITY MEASUREMENT

A recurrent interest of Thurstone was in the elusive realm of personality. We see evidence of his early attention to the writings of Freud and other psycho-analytic literature in his early book on *The Nature of Intelligence* (5). Although he felt that the center of psychology lay in this general field, he was unable to invent any experimental leverage for dealing with it. He therefore turned to other problems more amenable to rigorous analysis.

He and Thelma at one time developed a personality schedule patterned after the Woodworth questionnaire (98). In response to demand for it, he arranged for its publication by the University of Chicago Press. He wryly commented that he found that he was still owing the Press money after it had printed some 75,000 copies.

At the request of Beardsley Ruml, Thurstone spent a few months working with Elton Mayo in Philadelphia. He found the experience highly profitable but reported that he was unable to produce a written exposition of Mayo's psychological system.

When David Lenz was introducing the Rorschach test in this country, he and Thurstone discussed the possibility of objectifying the scoring and inter-pretation of the test. The speculation intrigued Thurstone, but his attention was already committed to scaling methods and other problems of test theory.

He returned to this early fascination shortly after World War II. His approach was to attempt to tease out the psychological hypotheses implicit in such tests as the Rorschach and to supplement the list with others related to the diagnostic value of various objective measures. He assembled a set of over 60 tests repre-senting various more or less plausible hypotheses concerning the outcropping of personality traits in objective-test performance. In general, the subjects would be unaware of the examiner's purpose. Many of the tests were projective for the subject but fairly well structured for the examiner. Thurstone felt that testing devices left open at both ends were hopeless for scientific study.

After Thurstone moved to Chapel Hill, he was still very actively intrigued by this area. Perhaps the most interesting objective test of personality he devised was that for color-form preference.

A fairly short temperament schedule was the product of factorial studies of personality questionnaires with many hundreds of items (166, 169). It contained 20 questions for each of seven scores. The schedule was planned for the appraisal of temperamental traits of normal persons who differ widely. A studied attempt was made to avoid terms appropriate only to the psychiatric clinic, not only in the questions asked but also in the terminology used to describe the traits.

The promising work in this field was by no means pursued to its limits.

Thurstone himself regarded the study of objective individual laboratory tests of temperament as one of the most challenging areas for future psychological research.

THURSTONE AS A TEACHER

Students were the lifeblood of Professor Thurstone. In a real sense, he needed to teach. He depended upon students sometimes as a sounding board for new ideas and again as a source of inspiration. But beyond that, he felt an obligation to stimulate and develop new talent. Thurstone's students displayed a marked productivity, probably the result of a kind of mutual selectivity — promising students flocked to him, and he in turn sought them out. The quality of the raw material alone is an insufficient answer, however. Thurstone devoted much time to individual consultation with students, listening to and evaluating their ideas, offering modifications or substitutions as they occurred to him, and generally inciting them in the direction of further creativity. The emphasis in his laboratory was never upon recapitulating results of earlier work but rather upon developing techniques or applying old ones in new contexts. Perhaps the opportunity for close collaboration with Professor Thurstone at the frontiers of research is the most prominent environmental influence in accounting for the eminence of many of his former students.

In his classes and seminars, Thurstone applied two quite different teaching techniques. His regular classroom periods were likely to be devoted to rather highly formalized lectures, exhibiting a masterly organization of subject matter presented with a simplicity bordering on the elegant. Teaching a class was never a haphazard chore for him. No matter how many times he had taught a subject, he clearly demonstrated fresh preparation for each class meeting. He did not want his classes to meet at a very early hour in the morning, but neither did he prefer them in the afternoon. The reason for this was that on a day his class was to meet he never felt quite comfortable about devoting himself to any other work until after he had discharged his responsibility to the class.

When in 1938 he was awarded an appointment as Charles F. Grey Distinguished Service Professor at the University of Chicago, where he had already been made a full professor three years after his original appointment in 1924, he could have been free to relinquish all teaching in order to devote full time to research. The same opportunity was available when Thurstone went to the University of North Carolina. With considerable self-insight, however, he elected in both cases to continue to expend a portion of his energies upon teaching. He profited from students perhaps as much as they gained from him. We thus can understand his attitude that a long commitment to a university appointment allowing full time for research is likely to be sterile for most individuals.

Thurstone also excelled in teaching by the seminar method. Weekly seminars, which were not informal talk sessions, were held at his home. Anyone with an idea was encouraged to present it to the seminar, which typically included several graduate students and faculty members in psychology, mathematical biophysics, or some other field related to mathematics or statistics; and often special visitors. The presentation itself was likely to be quite formal, but it did not have to deal with a completed theory or research project. Any new idea was welcome. Then, over coffee and Swedish rolls, came a more informal period of questions, criticisms, and often fruitful suggestions. Those who had been encouraged to participate in these seminars rarely permitted anything to interfere with their attendance. Some of them may even have designed their own homes to provide a permanent installation of a blackboard, a prominent characteristic of Thurstone living. In the Chapel Hill house is a retractable blackboard that can be available either to the study or to the spacious living room.

Just as Thurstone worked on his lectures to students, so he meticulously wrote complete manuscripts for public speeches. He would have felt that an informal, unprepared talk was an imposition on his audience. If he accepted an invitation to speak — and he did so frequently — his listeners could be assured that he would come prepared. He was generous with his time and displayed a not inconsiderable talent for interpreting psychological concepts to lay groups. For them, too, he was a gifted teacher.

As we have seen, the original interest in experimental approaches to learning and teaching was responsible for Thurstone's shift to psychology from engineering. He did not devote a great amount of time to learning research beyond his dissertation study (3), although two significant articles appeared in 1930: "The Learning Function" (93) and "The Relation between Learning Time and Length of Task" (94). Some of his former students and co-workers have continued to explore the application of quantitative approaches to learning data.

Again, while he did not actively conduct experimental investigations of teaching, he had definite convictions on methodology. He felt, for example, that most teaching was wasteful of time because of an erroneous assumption that extensive class discussion is educative. Thurstone held the belief, rather, that it was the instructor's responsibility to plan lectures and even illustrative examples with scrupulous care. He once said that he had never walked into a classroom without feeling a certain responsibility for as many man-hours as there were students, and never walked out without wondering whether he had succeeded in making it worthwhile for them to have come.

This outstanding teacher also had some revolutionary ideas about curriculum development, especially in relation to psychology. He suggested that a department should itemize all of the ideas, principles, and facts that should be included in the total departmental offerings and then should assemble them in appropriate sequences and groupings to constitute courses. Thus tiresome duplication could be avoided and prerequisites would have meaning. Changes in a course or new offerings would not be introduced without detailed discussion within a department, and new teaching material would be carefully prepared. Thurstone also thought that for graduate courses an effort should be made to reduce to an absolute minimum the amount of reading to be required of students. This strikes one as a refreshing point of view in the face of the preponderant opinion that advanced students should read everything ever written in their field. Thurstone pointed his finger especially at psychology, a field in which he found much of the writing to be expansive and verbose. He argued that the teacher might best summarize such writing in order to conserve student time.

A useful approach might be to apply Thurstone's ideas for curriculum overhaul and teacher preparation to much of the formal graduate teaching that is needed, and then combine it with the more informal seminars and on-the-job research training at which he also excelled. Were we to do this, the time necessary for the ordinary student to complete Ph.D. training could be reduced substantially, or at least expended more profitably.

CONTACTS WITH FOREIGN PSYCHOLOGISTS

Inevitably, a psychologist of Thurstone's achievements attracted the favorable attention of psychologists abroad, and he often referred with pride to the later attainments of foreign students who had come to this country to participate in the activities of his laboratory. Among these students were Charles Wang and E. H. Hsü from China; Mariano Yela from Spain; John Karlin, Melany E. Baehr, and Carol Pemberton, all of whom came from South Africa and later settled here; Nicholas Margineanu, who may still be a political prisoner in Rumania; Jean Cardinet from France; Sten Henrysson from Sweden; Per Saugstad from Norway; and Horace Rimoldi from Argentina. In addition, a number of post-Ph.D. fellows from this country chose the Psychometric Laboratory for a year of study, among these having been Allen L. Edwards, Lyle V. Jones, and J. E. Birren.

Inevitably, too, Thurstone was accorded the opportunity to teach and lecture in foreign countries. In 1948, both he and his wife held appointments as Visiting Professors at the University of Frankfurt. There were also opportunities for visiting lectures at Marburg, Heidelberg, Münster, Paris, and the International Congress of Psychology in Edinburgh; and a full month of lectures and consultation in Sweden.

Again in the spring of 1954, he was appointed Visiting Professor at the University of Stockholm. This trip included a period of several weeks at the Institute for International Research in Education at Frankfurt am Main, Germany; lectures at the University of London, Uppsala, Lund, Göteborg, Oslo, and Helsinki; and a memorable two days with Sir Godfrey and Lady Jennie Thomson in Edinburgh.

After the 1948 visit, Thurstone remarked upon the lack of psychological measurement in Europe, except in the case of the British Isles and Sweden. He was puzzled by the well-nigh universal European psychologists' confidence in graphology. But he commented, again perhaps with tongue in cheek, that this might be a better bet than the American preoccupation with the Rorschach test. Both, he felt, should be regarded as experimental procedures rather than as established techniques to be relied upon in clinics.

One previous return to Europe is worthy of mention — his 1923 attendance at the International Congress of Psychology at Oxford. There he met many of the European psychologists with whom he maintained contact in later years. He was also able to spend a week in Sweden, where he found after two or three days that he could speak Swedish with ease, even after an absence of some 22 years. This same experience was of course repeated on his later visits.

PROFESSIONAL AFFILIATIONS AND RECOGNITION

To Professor Thurstone came almost every honor that a psychologist could hope to achieve. His professional affiliations included the following: the American Psychological Association, of which he was president in 1932; the Division of Evaluation and Measurement of this Association, of which he was president in 1947; the Psychometric Society, which was founded largely by his impetus and of which he was the first president in 1936; the Midwestern Psychological Association, of which he was president in 1930; the Chicago Psychological Club, which elected him president in 1928; the Society for Promotion of Engineering Education, of which he was a Council member; the American Society of Human Genetics, which appointed him to its Advisory Editorial Committee; the American Statistical Association, in which he was on the Board of Directors; the Chaos Club, composed of representatives of several scientific fields in certain midwestern universities; the American Association for the Advancement of Science; the National Academy of Sciences; the American Academy of Arts and Sciences; and the American Philosophical Society. He was also elected Honorary Fellow of the British Psychological Society, of the Spanish Psychological Society, and of the Swedish Psychological Society. He was a member of the Editorial Board of the *Journal of Experimental Psychology* and the Editorial Council and Board of Editors of *Psychometrika*. He was the recipient of a 1949 award from the American Psychological Association for the best article published in any of the Association's journals (157), and in 1951 he received the Centennial Award from Northwestern University. The University of Göteborg granted him an honorary doctorate in 1954.

Leon Thurstone died in Chapel Hill, North Carolina, on September 29, 1955. From this survey of Thurstone's life and scientific activities, one can see that the literature of psychology is so replete with his contributions that it seems he must never have seriously considered a psychological problem without having contributed notably to its solution. He exhibited throughout his productive life a rare ability to capture the imagination of university colleagues and administrators, students, military leaders, industrialists, and representatives of foundations. He displayed a penetrating grasp of new problems and an inventiveness in solving them, a painstaking pursuit of complete solutions to problems, and an infinite degree of skill in imparting ideas to others and in inspiring them, too, toward creative accomplishment.

BIBLIOGRAPHY OF PUBLISHED WORKS
OF L. L. THURSTONE

Section A BOOKS, MONOGRAPHS, AND ARTICLES

Books and Monographs

(1) *Schemes and Precautions for Course in Qualitative Analysis, and the "Double-Oxide" and "Multiple-Equation" Methods of Balancing Equations.* Ithaca, New York: Author, 1908. 20 pp.

(2) *Freehand Lettering.* A course of exercises in single-stroke freehand lettering adapted for classes in mechanical drawing. Chicago: B. D. Berry Company, 1915.

(3) *The Learning Curve Equation.* Princeton, New Jersey: Psychological Review Company, 1919. (Also *Psychological Monographs*, **26,** 1919, No. 114. 51 pp.)

(4) *A Handbook of Clerical Tests.* Baltimore: The Johns Hopkins Press, 1923.

(5) *The Nature of Intelligence.* London: Routledge and Kegan Paul, Ltd.; New York: Harcourt, Brace & World, Inc., 1924. 167 pp.

(6) *Purpose of Psychological Tests.* Scranton, Pennsylvania: International Textbook Company, 1924. 22 pp.

(7) *The Fundamentals of Statistics.* New York: The Macmillan Company, 1925. 237 pp.

(8) (with E. J. Chave) *The Measurement of Attitude.* Chicago: University of Chicago Press, 1929. 97 pp.

(9) *The Reliability and Validity of Tests.* Ann Arbor, Michigan: Edwards Brothers, 1931. 113 pp. (Reprinted 1932 and 1939. Also Microfilm No. 1647, University of Chicago Library, Department of Photographic Reproduction.)

(10) (with Richard L. Jenkins) *Order of Birth, Parent-age, and Intelligence.* Chicago: University of Chicago Press, 1931. 135 pp.

(11) *The Theory of Multiple Factors.* Chicago: Author, 1933. 65 pp. (Also Microfilm No. 1648, University of Chicago Library, Department of Photographic Reproduction.)

(12) *A Simplified Multiple Factor Method and an Outline of the Computations.* Chicago: University of Chicago Bookstore, 1933. 25 pp. (Supplement to *The Theory of Multiple Factors.*)

(13) (with Leone Chesire and Milton Saffir) *Computing Diagrams for the Tetrachoric Correlation Coefficient.* Chicago: Distributed by University of Chicago Bookstore, 1933. 57 pp.

(14) (with M. W. Richardson, J. T. Russell, and J. M. Stalnaker) *Manual of Examination Methods.* Chicago: University of Chicago Bookstore, 1933. 177 pp. (Also Microfilm No. 1979, University of Chicago Library, Department of Photographic Reproduction.)

(15) *The Vectors of Mind.* Chicago: University of Chicago Press, 1935. 266 pp.

(16) (with J. R. Hamilton) *Safe Driving.* New York: Doubleday & Company, Inc., 1937.

(17) Primary Mental Abilities. *Psychometric Monographs*, No. 1. Chicago: University of Chicago Press, 1938. 121 pp. (See also Document 1317, Psychological Tests

Supplement to *Psychometric Monographs*, No. 1, American Documentation Institute, Washington, D.C.)

(18) (with Thelma Gwinn Thurstone) Factorial Studies of Intelligence. *Psychometric Monographs*, No. 2. Chicago: University of Chicago Press, 1941. 94 pp. (See also Document 1434, Psychological Tests Used in a Factorial Study of Eighth-Grade Children, American Documentation Institute, Washington, D.C.)

(19) *Code Aptitude Test*. Chicago: University of Chicago Press, 1944. (Includes reports on the use of the test, 1943–44, at the Naval Training School, University of Chicago.)

(20) A Factorial Study of Perception. *Psychometric Monographs*, No. 4. Chicago: University of Chicago Press, 1944. 148 pp. (Also Microfilm No. 1774, University of Chicago Library, Department of Photographic Reproduction.)

(21) *Multiple-Factor Analysis*. A Development and Expansion of *The Vectors of Mind*. Chicago: University of Chicago Press, 1947. 535 pp.

(22) *Applications of Psychology*. Essays to Honor Walter V. Bingham, ed. L. L. Thurstone. New York: Harper & Row, Publishers, 1952. 209 pp.

(23) *The Measurement of Values*. Chicago: University of Chicago Press, 1959. 322 pp. (A collection of published papers.)

Articles

(24) How to Save Niagara. *Scientific American*, **93,** July 1905, 27.

(25) A Curve which Trisects Any Angle. *Scientific American*, **73,** Supplement 1895, April 1912, 259–261.

(26) The Efficiency Propaganda. *Sibley Journal of Engineering*, April 1912, 262–268.

(27) Character and Temperament. *Psychological Bulletin*, **13,** October 1916, 384–387.

(28) A Statistical Method for the Treatment of School-Survey Data. *School Review*, **25,** May 1917, 322–330.

(29) A Method of Calculating the Pearson Correlation Coefficient without the Use of Deviations. *Psychological Bulletin*, **14,** January 1917, 28–32.

(30) A Notebook: Aid for Interviewers. (Issued by the Adjutant General of the Army for use of personnel officers.) Orange, New Jersey: Trade Test Division of the Committee on Classification of Personnel, 1918.

(31) A Course of Training for Radio Operators. Part II of *Emergency War Training for Radio Mechanics and Radio Operators, Bulletin No. 16*, 35–63. Issued by the Federal Board for Vocational Education. Washington, D.C.: Government Printing Office, 1918.

(32) Three Methods of Teaching Radio Telegraphy. *Journal of Educational Psychology*, **9,** October 1918, 467–470.

(33) Variability in Learning. *Psychological Bulletin*, **15,** June 1918, 210–212.

(34) Mental Tests for Engineering Students. *Proceedings of the Society for the Promotion of Engineering Education*, **27,** 1919, 113–121.

(35) A Standardized Test for Office Clerks. *Journal of Applied Psychology*, **3,** September 1919, 248–251.

(36) Mental Tests for College Entrance. *Journal of Educational Psychology*, **10,** March 1919, 129–142.

(37) Mental Tests for Prospective Telegraphers; A Study of the Diagnostic Value of

Mental Tests for Predicting Ability to Learn Telegraphy. *Journal of Applied Psychology*, **3,** March 1919, 110–117.

(38) A Scoring Method for Mental Tests. *Psychological Bulletin*, **16,** July 1919, 235–240.

(39) The Anticipatory Aspect of Consciousness. *Journal of Philosophy, Psychology, and Scientific Method*, **16,** October 1919, 561–568.

(40) What Is an Educational Motion Picture? *Visual Education*, April 1920, 3–7.

(41) The Problem of Melody. *The Musical Quarterly*, July 1920, 1–4.

(42) Report of Committee Number 22 on Intelligence Tests. *Proceedings of the Society for the Promotion of Engineering Education*, **28,** 1920, 349–361.

(43) Intelligence and Its Measurement. *Journal of Educational Psychology*, **12,** April 1921, 201–207.

(44) A Cycle-Omnibus Intelligence Test for College Students. *Journal of Educational Research*, **4,** November 1921, 265–278.

(45) The Course Schedules in a Professional Curriculum. *Engineering Education*, **12,** February 1922, 293–297.

(46) The Predictive Value of Mental Tests. *Educational Review*, **63,** January 1922, 11–22.

(47) A Data Sheet for the Pearson Correlation Coefficient. *Journal of Educational Research*, **6,** June 1922, 49–56.

(48) The Intelligence of Policemen. *Journal of Personnel Research*, **1,** June 1922, 64–74.

(49) The Calculation and Interpretation of Percentile Ranks. *Journal of Educational Research*, **6,** October 1922, 225–235.

(50) A Comparative Study of Clerical Tests. Part I, Arithmetic and Spelling; Part II, Classifying and Tabulating; Part III, Tests of Business Information; Part IV, Grammar, Reading, Letter Writing, Oral English; Part V, Proof Reading, Alphabetizing, Filing. *Public Personnel Studies*, **1,** October–December 1923. Washington, D.C.: Bureau of Public Personnel Administration, Institute for Government Research.

(51) Intelligence Tests for Engineering Students. *Engineering Education*, **13,** 1923, 263–318.

(52) Personnel Research. *Proceedings of the National Conference of Social Work*, 1923, 126–127.

(53) The Seventh International Congress of Psychology. *Psychological Bulletin*, **20,** October 1923, 558–561.

(54) The Stimulus-Response Fallacy in Psychology. *Psychological Review*, **30,** September 1923, 354–369.

(55) What Do We Measure by the Intelligence Test? *Hygeia*, **1,** September and October 1923, 349–353; 453–455.

(56) Intelligence Tests in the Civil Service: A Discussion of Fundamental Principles in the Development and Application of Intelligence Tests. *Public Personnel Studies*, **1,** October 1923, 4–24. Washington, D.C.: Bureau of Public Personnel Administration, Institute for Government Research. (Also in *Journal of Personnel Research*, **2,** March 1924, 431–441.)

(57) Arithmetic and Spelling. *Public Personnel Studies*, **1,** November 1923, 5–28. Washington, D.C.: Bureau of Public Personnel Administration, Institute for Government Research.

(58) Psychology in the Civil Service. (In Psychology in Business), *Annals of the American Academy of Political and Social Science*, **110,** November 1923, 194–199.

(59) The Civil Service Tests for Patrolmen in Philadelphia. *Public Personnel Studies*, **2,** January–February 1924, 1–5. Washington, D.C.: Bureau of Public Personnel Administration, Institute for Government Research.

(60) The Nature of General Intelligence and Ability, III. *British Journal of Psychology* (General Section), **14,** January 1924, 243–247. (This paper was read at the Seventh International Congress of Psychology at Oxford, July 1923.)

(61) The Principles of Vocational Guidance, III. *British Journal of Psychology* (General Section), **14,** April 1924, 353–361. (This paper was read at the Seventh International Congress of Psychology at Oxford, July 1923.)

(62) Influence of Freudism on Theoretical Psychology. *Psychological Review*, **31,** May 1924, 175–183.

(63) What Is Personnel Research? *Journal of Personnel Research*, **3,** June 1924, 52–56.

(64) The Significance of Psychology for the Study of Government and Certain Specific Problems Involving Both Psychology and Politics. *American Political Science Review*, **19,** February 1925, 7–19. (Round Table on Politics and Psychology, National Conference on the Science of Politics, held at Chicago, Illinois, September 8–12, 1924.)

(65) Vocational Guidance for College Students. *Journal of Personnel Research*, **3,** April 1925, 421–448.

(66) A Method of Scaling Psychological and Educational Tests. *Journal of Educational Psychology*, **16,** October 1925, 433–451.

(67) (with C. R. Mann) Vocational Guidance for College Students. (Rep. and Cir. Series), *National Research Council*, **3,** 1925, 421–448.

(68) Aspects of Public Opinion. *American Political Science Review*, **20,** February 1926, 126–127. (Report of the Third National Conference on the Science of Politics, held September 7–11, 1925, at New York City.)

(69) The Mental Age Concept. *Psychological Review*, **33,** July 1926, 268–278.

(70) The Scoring of Individual Performance. *Journal of Educational Psychology*, **17,** October 1926, 446–457.

(71) The Method of Paired Comparisons for Social Values. *Journal of Abnormal and Social Psychology*, **4,** January–March 1927, 384–400.

(72) Equally Often Noticed Differences. *Journal of Educational Psychology*, **18,** May 1927, 289–293.

(73) Psychophysical Analysis. *American Journal of Psychology*, **38,** July 1927, 368–389.

(74) A Law of Comparative Judgment. *Psychological Review*, **34,** July 1927, 273–286.

(75) The Unit of Measurement in Educational Scales. *Journal of Educational Psychology*, **18,** November 1927, 505–524.

(76) A Mental Unit of Measurement. *Psychological Review*, **34,** November 1927, 415–423.

(77) Three Psychophysical Laws. *Psychological Review*, **34,** November 1927, 424–432.

(78) Note on the Calculation of Percentile Ranks. *Journal of Educational Psychology*, **18,** December 1927, 617–620.

(79) A Note on the Spearman-Brown Formula. *Journal of Experimental Psychology*, **11,** February 1928, 62–63.

(80) Attitudes Can Be Measured. *American Journal of Sociology*, **33,** January 1928, 529–554.

(81) Reply to K. J. Holzinger's "Some Comments on Professor Thurstone's Method

of Determining the Scale Values of Test Items." *Journal of Educational Psychology*, **19,** February 1928, 117–124.

(82) The Measurement of Opinion. *Journal of Abnormal and Social Psychology*, **22,** January–March 1928, 415–430.

(83) The Absolute Zero in Intelligence Measurement. *Psychological Review*, **35,** May 1928, 175–197.

(84) An Experimental Study of Nationality Preferences. *Journal of General Psychology*, **1,** July–October 1928, 405–425.

(85) The Phi-Gamma Hypothesis. *Journal of Experimental Psychology*, **11,** August 1928, 293–305.

(86) Scale Construction with Weighted Observations. *Journal of Educational Psychology*, **19,** October 1928, 441–453.

(87) The Measurement of Psychological Value. In Smith, T. V., and W. K. Wright, eds., *Essays in Philosophy*. La Salle, Illinois: The Open Court Publishing Company, 1929, 157–174.

(88) Theory of Attitude Measurement. *Psychological Review*, **36,** May 1929, 222–241.

(89) Fechner's Law and the Method of Equal-Appearing Intervals. *Journal of Experimental Psychology*, **12,** June 1929, 214–224.

(90) (with Luton Ackerson) The Mental Growth Curve for the Binet Tests. *Journal of Educational Psychology*, **20,** November 1929, 569–583.

(91) (with Richard L. Jenkins) Birth Order and Intelligence. *Journal of Educational Psychology*, **20,** December 1929, 641–651.

(92) Commentary. In Rice, S. A., ed., *Statistics in Social Studies*. Philadelphia: University of Pennsylvania Press, 1930, 222 pp.

(93) The Learning Function. *Journal of General Psychology*, **3,** October 1930, 469–493.

(94) The Relation Between Learning Time and Length of Task. *Psychological Review*, **37,** January 1930, 44–53.

(95) (with Percy Bordwell, John H. Gray, and A. J. Carlson) University of Missouri: Report on the Dismissal of Professor DeGraff and the Suspension of Professor Meyer. *Bulletin of the American Association of University Professors*, **16,** February 1930, 3–35.

(96) Academic Freedom. A Practical Plan to Achieve the Right of Unhampered Thinking and Research for the Teacher. *Journal of Higher Education*, **1,** March 1930, 136–140.

(97) A Scale for Measuring Attitude toward the Movies. *Journal of Educational Research*, **22,** September 1930, 89–94.

(98) (with Thelma Gwinn Thurstone) A Neurotic Inventory. *Journal of Social Psychology*, **1,** February 1930, 3–30.

(99) Development of Personality Traits as an Object of College Instruction. *Annual Proceedings of the American Association of Collegiate Schools of Business* (1931). (This paper was read at the New Orleans meeting of the American Association of Collegiate Schools of Business, March 31, 1931.)

(100) Experimental Determination by Floyd H. Allport of Group Influence upon Mental Activity. In Rice, S. A., ed., *Methods in Social Science*. Chicago: University of Chicago Press, 1931, 694–696.

(101) The Measurement of Change in Social Attitude. *Journal of Social Psychology*, **2,** May 1931, 230–235.

(102) The Indifference Function. *Journal of Social Psychology*, **2**, May 1931, 139–167.

(103) Rank Order as a Psychophysical Method. *Journal of Experimental Psychology*, **14**, June 1931, 187–201.

(104) Influence of Motion Pictures on Children's Attitudes. *Journal of Social Psychology*, **2**, August 1931, 291–305.

(105) Multiple Factor Analysis. *Psychological Review*, **38**, September 1931, 406–427.

(106) A Multiple Factor Study of Vocational Interests. *Personnel Journal*, **10**, October 1931, 198–205.

(107) The Measurement of Social Attitudes. *Journal of Abnormal and Social Psychology*, **26**, October–December 1931, 249–269. (Presidential address for Midwestern Psychological Association, May 9, 1931.)

(108) (with Ruth C. Peterson) The Effect of a Motion Picture Film on Children's Attitudes toward Germans. *Journal of Educational Psychology*, **23**, April 1932, 241–246.

(109) Stimulus Dispersions in the Method of Constant Stimuli. *Journal of Experimental Psychology*, **15**, June 1932, 284–297.

(110) Isolation of Blocs in a Legislative Body by the Voting Records of Its Members. *Journal of Social Psychology*, **3**, November 1932, 425–433.

(111) The Error Function in Maze Learning. *Journal of General Psychology*, **9**, October 1933, 288–301.

(112) (with Ruth C. Peterson) Motion Pictures and the Social Attitudes of Children. In *Motion Pictures and Youth*. New York: The Macmillan Company, 1933, 75. (A preliminary edition was issued in 1932 under the title: The Effect of Motion Pictures on the Social Attitudes of High School Children. See microfilm No. 1696, University of Chicago Library, Department of Photographic Reproduction.)

(113) The Vectors of Mind. *Psychological Review*, **41**, January 1934, 1–32. (Presidential Address, American Psychological Association, 1933.)

(114) Unitary Abilities. *Journal of General Psychology*, **11**, July 1934, 126–132.

(115) (with J. E. Anderson, M. A. May, G. Murphy, R. S. Woodworth, and C. C. Brigham) Report of the Committee on Research in the Social Sciences. *Psychological Bulletin*, **31**, November 1934, 660–662.

(116) A Vocational Interest Schedule. *Psychological Bulletin*, **32**, November 1935, 719.

(117) The Isolation of Seven Primary Abilities. *Psychological Bulletin*, **33**, November 1936, 780–781.

(118) The Bounding Hyperplanes of a Configuration of Traits. *Psychometrika*, **1**, March 1936, 61–68.

(119) A New Conception of Intelligence. *Educational Record*, **17**, July 1936, 441–450.

(120) The Factorial Isolation of Primary Abilities. *Psychometrika*, **1**, September 1936, 175–182.

(121) A New Concept of Intelligence and a New Method of Measuring Primary Mental Abilities. *Educational Record*, **17**, Supplement No. 10, October 1936, 124–138.

(122) Elements in Intelligence. *Proceedings of the Annual Congress on Medical Education and Licensure*, American Medical Association, February 1937, 31–33.

(123) Psychology as a Quantitative Rational Science. *Science*, **85**, March 1937, 228–232. (Presidential Address, Psychometric Society, 1936.)

(124) Current Misuse of the Factorial Methods. *Psychometrika*, **2**, June 1937, 73–76.

(125) Ability, Motivation, and Speed. *Psychometrika*, **2,** December 1937, 249–254. (Also Abstract, *Psychological Bulletin*, **34,** 1937, 735–736.)

(126) The Perceptual Factor. *Psychometrika*, **3,** March 1938, 1–17.

(127) Shifty and Mathematical Components: A Critique of Anastasi's Monograph on the Influence of Specific Experience upon Mental Organization. *Psychological Bulletin*, **35,** April 1938, 223–236.

(128) Research and Psychology. *Bulletin of the Society for Social Research*, August 1938, 3–6.

(129) A New Rotational Method in Factor Analysis. *Psychometrika*, **3,** December 1938, 199–218.

(130) Factor Analysis as a Scientific Method with Special Reference to the Analysis of Human Traits. In Wirth, L., ed., *Eleven Twenty-Six; A Decade of Social Science Research*. Chicago: University of Chicago Press, 1940, 78–112.

(131) A Factorial Study of Visual Gestalt Effects. *Psychological Bulletin*, **37,** July 1940, 456. (Abstract.)

(132) Current Issues in Factor Analysis. *Psychological Bulletin*, **37,** April 1940, 189–236.

(133) Experimental Study of Simple Structure. *Psychometrika*, **5,** June 1940, 153–168.

(134) A Micro-Film Projector Method for Psychological Tests. *Psychometrika*, **6,** August 1941, 235–248.

(135) Experimental and Factorial Study of Perceptual Dynamics. *Psychological Bulletin*, **39,** July 1942, 452–453. (Abstract.)

(136) Research Note: In Search of New Tests. *Psychometrika*, **9,** March 1944, 69.

(137) Graphical Method of Factoring the Correlation Matrix. *Proceedings of the National Academy of Sciences*, **30,** June 1944, 129–134.

(138) Second-Order Factors. *Psychometrika*, **9,** June 1944, 71–100.

(139) Testing Intelligence and Aptitudes. *Hygeia*, **23,** 1945, 32–36; 50; 52; 54.

(140) Testing Intelligence and Aptitudes. *Public Personnel Review*, **6,** January 1945, 22–27.

(141) A Multiple Group Method of Factoring the Correlation Matrix. *Psychometrika*, **10,** June 1945, 73–78.

(142) The Effects of Selection in Factor Analysis. *Psychometrika*, **10,** September 1945, 165–198.

(143) The Prediction of Choice. *Psychometrika*, **10,** December 1945, 237–253.

(144) Primary Abilities. In Harriman, P. L., ed., *Encyclopedia of Psychology*. New York: Philosophical Library, 1946, 544–546.

(145) Psychophysics. In Harriman, P. L., ed., *Encyclopedia of Psychology*. New York: Philosophical Library, 1946, 640–644.

(146) A Note on the Experimental Study of English Style. *The American Psychologist*, **1,** February 1946, 62.

(147) Theories of Intelligence. *Scientific Monthly*, **62,** Supplement 5, February 1946, 101–112. (This paper was presented to the Chicago Literary Club, February 12, 1945.)

(148) Factor Analysis and Body Types. *Psychometrika*, **11,** March 1946, 15–21.

(149) A Single Plane Method of Rotation. *Psychometrika*, **11,** June 1946, 71–79.

(150) Comment on Nettler and Golding's Paper "The Measurement of Attitudes toward the Japanese in America." *American Journal of Sociology*, **52,** July 1946, 39–40.

(151) Note on a Reanalysis of Davis' Reading Tests. *Psychometrika*, **11,** September 1946, 185–188.

(152) The Calibration of Test Items. *The American Psychologist*, **2**, March 1947, 103–104.

(153) Factorial Analysis of Body Measurements. *American Journal of Physical Anthropology*, **5**, March 1947, 15–28.

(154) Psychophysical Methods. In Andrews, T. G., ed., *Methods of Psychology*. New York: John Wiley & Sons, Inc.; London: Chapman & Hall, Ltd., 1948, 124–157.

(155) Tests for Primary Mental Abilities. In Kaplan, O. J., ed., *Encyclopedia of Vocational Guidance*. New York: Philosophical Library, Inc., 1948, 1099–1102.

(156) The Improvement of Examinations. *American Association of University Professors Bulletin*, **34**, Summer 1948, 394–397.

(157) Psychological Implications of Factor Analysis. *The American Psychologist*, **3**, September 1948, 402–408. (Also Implicaciones psicológicos del análisis factorial, *Rev. Psicol. Gen. Apl.*, Madrid, **5**, 1950, 19–35.) (Presidential Address, American Psychological Association, Division on Evaluation and Measurement, Detroit, Michigan, September 9, 1947.)

(158) The Rorschach in Psychological Science. *Journal of Abnormal and Social Psychology*, **43**, October 1948, 471–475. (This paper was presented to the Illinois Association for Applied Psychology in Chicago, November 18, 1947.)

(159) The Edge-Marking Method of Analyzing Data. *Journal of American Statistical Association*, **43**, September 1948, 451–462.

(160) Primary Mental Abilities. *Science*, **108**, November 1948, 585 (Abstract). (Read at the Symposium of Human Individuality, American Association for the Advancement of Science meeting, September 14, 1948, in Washington, D.C.)

(161) Analysis of Human Abilities. In *Armed Forces Familiarization Course in Military Psychology*. Washington: American Psychological Association, 1949.

(162) Note about the Multiple Group Method. *Psychometrika*, **14**, March 1949, 43–45.

(163) Primary Abilities. *Occupations*, **27**, May 1949, 527–529.

(164) Primary Mental Abilities. In American Association for the Advancement of Science. *Centennial*. (Collected papers presented at the Centennial Celebration, Washington, D.C., September 13–17, 1948.) Washington: American Association for the Advancement of Science, 1950, 313 pp.

(165) Methods of Food Tasting Experiments. *Proceedings of the Second Conference on Research*, March 1950, 85–91. (Sponsored by The Council on Research, American Meat Institute.)

(166) The Factorial Description of Temperament. *Science*, **111**, (April 1950), 454–455 (Abstract). (Paper read at Annual Meeting of the National Academy of Sciences, Washington, D.C., April 24–26, 1950.)

(167) Some Primary Abilities in Visual Thinking. *Proceedings of the American Philosophical Society*, **94**, December 1950, 517–521.

(168) L'Analyse Factorielle Méthode Scientifique. *L'Année Psychologique*, **50**, 1951, 61–75. Volume Jubilaire, Hommage á Henri Pieron. Paris: Presses Universitaires de France. (Translated by Jean Cardinet.) (Read at a common meeting of the American Psychological Association, the American Statistical Association, and the Psychometric Society on December 29, 1950.)

(169) The Dimensions of Temperament. *Psychometrika*, **16**, March 1951, 11–20.

(170) Experimental Methods in Food Tasting. *Journal of Applied Psychology*, **35**, June 1951, 141–145.

(171) (with James W. Degan) A Factorial Study of the Supreme Court. *Proceedings of*

the National Academy of Sciences, **37,** September 1951, 628–635. (Also *Science*, **113,** 1951, 478.) (Abstract.)

(172) Experimental Tests of Temperament. In *Essays in Psychology*. Dedicated to David Katz, eds. G. Ekman, et al. Uppsala: Almquist & Wiksells (1951), 248–262.

(173) Autobiography. In Langfeld, H. S., et al., eds., *A History of Psychology in Autobiography*, Vol. IV. Worcester, Massachusetts: Clark University Press, 1952, 295–321.

(174) Walter Van Dyke Bingham. *Personnel Psychology*, **5,** No. 3, 1952.

(175) Creative Talent. In *Applications of Psychology*. Essays to Honor Walter V. Bingham, ed. L. L. Thurstone. New York: Harper & Row, Publishers, 1952, 18–37. (Also *Proceedings of the 1950 Invitational Conference on Testing Problems*. Princeton, New Jersey: Educational Testing Service, 1951, 55–69.)

(176) An Experiment in the Prediction of Food Preference and the Prediction of Choice. *Proceedings of the Fourth Research Conference*, March 1952, 58–66. (Sponsored by the Council on Research, American Meat Institute, at the University of Chicago.)

(177) A Psychologist Discusses the Mechanism of Thinking. In *The Nature of Creative Thinking*, 1952, 35–43. (A monograph sponsored by Industrial Research Institute, Inc. This paper was read at a symposium presented May 5–7, 1952, at Skytop Lodge, Pennsylvania.)

(178) (with Allen L. Edwards) An Internal Consistency Check for Scale Values Determined by the Method of Successive Intervals. *Psychometrika*, **17,** June 1952, 169–180.

(179) The Measurement of Values. *Psychological Review*, **61,** January 1954, 47–58.

(180) Criteria of Scientific Success and the Selection of Scientific Talent. *Technical Report No. 4*, April 1954, 29–36. Office of Scientific Personnel, National Academy of Sciences, and National Research Council. (This paper was read at a meeting on November 14, 1953, of the Research Advisory Committee, Office of Scientific Personnel.)

(181) An Analytical Method for Simple Structure. *Psychometrika*, **19,** September 1954, 173–182.

(182) Some New Psychophysical Methods. In *A Symposium on Food Acceptance Testing Methodology*, October 1954, 100–104. (Sponsored by the Quartermaster Food and Container Institute, National Academy of Sciences, and National Research Council.)

(183) (with Lyle V. Jones) Psychophysics and the Normality Assumption: An Experimental Report. In *A Symposium on Food Acceptance Testing Methodology*, October 1954, 105–111. (Sponsored by the Quartermaster Food and Container Institute, National Academy of Sciences, and National Research Council.)

(184) A Method of Factoring Without Communalities. In *Proceedings of the 1954 Invitational Conference on Testing Problems*. Princeton, New Jersey: Educational Testing Service, 1955, 59–62.

(185) (with Lyle V. Jones) The Psychophysics of Semantics: An Experimental Investigation. *Journal of Applied Psychology*, **39,** February 1955, 31–36.

(186) Sir Godfrey Thomson. *Psychometrika*, **20,** September 1955, 171–172.

(187) The Criterion Problem in Personality Research. *Educational and Psychological Measurement*, **15,** Winter 1955, 353–361.

(188) (with Lyle V. Jones) The Rational Origin for Measuring Subjective Values. *Journal of American Statistical Association*, **52,** December 1957, 458–471.

Reports of American Council
on Education Psychological Examinations

Psychological Tests for College Freshmen. *The Educational Record*, **6,** April 1925, 69–83. (Also *The Educational Record*, **6,** October 1925, 282–294.)

The Psychological Test Program. *The Educational Record*, **7,** April 1926, 114–126.

Psychological Examinations for College Freshmen. *The Educational Record*, **8,** April 1927, 27.

1927 Norms, Psychological Examination. *The Educational Record*, **9,** April 1928, 156–182.

Psychological Examination for 1928. *The Educational Record*, **10,** April 1929, 105–115.

(with Thelma Gwinn Thurstone) The 1929 Psychological Examination. *The Educational Record*, **11,** April 1930, 101–128.

The 1930 Psychological Examination. *The Educational Record*, **12,** April 1931, 160–178.

The 1931 Psychological Examination. *The Educational Record*, **13,** April 1932, 121–136.

The 1932 Psychological Examination. *The Educational Record*, **14,** April 1933, 183–197.

(with Thelma Gwinn Thurstone) The 1933 Psychological Examination. *The Educational Record*, **15,** April 1934, 161–175.

The 1934 Psychological Examination. *The Educational Record*, **16,** April 1935, 226–240.

(with Thelma Gwinn Thurstone) The 1935 Psychological Examination. *The Educational Record*, **17,** April 1936, 296–317.

(with Thelma Gwinn Thurstone) The 1936 Psychological Examination for College Freshmen. *The Educational Record*, **18,** April 1937, 252–273.

(with Thelma Gwinn Thurstone) The 1937 Psychological Examination for College Freshmen. *The Educational Record*, **19,** April 1938, 209–234.

(with Thelma Gwinn Thurstone and Dorothy C. Adkins) The 1938 Psychological Examination. *The Educational Record*, **20,** April 1939, 263–300.

(with Thelma Gwinn Thurstone) The American Council on Education Psychological Examinations, 1939 Edition. Psychological Examinations, 1939. (American Council on Education Studies), Series V, *Council Staff Reports*, **4,** No. 2, May 1940, 37.

(with Thelma Gwinn Thurstone) Psychological Examination, 1940 Norms. (American Council on Education Studies), Series V, *Council Staff Reports*, **5,** No. 3, May 1941, 41.

(with Thelma Gwinn Thurstone) Psychological Examinations, 1941 Norms. (American Council on Education Studies), Series V, *Council Staff Reports*, **6,** No. 4, May 1942, 42.

(with Thelma Gwinn Thurstone) Psychological Examination for College Freshmen, 1942 Norms. (American Council on Education Studies), Series V, *Council Staff Reports*, **7,** No. 6, May 1943, 32.

(with Thelma Gwinn Thurstone) Psychological Examination for College Freshmen, 1943 Norms. (American Council on Education Studies), Series V, *Council Staff Reports*, **8,** No. 8, June 1944, 28.

(with Thelma Gwinn Thurstone) Psychological Examination for College Freshmen, 1944 Norms. (American Council on Education Studies), Series V, *Council Staff Reports*, **9,** No. 9, May 1945, 29.

(with Thelma Gwinn Thurstone) Psychological Examination for College Freshmen, 1945 Norms. (American Council on Education Studies), Series V, *Council Staff Reports*, **10,** No. 10, May 1946, 34.

(with Thelma Gwinn Thurstone) Psychological Examination for College Freshmen, 1946 Norms. (American Council on Education Studies), Series V, *Council Staff Reports*, **11,** No. 11, June 1947, 23.

(with Thelma Gwinn Thurstone) Psychological Examination for College Freshmen, 1947 Norms. The American Council on Education, 1948.

Psychometric Laboratory Reports of the University of Chicago

Report Number

1. Note about Factor Analysis of Reading Tests, 1938.
2. In Search of New Tests, 1941. (Also in *Psychometrika*, **9,** March 1944, 69.)
3. A Code Aptitude Test, January 1944.
4. The Centroid Method of Factoring, September 1944. (Also Chapter VIII in *Multiple-Factor Analysis*, 1947.)
5. Alternative Methods of Rotation. (Also Chapter XVII in *Multiple-Factor Analysis*, 1947.)
6. Second-Order Factors. (Also in *Psychometrika*, **9,** June 1944, 71–100.)
7. Data for Company 19 at the Naval Training School after Six Weeks of Instruction, January 1944.
8. Supplementary Report on Code Aptitude Test, March 1944.
9. (with Ledyard R Tucker and Virginia Brown) Definitions of Terms in Factor Analysis. General Comments on Definitions in Factor Analysis, March 15, 1944.
10. The Psychometric Laboratory, January 1944.
11. (by Virginia Brown) Frequency Distributions for Code Aptitude Test, March 1944.
12. Graphical Method of Factoring the Correlation Matrix, March 1944. (Also in *Proceedings of the National Academy of Sciences*, **30,** June 1944, 129–134.)
13. (by Virginia Brown) Code Aptitude Test Scores for Company 31 at the Naval Training School, April 1944.
14. (by Ledyard R Tucker) The Determination of Successive Principal Components without Computation of Tables of Residual Correlation Coefficients, May 1944.
15. (by Virginia Brown) Progress Report on Code Aptitude Tests, May 1944.
16. (by Virginia Brown) Final Progress Report on Code Aptitude Tests, July 1944.
17. (by T. Gaylord Andrews) Factor Analysis of the Allergies, December 1944.
18. Theories of Intelligence, February 1945. (Paper given at Chicago Literary Club, February 12, 1945. Also in *Scientific Monthly*, **62,** February 1946, 101–112.)
19. A Multiple Group Method of Factoring the Correlation Matrix, June 1945. (Also in *Psychometrika*, **10,** June 1945, 73–78.)
20. A Single Plane Method of Rotation, June 1946. (Also in *Psychometrika*, **11,** June 1946, 71–79.)
21. Tests for Primary Mental Abilities, June 1945. (Also in *Encyclopedia of Vocational Guidance*, 1948, 1099–1102.)
22. Intelligence Quotients for Superior Adults, June 1945.
23. The Prediction of Choice, June 1945. (Also in *Psychometrika*, **10,** December 1945, 237–253.)
24. Factor Analysis and Body Types, September 1945. (Also in *Psychometrika*, **11,** March 1946, 15–21.)

25. Note on the Prediction of Choice with Correlated Ratings, October 1945. (Nos. 23 and 25 reprinted together. The Prediction of Choice.)

26. Psychophysics, November 1945. (Also in *Encyclopedia of Psychology*, 1946, 640–644.)

27. Primary Abilities, November 1945. (Also in *Encyclopedia of Psychology*, 1946, 544–546.)

28. A Note on the Experimental Study of English Style, December 1945. (Also in *The American Psychologist*, **1,** February 1946, 62.)

29. Analysis of Body Measurements, March 1946. (Also in *American Journal of Physical Anthropology*, **5,** March 1947, 15–28.)

30. The Selection of Talent, March 1946.

31. Comment on Gwynne Nettler's Paper "Known-Group Validation in the Measurement of Attitudes toward the Japanese in America," April 1946. (Also in *American Journal of Sociology*, **52,** July 1946, 39–40.)

32. Note on the Analysis of Reading Tests, April 1946. (Also in *Psychometrika*, **11,** September 1946, 185–188.)

33. Note on the Multiple Group Method of Factoring. (Cancelled) (In *Psychometrika*, **14,** March 1949, 43–45.)

34. The Calibration of Test Items, October 1946. (Also in *The American Psychologist*, **2,** March 1947, 103–104.)

35. Mechanical Aptitude. No. 1. Research Plan for the Project, October 1946.

36. Navy Mechanical Aptitude Project. No. 2. Progress Report, January 1947.

37. The Objective Study of Temperament, January 1947.

38. Report for Dr. John G. Lynn, April 1947.

39. An Interest Schedule, June 1947.

40. Psychophysical Methods, May 1947. (Also Chapter V in *Methods of Psychology*. New York: John Wiley & Sons, Inc., 1948.)

41. The Improvement of School Examinations, June 1947. (Also in *American Association of University Professors Bulletin*, **34,** Summer 1948, 394–397.)

42. The Dimensions of Temperament, June 1947.

43. (by Robert L. Chapman) The MacQuarrie Test of Mechanical Ability, August 1947.

44. Psychological Implications of Factor Analysis, September 1947. (Also in *The American Psychologist*, **3,** September 1948, 402–408. Presidential Address, APA, Division V, September 9, 1947.)

45. (by James W. Degan) A Note on the Effects of Selection in Factor Analysis, November 1947.

46. The Rorschach in Psychological Science, November 1947. (Paper presented to Illinois Association for Applied Psychology, Chicago, November 18, 1947. Also in *Journal of Abnormal and Social Psychology*, **43,** October 1948, 471–475.)

47. (with Thelma Gwinn Thurstone) Mechanical Aptitude. Report of the First Year of the Study, October 1947.

48. The Edge-Marking Method of Analyzing Data, February 1948. Also in *Journal of American Statistical Association*, **43,** September 1948, 451–462.

49. (by Mariano Yela) Application of the Concept of Simple Structure to Alexander's Data, July 1948.

50. Primary Mental Abilities, September 1948. (Paper given at Symposium on Human

Individuality, American Association for the Advancement of Science, Washington, D.C., September 1948. Also in *Science*, **108,** November 1948, 585.) (Abstract.)

51. Psychological Assumptions in Factor Analysis, February 1949. (Paper given at Twelfth International Congress of Psychology, Edinburgh, July 24, 1948.)

52. Experimental Methods in Food Tasting, June 1950. (Paper given at Research Conference, Council on Research, American Meat Institute, March 24, 1950.)

53. The Factorial Description of Temperament, June 1950. (Paper given at National Academy of Sciences, Washington, D.C., April 24, 1950. Also in *Science*, **111,** April 1950, 454–455.) (Abstract.)

54. (with Thelma Gwinn Thurstone) Mechanical Aptitude II. Description of Group Tests, March 1949.

55. Mechanical Aptitude III. Analysis of Group Tests, May 1949.

56. (with Thelma Gwinn Thurstone) Mechanical Aptitude IV. Description of Individual Tests, May 1949.

57. Mechanical Aptitude V. Individual and Group Tests of Mechanical Aptitude, May 1949.

58. (by James W. Degan) Mechanical Aptitude VI. A Reanalysis of the Army Air Force Battery of Mechanical Tests, September 1950.

59. Some Primary Abilities in Visual Thinking, August 1950. (Paper given at the American Philosophical Society, Philadelphia, April 21, 1950. Also in *Proceedings of the American Philosophical Society*, **94,** No. 6, December 1950, 517–521.)

60. Apparatus for Studying Continuous Apparent Movement, September 1950.

61. Creative Talent, December 1950. (Also Chapter 2 in *Applications of Psychology*. New York: Harper & Row, Publishers, 1952. Paper given at Invitational Conference on Testing Problems, New York, October 28, 1950.)

62. (with Carol Pemberton) An Analysis of Mechanical Aptitude. Summary of Previous Reports, January 1951.

63. (by Melany E. Baehr) A Factorial Study of Temperament, February 1951.

64. (with James W. Degan) A Factorial Study of the Supreme Court, March 1951. (Paper given at National Academy of Sciences, Washington, D.C., April 23, 1951. Also in *Proceedings of the National Academy of Sciences*, **37,** September 1951, 628–635, and *Science*, **113,** 1951, 478.) (Abstract.)

65. Factor Analysis as a Scientific Method, March 1951. (Paper given at a common meeting of the American Psychological Association, the American Statistical Association, and the Psychometric Society, December 29, 1950. Also in *L'Année Psychologique*, **50,** 1951, 61–75. Translated by Jean Cardinet.)

66. (by Per Saugstad) Incidental Memory and Problem Solving, March 1951.

67. Experimental Tests of Temperament, April 1951. (Also in *Essays in Psychology*. Uppsala: Almquist & Wiksells, 1951.)

68. An Experiment in the Prediction of Choice, April 1951.

69. (by Allen L. Edwards) Psychological Scaling by Means of Successive Intervals, May 1951.

70. (by Thomas Jeffrey and Jonathan Wegener) A Response Timer, May 1951.

71. (by Lyle V. Jones) Primary Mental Abilities in the Stanford-Binet, Age 13, June 1951.

72. Objective Tests of Temperament. Tests of Verbal Associations, July 1951.

73. (by James E. Birren) A Factorial Analysis of the Wechsler-Bellevue Scale Given to an Elderly Population, October 1951.

74. Growth of a Social Group. (Cancelled.)
75. (by Lyle V. Jones) Second-Order Factors in Tests, March 1952.
76. (by James E. Birren, William R. Allen, and H. G. Landau) Speed, Accuracy, and Difficulty, May 1952.
77. The Measurement of Values, May 1952. (Read at the Southern Society of Philosophy and Psychology in Knoxville, Tennessee, April 11, 1952.)
78. The Criterion Problem in Personality Research, May 1952. (Read in a symposium of the Illinois Psychological Association at Northwestern University, April 5, 1952.)
79. Word Association with Homonyms, July 1952.
80. Progress Report on a Color-Form Test. Research project on objective tests of temperament, July 1952.
81. The Scientific Study of Inventive Talent, July 1952. (Read at a meeting of the Industrial Research Institute, Skytop, Pennsylvania, May 6, 1952.)

Psychometric Laboratory Reports
of the University of North Carolina

Report Number

1. The Development of Objective Measures of Temperament, April 1953. (Read as an invitation lecture at the meetings of the American Psychological Association on September 4, 1952, in Washington, D.C.)
2. Classification Test, May 1953.
3. (with J. J. Mellinger) The Stroop Test, May 1953.
4. (with Thelma Gwinn Thurstone and Herluf H. Strandskov) A Psychological Study of Twins. 1. Distributions of Absolute Twin Differences for Identical and Fraternal Twins, June 1953.
5. (by J. J. Mellinger) A Nine-Fold Point Correlation. A Measure of Association between Questionnaire Item Responses and Quantitative Test Scores, July 1953.
6. Analytical Method for Simple Structure, July 1953.
7. Some New Psychophysical Methods, October 1953. (This paper was prepared for a symposium sponsored by the National Research Council Advisory Board on Quartermaster Research and Development at the Palmer House, Chicago, on October 9, 1953. Also in *A Symposium on Food Acceptance Testing Methodology*, sponsored by the Quartermaster Food and Container Institute, National Academy of Sciences and National Research Council, October 1954, 101–104.)
8. (by Dorothy C. Adkins) The Simple Structure of the American Psychological Association, October 1953. (Address of the retiring President of the Division on Evaluation and Measurement of the American Psychological Association at Cleveland, Ohio, on September 7, 1953, presented at a dinner meeting held jointly with the Psychometric Society.)
9. Criteria of Scientific Success and the Selection of Scientific Talent, November 1953. (This paper was prepared for a conference called by the Advisory Committee on Fellowship Selection of the National Research Council in Washington, D.C., on November 14, 1953. Also Technical Report No. 4, April 15, 1954, 29–36, Office of Scientific Personnel, National Academy of Sciences and National Research Council.)
10. (by W. A. Gibson) Simultaneous Absolute Scaling for Several Groups, March 1954.
11. (by J. J. Mellinger) An Exploratory Study on the Selection of Creative Talent, September 1954.

12. (with Thelma Gwinn Thurstone and Herluf Strandskov) A Psychological Study of Twins. 2. Scores of One Hundred and Twenty-five Pairs of Twins on Fifty-nine Tests, January 1955.
13. The Rational Origin for Measuring Subjective Values, January 1955.
14. The Differential Growth of Mental Abilities, March 1955.

Tests

Examination in Clerical Proficiency, Form 1. Also Form 2, Form E, and Form F.

Oral Trade Tests, Committee on Classification of Personnel in the Army, Trade Test Division, 1918.

Thurstone's Hand Test. Chicago: C. H. Stoelting Company, 1918.

Thurstone's Miscellaneous Intelligence Test. Chicago: C. H. Stoelting Company, 1918.

Thurstone's Spatial Relations Test, A and B. Chicago: C. H. Stoelting Company, 1918.

Wheels Tests. Chicago: C. H. Stoelting Company, 1918. (This was the first form of the mechanical movements test.)

Intelligence Tests for College Students, Form 1481. Pittsburgh: Carnegie Institute of Technology, 1919.

Thurstone Cycle-Omnibus Intelligence Test for College Students. Range: high school seniors and college freshmen. Bloomington, Illinois: Public School Publishing Company, 1919. (See *Journal of Educational Research*, **4**, 1921, 265–278.)

Thurstone's Intelligence Test (IV). Also Supplement to Test IV. Chicago: C. H. Stoelting Company, 1919.

Thurstone's Test of Engineering Aptitude for College Freshmen and High School Seniors. Pittsburgh: Carnegie Institute of Technology, 1919. (There are five tests in the engineering series, published by World Book Company, now Harcourt, Brace & World, Inc.)

Thurstone's Vocational Guidance Tests. Algebra, Arithmetic, Geometry, Physics, and Technical Information. Range: high school seniors and college freshmen. New York: Harcourt, Brace & World, Inc., 1919.

Thurstone Proficiency Test for Typists. New York: Harcourt, Brace & World, 1920.

Thurstone Employment Tests. Examination in clerical work and examination in typing. New York: Harcourt, Brace & World, Inc., 1922.

Thurstone's Psychological Examination. Chicago: C. H. Stoelting Company, 1922, 1923, 1924.

(with Thelma Gwinn Thurstone) Ingenuity Test. Chicago: C. H. Stoelting Company, 1923.

Psychological Examination for High School Graduates and College Freshmen. Washington, D.C.: American Council on Education. (Annual editions 1924 to 1947, inclusive.)

Thurstone Lettering Test. See Smith, H., and W. W. Wright, second revision of the Bibliography of Educational Measurement, *Bulletin of the School of Education*, Indiana University, **4**, No. 2, 1927.

Thurstone's Proverbs Test. Supplement to Test IV. Chicago: C. H. Stoelting Company. See Bronner, A. F., W. Healy, G. M. Lowe, and M. E. Shimberg, *A Manual of Individual Mental Tests and Testing*. Boston: Little, Brown & Company, 1927.

Thurstone's Reasoning Test A and B. Chicago: C. H. Stoelting Company. See Bronner, A. F., W. Healy, et al., *A Manual of Individual Mental Tests and Testing*. Boston: Little, Brown & Company, 1927.

(with Thelma Gwinn Thurstone) Personality Schedule. Range: high school, college, and adult. Chicago: The University of Chicago Press, 1929, 4–23. (Form A, 1928; Form B (alternate), 1929.) (Also published by Cambridge University Press, 1930. See A Neurotic Inventory, *Journal of Social Psychology*, **1**, 1930, 3–30.)

(with Thelma Gwinn Thurstone) Psychological Examination for Grades Nine to Twelve. Washington, D.C.: American Council on Education. (Annual editions 1933 to 1941, inclusive.)

Psychological Examination for College Freshmen, Experimental Machine-Scoring edition. Washington, D. C.: American Council on Education, 1937.

Psychological Examination for Grades 9 to 12, Machine-Scoring. Washington, D.C.: American Council on Education. (Annual editions 1938 to 1941, inclusive.)

Tests for the Primary Mental Abilities, Experimental edition. Washington, D.C.: American Council on Education, 1938.

Psychological Examination for College Freshmen, Machine-Scoring. Washington, D.C.: American Council on Education. (Annual editions 1938 to 1947, inclusive.)

Chicago Primary Mental Abilities Tests, Experimental edition. 1940.

(with Thelma Gwinn Thurstone) The Chicago Tests of Primary Mental Abilities. Washington, D. C.: American Council on Education, 1942.

(with Thelma Gwinn Thurstone) The Chicago Tests of Primary Mental Abilities. Single booklet edition. Chicago: Science Research Associates, 1943.

(with Thelma Gwinn Thurstone) Thurstone Test of Mental Alertness. Form AH, Form AM. Chicago: Science Research Associates, 1943 and 1948.

(with Thelma Gwinn Thurstone) United States Coast Guard Academy Scholastic Examination. Washington, D.C.: American Council on Education, 1945.

(with Thelma Gwinn Thurstone) Tests of Primary Mental Abilities, for ages 5 and 6. Chicago: Science Research Associates, 1946. (See *Journal of Consulting Psychology*, **11**, 1947, 341.)

SRA Verbal Form. Form AH, Form AM. High school — college. Chicago: Science Research Associates, 1947. (See *Journal of Consulting Psychology*, **11**, 1947, 341.)

Thurstone Interest Schedule. Revision of the Vocational Interest Schedule. High school — adult. New York: Psychological Corporation, 1947. (See *Journal of Consulting Psychology*, **12**, 1948, 63.)

(with Thelma Gwinn Thurstone) SRA Primary Mental Abilities, for ages 11 to 17. Form AH and Form AM. Chicago: Science Research Associates, 1947. (See *Journal of Consulting Psychology*, **11**, 1947, 340.)

(with Thelma Gwinn Thurstone) SRA Primary Mental Abilities, Elementary, for ages 7 to 11. Form AH. Chicago: Science Research Associates, 1948.

(with Thelma Gwinn Thurstone) SRA Primary Mental Abilities, Intermediate, for ages 11 to 17. Form AM, Form AH. Chicago: Science Research Associates, 1948.

Thurstone Temperament Schedule. Chicago: Science Research Associates, 1949, 1950.

Color-Form Film Test. Psychometric Laboratory, University of North Carolina, 1952.

(Twenty-five research tests in) *Manual for Kit of Selected Tests for Reference Aptitude and Achievement Factors*. Princeton, New Jersey: Educational Testing Service, 1954.

(with Thomas E. Jeffrey) Concealed Figures Test, Education-Industry Service. Chicago: University of Chicago Press, 1956.

(with Thomas E. Jeffrey) Figure Grouping Test, Education-Industry Service. Chicago: University of Chicago Press, 1956.

(with Thomas E. Jeffrey) Flags Test, Education-Industry Service. Chicago: University of Chicago Press, 1956.

(with Thomas E. Jeffrey) Gestalt Completion Test, Education-Industry Service. Chicago: University of Chicago Press, 1956.

(with Thomas E. Jeffrey) Identical Forms Test, Education-Industry Service. Chicago: University of Chicago Press, 1956.

(with Thomas E. Jeffrey) Mechanical Movements Test, Education-Industry Service. Chicago: University of Chicago Press, 1956.

(with Thomas E. Jeffrey) Paper Puzzles Test, Education-Industry Service. Chicago: University of Chicago Press, 1956.

(with Thomas E. Jeffrey) Weights and Pulleys Test, Education-Industry Service. Chicago: University of Chicago Press, 1956.

Microfilms

The following microfilms may be obtained from the University of Chicago Library, Department of Photographic Reproduction.

Report Number

1647　The Reliability and Validity of Tests. Ann Arbor, Michigan: Edwards Brothers, 1939.

1648　The Theory of Multiple Factors. Ann Arbor, Michigan: Edwards Brothers, 1934.

1696　(with Ruth Peterson) The Effect of Motion Pictures on the Social Attitudes of High School Children. Ann Arbor, Michigan: Edwards Brothers, 1932.

1741　(by Jean Cardinet) Esthetic Preferences and Personality.

1767　(with Thelma Gwinn Thurstone) Mechanical Aptitude II. Description of Group Tests with Sample Items. (Report No. 54, The Psychometric Laboratory, University of Chicago, March 1949.)

1768　(with Thelma Gwinn Thurstone) Mechanical Aptitude — Complete Set of Group Tests.

1771　Measurement of Social Attitudes (collection of attitude scales).

1772　Psychometric Laboratory Reports (includes 3, 15, 16, 17, 18, 22, 23, 24, 25, 29, 30, 32, 34, 39, 40, 41, 42, 43, 44, 45, 46, 47).

1774　A Factorial Study of Perception. Chicago: University of Chicago Press, 1944.

1844　Mechanical Aptitude III. Analysis of Group Tests. (Report No. 55, The Psychometric Laboratory, University of Chicago, May 1949.)

1845　(with Thelma Gwinn Thurstone) Mechanical Aptitude IV. Description of Individual Tests. (Report No. 56, The Psychometric Laboratory, University of Chicago, May 1949.)

1979　(with M. W. Richardson, J. T. Russell, and J. M. Stalnaker) Manual of Examination Methods. Chicago: University of Chicago Bookstore, 1933.

T1136　(by Frances Smith) Word Reactions and Temperament, 1951.

T1279　(by Carol Pemberton) The Speed and Flexibility of Closure Factors, 1951. (Library catalog no.: BF 1999.)

The following microfilms and photocopies may be obtained from the American Documentation Institute, Library of Congress, Washington, D.C.

Document Number

1317   Psychological Tests Used in a Study of Mental Abilities, Psychological Tests Supplement to *Psychometric Monographs*, No. 1, Primary Mental Abilities.

1329   Psychological Tests Used in a Factorial Study at the Hyde Park High School, Chicago, Illinois, 1937. (*Psychometrika*, **5**, No. 2, June 1940.)

1337   Psychological Tests Used in a Factorial Study at the Lane Technical High School, Chicago, Illinois, 1936. (*Psychometrika*, **3**, No. 1, March 1938.)

1434   Psychological Tests Used in a Factorial Study of Eighth-Grade Children. Psychometric Society.

2

SOME SYMMETRIES AND DUALITIES AMONG MEASUREMENT DATA MATRICES

Clyde H. Coombs
University of Michigan

2 SOME SYMMETRIES AND DUALITIES AMONG MEASUREMENT DATA MATRICES[1]

From the responses that individuals make to stimuli we seek to measure the individuals or the stimuli or both, to scale them, or in a general sense, to arrive at an inferential classification of them. This has led to a considerable variety of abstract systems, which we call measurement models, designed for mapping some particular kind of response variable into a psychological space. A psychological space is a representation in which the individuals and/or stimuli are mapped into points and the relations among the points in the space reflect the responses, the interactions of individuals and stimuli.

Consideration of the variety of models has led to the construction of the Theory of Data (Coombs, 1960), which is a simple abstract system for classifying and interrelating these models. We shall first summarize the Theory of Data and some of these relations.

The important axiom in the system is that all psychological measurement data may be viewed as *interpretations* in which each of the following three dichotomies is satisfied:

(1) A relation exists on a pair of points or a pair of dyads.
(2) The members of a pair of points either represent two distinct sets or the same set.
(3) The relation is either an order relation ($>$) or a proximity relation (0).

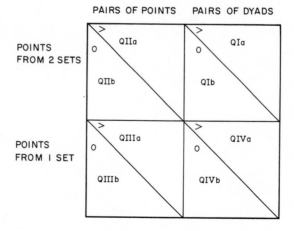

FIGURE 2.1. *The eight classes of data*

These three dichotomies generate eight classes, as pictured in Figure 2.1. As can be seen, there are four principal quadrants, each divided in two by the order relation-proximity relation dichotomy.

[1] This research was supported in part by Research Grant M-4236, National Institute of Mental Health, Public Health Service.

If names were given to these quadrants in terms of the kind of behavior that is most typically associated with them, the labels would come out as in Figure 2.2.

SINGLE STIMULUS DATA OR INDIVIDUAL–STIMULUS COMPARISON	PREFERENTIAL CHOICE DATA INDIVIDUAL–STIMULUS DIFFERENCES COMPARISON
STIMULUS COMPARISON DATA	SIMILARITIES DATA OR STIMULUS DIFFERENCES COMPARISON

FIGURE 2.2. *Behavioral referents for the data quadrants*

The data of QI and QII yield what are called joint spaces because there are two sets of points involved. Typically, the two sets are identified with individuals and stimuli, but this is not necessarily or exclusively the case. Torgerson's (1958, Chapter 10) model for categorical judgment, in QIIa, for example, identifies the stimuli with one set of points and the category boundaries with the other set of points.

The data of QIII and QIV yield what may be called stimulus spaces, because there is only one set of points involved, all identified with stimuli.

Models *within* any one of the octants are all intimately related, as they are all concerned with processing what is basically the same kind of data. These intra-octant relations are a long and complicated story, which we shall bypass now. Instead, we shall speak of some of the relations between octants.

The clearest and easiest way to see some of these interrelations is in terms of three basic measurement data matrices. These three matrices may be called a dominance matrix, a symmetric proximity matrix, and a conditional proximity matrix. We shall discuss each of these kinds of matrices in turn, and then present an analysis of a conditional proximity matrix because such a matrix has some quite unique features.

THE DOMINANCE MATRIX

The dominance matrix is the most common and is the one that has received the most attention. The matrix is square, with a stimulus labeling a row and the corresponding column. The entry in the cell corresponding to row j and column k is a response measure which reflects a dominance relation between j and k. This may be a "1" to indicate that j defeated k in competition or that j

was judged prettier than k. Very commonly, however, it is a number between 0 and 1 to represent the proportion of times that j dominated k, $p(j > k)$. We will discuss dominance matrices, which are probabilistic, because they are most common. A dominance matrix is an example of QIIIa data in that the basic observations are order relations on pairs of points, all from the same set.

The entry in the (k,j) cell of a probabilistic dominance matrix is the complement of that in the (j,k) cell. Because a simple transformation, $p \rightarrow (2p - 1)$, yields a skew symmetric matrix, we shall speak of the dominance matrix as being skew symmetric.

The analysis of such a matrix by Thurstone's model for comparative judgment (1927) could not be more familiar to any other audience. It may be merely added, then, that the Bradley–Terry–Luce (BTL) model for choice behavior (Bradley and Terry, 1952; Luce, 1959) is also designed for such a data matrix.

Now let us consider a special kind of submatrix, one formed from a rectangle of data all on one side of the diagonal, as in Figure 2.3. Such a submatrix is called an off-diagonal submatrix. It is characterized by the fact that the row elements and the column elements are distinct — they form two disjoint subsets of the original set of elements that border the complete matrix.

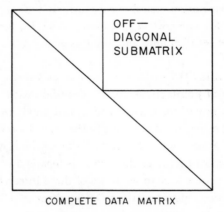

FIGURE 2.3. *A data matrix and an off-diagonal submatrix*

Such a submatrix is one in which the data consist of the proportion of times an element in one set dominates an element in another set. Here we are dealing with an order relation on a pair of points that are from two distinct sets, QIIa data.

It is not uncommon for a data matrix in QIIa to be bordered with individuals as rows and with stimuli as columns, and to have cell entries, then, that reflect a dominance relation between an individual and a stimulus, as in an arithmetic test. Such a data matrix is QIIa because we do not directly observe a dominance relation between pairs of individuals or between pairs of items, but only between pairs of elements from distinct sets. This is what, in Figure 2.2, distinguished single-stimulus data from stimulus comparison data, and, correspondingly, the off-diagonal submatrix from the complete matrix.

Thurstone's model for comparative judgment is designed for the intact QIIIa data matrix. This model was adapted for an off-diagonal submatrix by Torgerson in his model for categorical judgment (1958). It yields two sets of scale values, one for the row elements and one for the column elements. So Torgerson's model is a QIIa adaptation of Thurstone's QIIIa model.

Rasch's recent work (1960, p. 75, Equation 10.1) on a model for the probabilistic behavior of individuals in response to test items may be regarded as related to the BTL QIIIa model in the same way that Torgerson's is related to Thurstone's. Rasch maps the individual and the item into measures on an ability scale, ξ_i for the individual and ζ_j for the problem; and then defines the probability of the individual solving the problem $p(i > j)$ as:

$$p(i > j) = \frac{\xi_i}{\xi_i + \zeta_j} \tag{2.1}$$

This may be recognized as the same relation found in the BTL model in which i and j are elements of the same set rather than of distinct sets.

Now instead of asking which of a pair of stimuli is greater, suppose that we present pairs of dyads and ask in which dyad the pair of stimuli is more alike. The judgment that one pair of stimuli is more alike than another pair we may interpret as signifying that the distance between the one pair of stimulus points is less than the distance between the other pair. This is an order relation on a pair of points in which the points are distances. So clearly we can construct a dominance matrix in QIIIa in which the row and column elements are distances.

Either the Thurstone or the BTL model, appropriately modified for similarities data, could be applied to scale these distances, where each distance is a point on a unidimensional scale.

A weaker alternative is simply to construct an ordinal scale of these distances by requiring weak stochastic transitivity. This corresponds to permuting the columns of the matrix, and of course the corresponding rows, in a search for a pattern in which all entries above the diagonal are at least 0.5. We call this a triangular pattern and the method, triangular analysis. Its relation to Guttman scalogram analysis should be pointed out in passing. Scalogram analysis is a QIIa method designed for the analysis of an off-diagonal submatrix of a QIIIa dominance matrix, and triangular analysis is just another name for it that the author finds desirable for other purposes.[2] But triangular analysis in QIIIa must be distinguished from triangular analysis in QIIa (scalogram analysis), because rows may be permuted independently of columns in the latter but not in the former.

[2] One purpose is to distinguish it from another related method called parallelogram analysis.

These interpoint distances having been scaled, the data correspond to QIVa, similarities data, and may be analyzed by a multidimensional psychophysical model such as the Young-Householder (1938)—Torgerson (1958) model if the distances are measured on a ratio scale. If the interpoint distances are measured only on an ordinal scale, they may be analyzed by a nonmetric model such as Shepard's (1962a, 1962b) or Hays' which is described on p. 55ff.

We see in Figure 2.2 that preferential choice data is identified with QIa. If an individual says he prefers one stimulus to another, we may interpret this as a judgment that the distance from his ideal point to the one stimulus is less than the distance to the other stimulus. In such a data matrix, then, we have order relations on pairs of distances in which each distance is between pairs of points corresponding to disjoint sets, e.g., individuals and stimuli.

A QIa preferential choice data matrix may be seen to be a special submatrix of a QIVa similarities matrix. In QIa we have two disjoint sets of points and the relative distances of the elements of one set from each of the elements of the other set. The distances being compared in QIa are what might be called conjoint distances, because they always have one terminus in common. In QIVa all pairs of distances may be compared, both conjoint and disjoint distances. So we see that QIa data are a very restricted portion of the total potential data we might like to have. But, unfortunately, we are sometimes limited to such observations. You may be able to observe my preference for chocolate creams over peanut brittle and John Jones' preference for chocolate creams over peanut brittle but you may not be able to observe whether I prefer John to chocolate creams.

We have indicated some of the interrelations found within the category of dominance matrices, and we find that they take us through all four quadrants, that is, we find relations between points from the same set and from distinct sets, and relations between distances, all pairs of distances, and only pairs of conjoint distances. Whether we deal with the stimulus points themselves or their interpoint distances, there is a sense in which, if we could get all the data, we would have a QIIIa matrix initially. If we were dealing with the stimulus points, we would get a unidimensional stimulus scale. If we were dealing with the interpoint distances, we would analyze them by a QIVa model, after scaling these interpoint distances, and we could arrive at a multidimensional stimulus space.

If we had somewhat less than all the data, and in a particular sense, then we would analyze it in QIIa if we were dealing with the stimulus points or in QIa if we were dealing with interpoint distances.

We turn now to the discussion of proximity matrices. The discussion of the dominance matrix has involved somewhat more intricate relations than we need to be concerned with in the discussion of proximity matrices. The reason for this is that a dominance matrix is sometimes bordered by stimuli and sometimes bordered by pairs of stimuli, interpoint distances. Models for the analysis of a dominance matrix and its off-diagonal submatrix are different, depending upon whether the matrix is bordered by stimuli or by interpoint distances. Proximity matrices, on the other hand, are generally only bordered by stimuli. We do not, at the current stage of development, need to consider proximity matrices bordered by interpoint distances.

THE SYMMETRIC PROXIMITY MATRIX

Let us turn now to the symmetric proximity matrix. This matrix is square, with a stimulus labeling a row and the corresponding column. The entry in the cell of row j column k is some measure of proximity, for example, commonly, the proportion of times the two stimuli are judged alike, or confused, or otherwise not discriminated, but in a symmetric sense. The proportion is an estimate of a joint probability, $p(jk)$, and is equal to the entry $p(kj)$ in row k column j.

The usual inference is that such a probability may be interpreted in terms of the proximity of the corresponding pair of stimulus points in a psychological space; and because the probability is a joint probability, the matrix is called a symmetric proximity matrix, a QIIIb data matrix.

The Goodman (1951)–Galanter (1956) model was designed for the symmetric proximity matrix with a *one* or *zero* in each of its cells. This model is a set theoretic model, leading under certain conditions to an ordinal scale of the stimuli.

Hefner (1958), in his Ph.D. thesis at Michigan, adapted Thurstone's comparative judgment model to the analysis of a symmetric proximity matrix with probabilities in its cells to arrive at a ratio scale measure of the interpoint distances. The distribution of squared distances between two points each drawn from a multivariate normal is noncentral χ^2 with r degrees of freedom. The noncentrality parameter is the difference between the means of the two multivariate normal distributions, and the number of degrees of freedom is the dimensionality of the space. There are some theoretical problems and some experimental problems that need study before this development can be considered usefully operational.

An off-diagonal submatrix of a symmetric proximity matrix would be a QIIb matrix in which one had the proportion of times each row element and column element had been proximal in a symmetric sense. For example, if a fraternity and sorority with the same number of members had a joint dance, and if everyone danced every dance, then a matrix of the number of times each pair of individuals danced together would be an off-diagonal symmetric proximity matrix. This kind of data matrix does not very commonly arise in psychological research.

A row of this off-diagonal submatrix leads simply and directly to an individual's preference order I scale (Coombs, 1958) over the column elements, which is QIa data and may be analyzed by unfolding theory to obtain a joint space. At the same time, a column of this matrix leads directly to a preference order I scale over the row elements and may be similarly analyzed. This symmetry in the freedom to analyze both row I scales and column I scales is what distinguished the off-diagonal submatrix of a symmetric proximity matrix from that of a conditional proximity matrix.

In summary, the complete symmetric proximity matrix leads to QIVa data and a stimulus space, and an off-diagonal submatrix leads to QIa data and a joint space.

THE CONDITIONAL PROXIMITY MATRIX

This is the third kind of basic measurement data matrix in psychology, and the one to which we shall devote the most attention, including an illustration of a multidimensional analysis of such a matrix. This matrix, like all the other basic matrices, is square with a stimulus labeling a row and the corresponding column. The entry in the cell corresponding to row j and column k may be any measure of conditional proximity, for example, the proportion of times the column stimulus has been judged to be proximal to the row stimulus. The proportion is an estimate of the probability that given j the individual responds with k, $p(k|j)$, a conditional probability.

As a concrete instance, the individual may be given one of half a dozen brands of cigarettes to smoke and asked to identify the brand. Each brand he smokes corresponds to a row of the matrix, and each possible identification is a column of the matrix. Clearly the matrix is in general nonsymmetric. We would not expect that the probability with which he will identify a Camel cigarette as an Old Gold will equal the probability with which he will identify an Old Gold as a Camel.

This conditional proximity matrix is like an $S–R$ matrix in which the responses are identified with the stimuli in a one-to-one manner. The symmetric proximity matrix is like an $S–S$ matrix.

Another way of characterizing the difference between symmetric and conditional proximity data is to say that proximity data may be either absolute or relative. If absolute, then we have symmetric proximity data. If relative, we have conditional proximity data.

We give our attention, now, to the conditional proximity matrix, one that may be described as an $S–R$ matrix or as relative proximity data. We might make the reasonable inference that a probability in a cell of a conditional proximity matrix reflects a proximity relation between the corresponding row and column points, but there is an important difference between conditional proximity data and either of the other two kinds. Two conditional probabilities in the same *row* of the matrix may be interpreted to signify the relative proximity of the corresponding column elements to that row element. But conditional probabilities in different rows are not comparable in this sense, because of the inherent lack of symmetry.

Such data are QIIIb data in the sense that a stimulus is presented and a response is made; this is interpreted as a proximity relation on the corresponding pair of points, all in the same set. This proximity relation, however, is conditional and not symmetric.

If we take an off-diagonal submatrix of such a conditional proximity matrix, we have a QIIb matrix. This is the kind of matrix we would have if we observed the relative frequency with which an element of one set was identified with each of the elements in another set. For example, if we observed the probabilities with which an individual endorsed different items on an attitude scale or the probability with which he bought and smoked different brands of cigarettes, we would have such an off-diagonal submatrix. A row of this matrix leads directly to a preference order I scale over the column elements and may be analyzed by the unfolding technique as QIa data. Because the conditional probabilities in different rows are not comparable, however, column I scales should not be so analyzed.

An off-diagonal submatrix of a conditional proximity matrix may arise in a concept formation experiment in which there is a many-one mapping of stimuli into response categories.

In general, a QIIb matrix is a submatrix of a QIIIb matrix which may be either a symmetric or a conditional proximity matrix. In either case row I scales may be analyzed, but column I scales may be analyzed only in the case that the parent matrix be a symmetric proximity matrix. It is not clear to me how one may be sure, in the case of a QIIb matrix, which the parent matrix may be; but, in all instances examined by the author, the parent matrix may be inferred to be a conditional proximity matrix.

The conditional probabilities in a row of the complete matrix in QIIIb may be used to rank order the distances of all the column stimulus points from the given row stimulus. We will assume that, if stimulus j is more often identified as stimulus k than as stimulus l, the distance between stimulus j and k is less than the distance between j and l. We thus have order relations on distances between pairs of stimuli, QIVa data, and we may hope to analyze such data by a QIVa model.

Before pursuing this analysis further let us make some general remarks about these three kinds of basic data matrices. The examples have been those of probabilistic data matrices, but these matrices are not limited to that particular response characteristic. If, for example, we condition the GSR to one stimulus and observe the magnitude of the conditioned response to other stimuli, we might interpret this as a conditional proximity matrix. A correlation matrix is a symmetric proximity matrix. A sociometric matrix in regard to who bosses whom is a dominance matrix. In general, frequency, amplitude, and latency are three broad categories of response measures, in addition to verbal judgments, that might appear in any one of these matrices.

Let us turn, now, to an example of the complete conditional proximity matrix and discuss its analysis with an example.

AN ANALYSIS OF A CONDITIONAL PROXIMITY MATRIX

Since it might be interesting to analyze similarities among psychological journals, we selected 10 journals; eight of them were APA journals and two were not — *Psychometrika* and the *American Journal of Psychology*. The journals are listed in Table 2.1 in alphabetical order.

TABLE 2.1. *Codes for Journals*

A.   American Journal of Psychology (AJP)
B.   Journal of Abnormal and Social Psychology (JASP)
C.   Journal of Applied Psychology (JAP)
D.   Journal of Comparative and Physiological Psychology (JCPP)
E.   Journal of Consulting Psychology (JCP)
F.   Journal of Educational Psychology (JEdP)
G.   Journal of Experimental Psychology (JExP)
H.   Psychological Bulletin (PB)
I.   Psychological Review (PR)
J.   Psychometrika (Pka)

For the calendar year 1960, we tallied[3] the number of references that each of the journals made to the others in the set. Table 2.2 contains the raw data.

TABLE 2.2. *Number of References in Row-Journal to Column-Journal,* 1960

	A	B	C	D	E	F	G	H	I	J	Other
A	122	4	1	23	4	2	135	17	39	1	319
B	23	303	9	11	49	4	55	50	48	7	1200
C	0	28	84	2	11	6	15	23	8	13	432
D	36	10	4	304	0	0	98	21	65	4	744
E	6	93	11	1	186	6	7	30	10	14	843
F	6	12	11	1	7	34	24	16	7	14	358
G	65	15	3	33	3	3	337	40	59	14	531
H	47	108	16	81	130	14	193	52	31	12	1095
I	22	40	2	29	8	1	97	39	107	13	497
J	2	0	2	0	0	1	6	14	5	59	221

This is quite literally a count of the extent to which a journal "uses" another journal, and we shall relate this to their conditional similarity. Our intent is to map each journal into a point in a Euclidean space in such a manner that the rank order of the other nine points from each point in turn will correspond to the rank order of the similarity of the other nine journals to the one in question.

For various reasons we eliminated two of these journals from the analysis reported here. These were the *Psychological Bulletin* and the *Psychological Review*. This matrix was reduced to an 8 × 8 matrix, with rows H and I and the corresponding columns struck out of Table 2.2.

The numbers in a row of the table might be interpreted as indicating the relative similarity of the column journals to that row journal by assuming, for

[3] This tabulation was made by Mike Levine at Stanford University.

example, that if Journal A refers more often to Journal B than to C, then A is more similar to B than to C.

However, some journals publish more articles than other journals, and one might argue that if Journal A refers to 10 articles out of 200 published in Journal B and to 10 out of 100 published in C, then Journal A is more similar to C than to B. Hence, one should correct the column entries for the size of the pool of articles that could be referred to in that column journal. As an estimate of the size of such pools, we used the column sums and removed their main effect.

Also, some journals tend to make more references than do other journals, so we corrected for row main effects also.

The result of removing the main effects due to differences in sheer bulk of publications and to number of references is to yield a residual matrix of inter-actions, reported as Table 2.3. This is the matrix of which we shall make a nonmetric multidimensional analysis.

TABLE 2.3. *Residual Matrix: The Matrix of Interactions*

	A	B	C	D	E	F	G	J
A	89.625	−54.000	−14.500	−23.750	−28.375	− 4.875	50.500	−14.625
B	−30.500	223.875	−27.625	−56.875	− 4.500	−24.000	−50.625	−29.750
C	−15.750	−13.375	85.125	−28.125	− 4.750	15.750	−52.875	14.000
D	−16.875	−68.500	−32.000	236.750	−52.875	−27.375	− 7.000	−32.125
E	−30.375	31.000	− 8.500	−49.750	149.625	− 4.875	−81.500	− 5.625
F	− 3.500	−23.125	18.375	−22.875	− 2.500	50.000	−37.625	21.250
G	10.000	−65.625	−35.125	−36.375	−52.000	−26.500	229.875	−24.250
J	− 2.625	−30.250	14.250	−19.000	− 4.625	21.875	−50.750	71.125

For each row journal we may rank the column journals in order of increasing distance from it. This gives us what is essentially each journal's preference order I scale over the other journals and suggests analysis by multidimensional unfolding.

In Table 2.4 are the stimulus I scales for each journal obtained directly from Table 2.3.

TABLE 2.4. *Rank Order of the Column-Journals from Each Row-Journal*

A	G	F	C	J	D	E	B
B	E	F	C	J	A	G	D
C	F	J	E	B	A	D	G
D	G	A	F	C	J	E	B
E	B	F	J	C	A	D	G
F	J	C	E	A	D	B	G
G	A	J	F	C	D	E	B
J	F	C	A	E	D	B	G

There are two testable conditions that a conditional proximity matrix must meet to satisfy a metric space: (1) each point must be at least as near to itself as to any other point and (2) distance must be transitive.

The first condition requires that the diagonal entry in the residual matrix be at least as large as any other entry in that row. This assumption of a single-peaked gradient requires that a journal refer to itself at least as often as to any other journals after removing the main effects. We see that this condition is satisfied.

The second condition is one of transitivity of distances. How this condition may be tested may be seen as follows. Any triple of points defines a triangle in the space. From each corner of the triangle the data yield an order relation on the lengths of the two adjacent sides. This has been illustrated in Figure 2.4, using the data from the residual matrix for Journals A, B, and C.

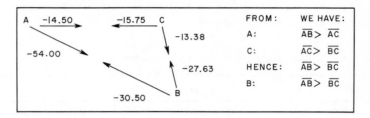

FIGURE 2.4. *Illustrating the test for transitivity of distance*

From row A we see that, according to A's residuals, C is nearer to A than B is, hence $\overline{AB} > \overline{AC}$. From row C we observe that B is nearer C than A is, hence $\overline{AC} > \overline{BC}$. By transitivity, then, B should be nearer C than to A, so $\overline{AB} > \overline{BC}$, which means that Journal B must make more references to C than to A after removing main effects. In this manner, the order relation on the residuals in B's row provides an experimentally independent confirmation or contradiction of the distance relations in this triangle.

This is actually only part of the test of transitivity. Every such triangle may be tested, but in addition there are many longer chains of distances involving disjoint pairs of distances which may also be tested for intransitivity. One does not, of course, need to test each separate triple of distances. Instead, one may test them all at once by using triangular analysis. The method involves merging the distance relations implied by each stimulus I scale in Table 2.4 into a common partial order of distances if it exists. The easiest way the author has found to do this is to make a triangular analysis of the distances. This is illustrated by Table 2.5.

A 1 in a cell of this matrix indicates that the row-distance is greater than the column-distance. A 0 indicates the contrary. A *dash* in a cell indicates a pair of distances that were not compared; these occur between pairs of disjoint distances which are never compared in a conditional proximity matrix. Entries below the diagonal are redundant and have been omitted except for 1's which make it easy to spot the errors in the triangular pattern. If all distance relations were

TABLE 2.5. *Triangular Pattern Which Minimizes the Sum Total of Differences between Residuals That Must Be Changed*

	$\overline{BD}$	$\overline{BG}$	$\overline{AB}$	$\overline{EG}$	$\overline{DE}$	$\overline{AE}$	$\overline{CG}$	$\overline{FG}$	$\overline{GJ}$	$\overline{BJ}$	$\overline{DJ}$	$\overline{CD}$	$\overline{BF}$	$\overline{DF}$	$\overline{AD}$	$\overline{AC}$	$\overline{BC}$	$\overline{CE}$	$\overline{DG}$	$\overline{EJ}$	$\overline{AJ}$	$\overline{CJ}$	$\overline{AF}$	$\overline{AG}$	$\overline{EF}$	$\overline{BE}$	$\overline{CF}$	$\overline{FJ}$
$\overline{BD}$	–	–	–	–	–	–	–	–	–	–	–	–	–	–	–	–	–	–	–	–	–	–	–	–	–	–	–	–
$\overline{BG}$		–	–	–	–	–	–	–	–	–	–	–	–	–	–	–	–	–	–	–	–	–	–	–	–	–	–	–
$\overline{AB}$			–	–	–	–	–	–	–	–	–	–	–	–	–	–	–	–	–	–	–	–	–	–	–	–	–	–
$\overline{EG}$				–	–	–	–	–	–	–	–	–	–	–	–	–	–	–	–	–	–	–	–	–	–	–	–	–
$\overline{DE}$					–	–	–	–	–	–	–	–	–	–	–	–	–	–	–	–	–	–	–	–	–	–	–	–
$\overline{AE}$						–	–	–	–	–	–	–	–	–	–	–	–	–	–	–	–	–	–	–	–	–	–	–
$\overline{CG}$							–	–	–	–	–	–	–	–	–	–	–	–	0	–	–	–	–	–	–	–	–	–
$\overline{FG}$								–	–	–	–	–	–	–	–	–	–	–	0	–	–	–	–	–	–	–	–	–
$\overline{GJ}$									–	–	–	–	–	–	–	–	–	–	0	–	–	–	–	–	–	–	–	–
$\overline{BJ}$										–	–	–	–	–	–	–	–	–	–	–	–	–	–	–	–	–	–	–
$\overline{DJ}$											–	–	–	–	–	–	–	–	–	–	–	–	–	–	–	–	–	–
$\overline{CD}$												–	–	–	–	–	–	–	–	–	–	–	–	–	–	–	–	–
$\overline{BF}$													–	–	–	–	0	–	–	–	–	–	–	–	–	–	–	–
$\overline{DF}$														–	–	–	–	–	–	–	–	–	–	–	–	–	–	–
$\overline{AD}$															–	–	–	–	–	–	–	–	–	–	–	–	–	–
$\overline{AC}$																–	–	–	–	–	0	–	–	–	–	–	–	–
$\overline{BC}$																	–	–	–	–	–	–	–	–	–	–	–	–
$\overline{CE}$																		–	–	–	–	–	–	–	–	–	–	–
$\overline{DG}$							1	1	1										–	–	–	–	–	–	–	–	–	–
$\overline{EJ}$																				–	–	–	–	–	–	–	–	–
$\overline{AJ}$																					–	–	–	–	–	–	–	–
$\overline{CJ}$																						–	–	–	–	–	–	–
$\overline{AF}$																							–	–	–	–	–	–
$\overline{AG}$																								–	–	–	–	–
$\overline{EF}$																									–	–	–	–
$\overline{BE}$																										–	–	–
$\overline{CF}$																											–	–
$\overline{FJ}$																												–

transitive, an arrangement of this matrix would exist that would have no 1's below the diagonal.

We see that there are 1's below the diagonal, and this implies that there are intransitivities. In fact, for Table 2.5, there are a total of 24 intransitive triples of distances out of a total of 3276 triples, 0.0073, or three-fourths of one percent (Chapter 17 of Coombs (1964) describes the procedures for obtaining the number of transitive triples). We might reasonably conclude that these are due to error and that the distance relations are basically transitive.

In order to construct a geometric representation of these relations, we must violate any intransitivities. Equivalently, we may deliberately change the data and make all the relations transitive. Now, any particular intransitive cycle of k elements can be made transitive by cutting it at any one of k different places, and we must decide which would do the least violence to the basic data.

The 1's below the diagonal in Table 2.5 correspond to the links that would be cut in their respective intransitive cycles if this triangular pattern were accepted. To each such link corresponds a difference between the column element residual and the row element residual. To break a link is effectively to reduce this difference to zero, that is, to violate this difference, and so the criterion used to accept a triangular pattern was that it minimizes the sum of these differences between residuals which would be violated.

A simpler criterion would be to minimize the number of intransitive triples. The criterion used instead weights each such triple according to the strength of the quantitative evidence for preserving it.

For Table 2.5, corresponding to the 1's below the diagonal, we have the following differences between residuals which are violated by this triangular pattern:

$$
\begin{aligned}
\overline{CG} - \overline{DG} &= -35.125 - (-36.375) = 1.250 \\
\overline{FG} - \overline{DG} &= -26.500 - (-36.375) = 9.875 \\
\overline{GJ} - \overline{DG} &= -24.250 - (-36.375) = 12.125 \\
\overline{BF} - \overline{BC} &= -24.000 - (-27.625) = 3.625 \\
\overline{AC} - \overline{AJ} &= -14.500 - (-14.625) = 0.125 \\
&\qquad\qquad\qquad\qquad\quad \sum = 27.000
\end{aligned}
$$

We see that the sum of the differences between residuals which would be violated here is 27. Since no other triangular pattern that led to a smaller value could be found, this was accepted as the minimum.

The final resulting partial order of distances is given in Figure 2.5, which comes from the order of the columns in Table 2.5.

Perhaps the best way to see just what changes have been made is to compare the revised stimulus I scales, Table 2.6, with those given in Table 2.4. The arrow in A's I scale indicates that J was moved forward from behind C to in front of C. In B's I scale, C was moved from behind F to in front of F. In G's I scale, D was moved from behind C to in front of J. These revised I scales are the data, then, for which we seek a geometric representation.

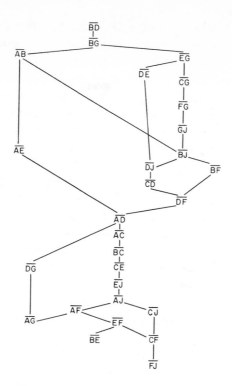

FIGURE 2.5. *Final partial order on interpoint distances*

TABLE 2.6. *Revised I Scales, Showing Changes in Originals*

A	G	F	J	C	D	E	B
B	E	C	F	J	A	G	D
C	F	J	E	B	A	D	G
D	G	A	F	C	J	E	B
E	B	F	J	C	A	D	G
F	J	C	E	A	D	B	G
G	A	D	J	F	C	E	B
J	F	C	A	E	D	B	G

Having obtained a transitive partial order of the interpoint distances, we are ready to make a multidimensional analysis of them.

The method of analysis has been described elsewhere in some detail. It is an algorithm based on William Hays' modification of his method for the multidimensional unfolding of preferential choice data (Hays and Bennett, 1961). The method is a nonmetric analogue to a principal components factor analysis. Every triple of points defines a triangle, and for each triangle we know its longest side. We speak of an axis as fitting or satisfying a triangle if the longest side of the triangle has the longest projection on that axis.

For example, in Figure 2.4 we saw that the triangle *ACB* has the line *A–B* as its longest side. To fit this triangle, *C* must project on some axis between *A* and

B, so that the side A–B has the longest projection on the axis. In listing a triple of points, we follow the convention here of listing each triple so that the ends of the longest side are the first and last letter in the triple. So, because C must project between A and B, we list this triple of points in the order ACB.

We locate the first dimension so as to fit as many triangles as possible, with priority to the largest triangles in the space. This is most conveniently done by using the I scales of the end points of the longest line in the space. In these data, the longest line is B–D, as may be seen from the partial order on distances, Figure 2.5.

If one dimension were to satisfy the data, B's I scale and D's I scale would be mirror images, and we would have the rank order of the projections of the other points between them immediately. If their I scales are not mirror images, we merge them into a common partial order, thereby fitting a maximum number of the largest triangles, and resolve the partial order by fitting as many as possible of the remaining triangles.

For example, in Table 2.6 we have B's I scale and D's I scale. If we put these in juxtaposition, as in Table 2.7, with D's I scale reversed for clarity, we see that their common partial order is as shown.

TABLE 2.7. *The Line B–D as First Dimension*

B's I scale	:	B	E	C	F	J	A	G	D
D's I scale (rev)	:	B	E	J	C	F	A	G	D

Their Common Partial Order

$$B - E\underset{J}{\overset{}{-}}C - F - A - G - D$$

Resolution of Partial Order

CJ		FJ
$AJC \Rightarrow CJ$		$AFJ \Rightarrow JF$
$BCJ \Rightarrow CJ$		$BFJ \Rightarrow FJ$
$DCJ \Rightarrow JC$		$CFJ \Rightarrow FJ$
$CJE \Rightarrow JC$		$DFJ \Rightarrow JF$
$CFJ \Rightarrow CJ$		$EFJ \Rightarrow FJ$
$CJG \Rightarrow CJ$		$FJG \Rightarrow FJ$
	$\therefore CFJ$	

Solution

$$B \quad E \quad C \quad F \quad J \quad A \quad G \quad D$$

To resolve this partial order we need to locate J relative to C and F; so we look at all triples involving CJ and FJ, see what order each triple implies, and select that order which fits the largest number of them. The result is the solution at the bottom of the table.

Altogether there are 56 triangles in the space, of which 47 (84 percent) are fitted by the line B–D as first dimension.

The line B–G, the second longest line in the space, was also tried as an alternative first dimension, which is like making a rotation. The result is given in Table 2.8. Since this solution fitted 49 of the 56 triangles, or 87.5 percent, it was chosen for the first dimension.

TABLE 2.8. *The Line B–G as First Dimension*

B's I scale :	*B E C F J A G D*
G's I scale (rev) :	*B E C F J D A G*

Their Common Partial Order

$$B - E - C - F - J \underset{\searrow}{} A - G$$
$$D$$

Resolution of Partial Order

AD	*DG*
BAD $\Rightarrow$ *AD*	*BGD* $\Rightarrow$ *GD*
CAD $\Rightarrow$ *AD*	*CDG* $\Rightarrow$ *DG*
DAE $\Rightarrow$ *AD*	*EDG* $\Rightarrow$ *DG*
DAF $\Rightarrow$ *AD*	*FDG* $\Rightarrow$ *DG*
AGD $\Rightarrow$ *AD*	*AGD* $\Rightarrow$ *GD*
DAJ $\Rightarrow$ *AD*	*GDJ* $\Rightarrow$ *DG*

$\therefore$ *ADG*

Solution

B   E   C   F   J   A   D   G

Because there are triples that remain unsatisfied, another dimension is called for. For the second, and all further dimensions, we merely take the triples that are still not fitted and construct a partial order that satisfies the maximum number of them. There are only seven unsatisfied triangles remaining. With so few, one may directly construct a partial order to embed as many of these as possible. The solution is immediate and satisfies all seven of the unfitted triangles. The unfitted triangles and the solution are presented in Table 2.9.

TABLE 2.9. *Solution for the Second Dimension*

Unfitted Triangles

AGD	*CFE*
AFJ	*CJE*
BGD	*DFJ*
DCJ	

Their Best Partial Order

(AB)   G   D   C   F   J   E

To assist in arriving at an interpretation, the two dimensions are summarized in Table 2.10, and a possible product space of the two orders is shown in Figure 2.6.

TABLE 2.10. *The Final Two Dimensions*

K^1		K^2	
B.	J. Abnorm. Soc. Psychol.	*A.*	Amer. J. Psychol.
E.	J. Consult. Psychol.	*B.*	J. Abnorm. Soc. Psychol.
C.	J. Appl. Psychol.	*G.*	J. Exp. Psychol.
F.	J. Educ. Psychol.	*D.*	J. Compar. Physio. Psychol.
J.	Psychometrika	*C.*	J. Appl. Psychol.
A.	Amer. J. Psychol.	*F.*	J. Educ. Psychol.
D.	J. Compar. Physio. Psychol.	*J.*	Psychometrika
G.	J. Exp. Psychol.	*E.*	J. Consult. Psychol.

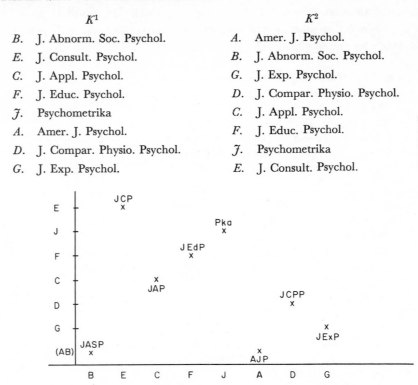

FIGURE 2.6. *The configuration*

The first dimension might variously be interpreted as soft–hard, field–laboratory, real–artificial, significant–rigorous, and so on. The figure does not adequately reflect the metric relations or the relative lengths of the two dimensions, because the first dimension quite dominates the space, fitting 87.5 percent of the triangles.

The interpretation of the second dimension is less obvious. The first four journals are ordinarily associated with academic psychology, and the last four more often with service and application, so we might tentatively label this dimension academic-applied.

The author was frankly somewhat surprised that the data satisfied the conditions for a metric space as well as they did, and also that a single dimension satisfied so much of the data.

SUMMARY

After a very brief review of the basis of the theory of data and the resulting classification of kinds of data, we suggested that measurement data could also be categorized in terms of three basic kinds of data matrices when they are intact or complete. Off-diagonal submatrices of these are QII data matrices.

The data of QI and QIV involve relations on interpoint distances. Such relations are obtained from these same three basic matrices, either by bordering the matrices with interpoint distances or by a transformation of a response measure into a measure of distance. Once one has the measures of interpoint distances, these measures may be analyzed by multidimensional methods in QIa or QIVa, and it no longer matters which of the three basic kinds of matrices was the parent matrix.

As an example we took a conditional proximity matrix and made a nonmetric multidimensional analysis. The first phase of such an analysis requires testing for transitivity of distance, correcting intransitivities if they exist, and establishing a partial order on them. The second phase is the multidimensional analysis of the partial order.

Both of these phases would also be required in the analysis of a dominance matrix bordered by interpoint distances. With a symmetric proximity matrix the situation is not so clear. The first phase may or may not be necessary, depending upon the assumptions one makes and the nature of the data. In the case of a correlation or covariance matrix, for example, it would be a simple matter to construct an order relation on distances and make a nonmetric factor analysis. This would not be advisable, of course, since it would be throwing away information. But it is clear that we can perform nonmetric factor analyses of data matrices that are not suitable for conventional methods of factoring.

3

INTERCULTURAL STUDIES
OF ATTITUDES

Harold Gulliksen

Princeton University
and Educational
Testing Service

3 INTERCULTURAL STUDIES OF ATTITUDES[1]

From one point of view, the origin of this paper dates back to 1928 when I was a student at Ohio State University. Professor Thurstone came to Ohio State and gave a seminar describing his "New Scaling Methods." He showed how psychophysics could be extended to deal with stimuli for which there was no physical measure that correlated with the subjective measurements. Some of the psychophysical procedures that had been used to measure the brightness of a light or the pitch of a sound could be used to measure numerous other subjective characteristics, such as the strength of an attitude, the value of a gift, or the beauty of a picture. To me this was a tremendously striking development — the heart of the subject matter of psychology. All of the subjective qualities about which one formerly had said, "Oh, what can you do about subject matter X? It is all a matter of opinion, and opinions differ," were now available for scientific study. Psychological scaling methods were an exact tool to deal with this vast array of subject matter. I very much wanted to be a part of the initial development of a field as important as this. In the summer of 1929, I went to the University of Chicago for the summer session and began my work there, taking Professor Thurstone's course on Psychophysical Scaling Methods.

His work demonstrated the usefulness and power of these new psychophysical methods — the method of paired comparisons, the successive intervals method, the extension of paired comparisons theory to rank-order data, and the method of response similarities (Thurstone, 1927; 1928a; 1928b; 1929; 1931a). He then became interested in developing methods of factor analysis for the determination of primary mental abilities, and his major efforts moved to the mental ability field. In teaching at Princeton, in 1945, I was impressed with the need for further developments in scaling methods.

DEVELOPMENTS IN SCALING METHODS

Several things were noted that might be done in order to secure more widespread and appropriate use of the psychological scaling methods.

Theoretical Developments

The first need had to do with several aspects of the theoretical development that were not as yet complete. Linear scaling methods had been developed only for the analysis of group data. In the field of multidimensional scaling the early work of Klingberg (1941), Richardson (1938), and Young and Householder (1938) had not been followed up. Development of multidimensional methods

[1]The research is supported jointly by the Office of Naval Research under Contract Nonr 1858(15) and the National Science Foundation Grant G-22889 with Princeton University, and by Educational Testing Service. This work made use of computer facilities at Princeton University that are supported, in part, by National Science Foundation Grant NSF-GP579. The Rockefeller Foundation supported meetings to plan some of these studies.

was needed in order to supplement the linear scaling methods where appropriate. Such work was carried out by Messick (1956) and Torgerson (1952; 1958). Recently Shepard (1962a; 1962b), at the Bell Telephone Laboratories, generalized the multidimensional scaling procedures to the assuming of the "best-fitting" monotonic relationship between the responses of the subjects and the interpoint distances. Computer programs for determining interpoint distances and point coordinates from subjects' judgments, using only this monotonic assumption, have been developed by Roger Shepard, Joseph Kruskal, and Warren Torgerson. This generalization of multidimensional scaling greatly increases the range of data to which the procedure may usefully be applied.

The possibility that various members of a group did not see exactly the same scale had to be recognized. In any values study, for example, some people in the group might value A very much more than B, while for others the reverse might be true. Some way was needed to give appropriate scope to individual differences in the analysis, preferably without going to the extreme of saying that one must develop a separate and independent scale for each individual. These considerations led Ledyard Tucker (1955; 1960a; 1960b) to the development of what he has termed the vector model in scaling, an application of factor analysis to determine the major points of view that are exhibited by the group of judges. Perhaps I can best illustrate this with the very simple setup illustrated in Table 3.1,[2] in which there are four objects, A, B, C, and D, being judged by three judges, X, Y, and Z. Assume that each of these three judges is a type case and that there are many other judges like X, many others like Y, and many like Z.

If we follow the usual procedure of averaging ratings, then object A gets an average rating of 2. The other three get an average rank of $2\frac{2}{3}$; so on the average A is clearly the first. If A, B, C, and D are four people, and we have a political caucus situation where the party convention must agree on a candidate, Mr. A would win, because none of the other three candidates could swing enough votes from those who rate him very low. So, from one point of view, the average scale value could be regarded as a correct representation of the results. But let us assume we are dealing with a market situation and that A, B, C, and D are commodities. On the basis of the highest average for A, one concern might put out commodity A as the best one. The other companies, who put out B, C, and D, would get all of the sales, however. A would not get any sales, since for every customer, there would always be something preferable to A.

Essentially the analytical procedure is a factoring procedure. We might represent these four items by putting B, C, and D at the vertices of an equilateral triangle and A inside the triangle. The different people concerned then would be thought of as vectors through this two-space. Each person's point of view could be correctly represented by a simple diagram such as is shown in Figure 3.1.

[2] Tables 3.1 through 3.14 appear in numerical order at the end of this chapter.

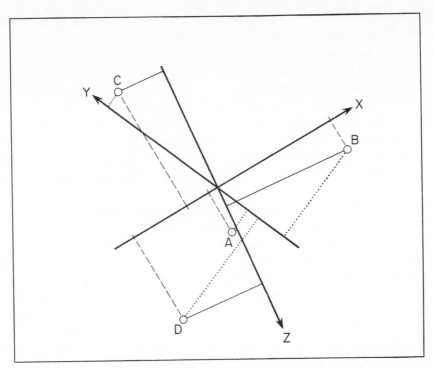

FIGURE 3.1. *Illustrative preference structure. Adapted from L. R Tucker, Dimensions of Preference. Research Memorandum 60-7, Educational Testing Service, Princeton, N. J., 1960. (Multilithed report)*

A simplified description of this procedure is that one obtains the scale values of the set of objects for each judge. These scale values are arranged in an "objects" by "persons" matrix. The rank of this matrix indicates the number of dimensions in which the stimulus vectors and the person vectors would be placed in order to represent the experimentally observed relationships. As illustrated in Figure 3.1, the scale value for each object, for each judge, can be approximated as the scalar product of the vector representing that judge by the vector representing that particular object. Judge X would rate B as best, A next, C third, and D poorest, as shown by the dashed lines on the graph. Judge Y sees the world from a different point of view, according to which C is best, A next, then D, and B lowest, as shown by the dotted lines on the graph. Judge Z, as shown by the solid lines, gives the order as D, A, B, C. In other words, objects A, B, C, and D have at least two relevant characteristics, since this is a two-dimensional graph. The three judges are weighting these characteristics differently and, hence, express different opinions regarding the optimum.

We now have both linear and multidimensional methods for use with a *group*, at the other extreme with *individuals*, and an intermediate situation with the *vector model*. These developments, represented by the six cells in the following chart, give a reasonably complete set of methods for dealing with various scaling situations.

	Linear	*Multidimensional*
Group		
Vector		
Individual		

Development of Labor-Saving Methods

A second need in the development of scaling methods arose from the fact that the work involved in a method such as paired comparisons is quite laborious

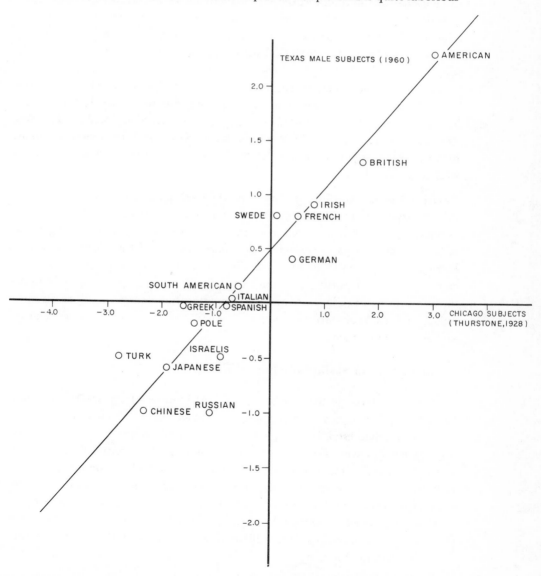

FIGURE 3.2. *Comparison of scale values for Nationality Preferences. (1928 vs. 1960)*

for the subject. In considering this difficulty, Tucker (1960b) thought of using multiple rank orders. John Tukey identified such designs as balanced incomplete block designs and balanced lattice designs. The method has been described by Gulliksen and Tucker (1961). Setting up the experimental procedure in this way, rather than as a complete paired comparisons schedule, facilitates the covering of a good many stimuli without unreasonable fatigue for the subjects or without unreasonable consumption of experimental time.

Other developments were needed to reduce the burden of computational labor. The analytical work involved, both in the regular linear and multidimensional methods and in the vector methods, turns out to be considerable.

With the advent of the electronic computer, however, programs are now available for paired comparisons, successive intervals, and multidimensional methods; as a result, the analytical work is speeded up and made tremendously less laborious.

Also, there was no convenient assemblage of descriptions of different scaling methods for study by the student. Recognizing this need, the Social Science Research Council engaged Warren Torgerson to write the book, *Theory and Methods of Scaling* (1958). This volume has proved to be extremely useful in making developments in scaling methods available to students and research workers in the field.

Relative Versus Absolute Judgments. Another point frequently raised was that methods such as paired comparisons were relative and not absolute methods; that is, one achieved a scaling of the objects by forcing a preference judgment on each pair even when the judge liked *all* of the objects, or *half* of them, or *none* of them. The results could scale in the same way in any of these cases. The idea of putting in a "neutral point," which requires the subject to make an absolute judgment, and then treating this neutral point as another object for paired comparisons is one way of having the subject give both relative and absolute judgments.

Applications of Scaling Methods

It was also possible that the potential contributions of the scaling methods to various psychological and sociological problems were not too clear. While many studies had established scale values for stimuli, there had been relatively few studies that went *beyond* the determination of scale values. In general, a method of measurement is a necessary but not a sufficient condition for the development of a science. So it seemed reasonable to suggest that studies should not end with the establishment of scale values but should go on to utilize these measurements in determining other laws of science (Gulliksen, 1961, pp. 12–14). General analytical methods for utilizing factor analysis and rotational procedures in determining parameters for various types of nonlinear functional relationships have been presented by Tucker (1958) and Cliff (1962).

Thurstone and Jones (1959) followed this principle in studies of various birthday gifts, in which the scale values were utilized to test a linear law of diminishing returns by the device of getting scale values for both single objects and double objects. The possibility of utilizing similar procedures for verifying various nonlinear laws was investigated. One study (Gulliksen, 1956) on the measurement of values compared a linear, a negative exponential, a logarithmic, and a square root law of diminishing returns. It utilized the scaling methods as the initial take-off point but went beyond them.

Norman Cliff's studies (1959; 1960) of adverb-adjective combinations are another illustration. The scale values of adverb-adjective combinations were used as the initial data of the study, but the major interest was in going beyond the initial scale values to see if some simple law could be devised giving the effect of adverbs on adjectives. In his studies, the multiplicative law has been verified — adverbs multiply adjectives. It is interesting to note that, in 1954, Thurstone (see Thurstone, 1959, p. 189) wrote, "It would be useful to have an index of affective intensity for adjectives in a dictionary. . . . Such affective indexes would be useful in translating a foreign language."

Harold Schiffman (1960) also utilized scaling procedures to study the combined influence of the characteristics of an *author* of a statement and the characteristics of the *content* of the statement on the *total effect* of this statement, and again found a very simple relationship. The author and the statement may each be regarded as a vector, and the total effect — or scale value of the "authored-statement" — is the scalar product of these two vectors.

BACKGROUND FOR ATTITUDES STUDY

The current study of international attitudes is another attempt to demonstrate the usefulness of psychological scaling methods for investigating problems of an abstract nature. It uses primarily the linear rather than multidimensional methods, but utilizes both group scaling and vector models, together with some of the experimental simplifications previously mentioned. The study is concerned generally with attitudes toward work. Since a person's occupation is sometimes considered as an index of status, it was considered important to study views of occupational prestige and reasons for work. Larger goals of life and nationality preferences were also studied.

If we review studies of occupational prestige and nationality preferences, we find that the authors have encountered several difficulties. Many investigators (Aberle, 1950; Coleman, 1957a; Davies, 1952; Hatt, 1950; Hyman, 1942; and Morris and Murphy, 1959) have indicated that the concept of one prestige hierarchy, or one ordering, is inadequate. They recognize that instead there may be several different orderings. A given average can be made up in several ways, as was suggested earlier. We may get a mid-scale prestige or preference value because most of the persons give that object a mid-scale rating, or we may get it because some persons rate the object very high and others rate it very low.

A number of possibilities have been suggested in the sociological literature to overcome this difficulty:

(1) Not only the mean rating but the variance of ratings over the group can be reported.

(2) It has been proposed by Benoit-Smullyan (1944), by Hatt (1950), and others that there are different parallel scales, and different sets of objects will have ratings along these different scales. This is analogous to what has been

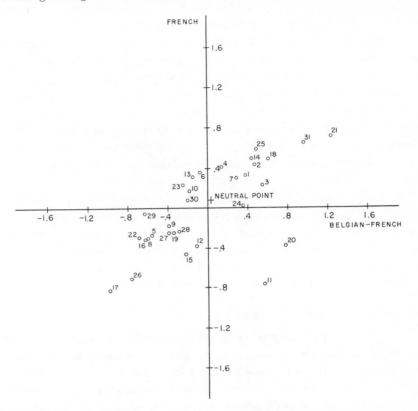

FIGURE 3.3. *Comparison of scale values of Occupations: French and Belgian-French. (The number near each point is the number of an item in the schedule. The items are shown in Table 3.4)*

termed partial ordering. Items within each scale can be compared, but items in one scale cannot be compared with those in another scale.

(3) Another approach is to define various arbitrary subgroups, such as urban vs. rural, educated vs. uneducated, Democrat vs. Republican, or wealthy vs. poor. These various subgroups, or combinations of them, are then treated separately, so that one can determine the extent to which the resulting scale values are different for members of these different groups. This approach has been used in some of the large-scale studies, such as those of Hall and Jones (1950) in England and North and Hatt (1947) in the United States.

(4) Paul Hatt (1950) has also suggested that one might define various subgroups of persons not by arbitrary categories, as in (3) above, but by inter-correlations among persons, setting some arbitrary cut-off point, such as where

the average intercorrelation drops below 0.60 or 0.40; one then would secure by cut-and-try methods a number of subgroups within each of which the average intercorrelation was at or above the specified limit.

Instead of attempting to predefine subgroups whose members will have a uniform opinion or to set some arbitrary criterion of intercorrelations for the

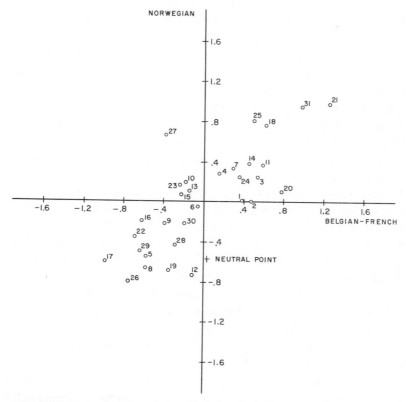

FIGURE 3.4. *Comparison of scale values of Occupations: Norwegian and Belgian-French. (The number near each point is the number of an item in the schedule. The items are shown in Table 3.4)*

determination of a subgroup, it is possible to ask directly how many different points of view (with respect to hierarchical order) are held by the group. Do some persons in the group see things one way and some another? We may obtain the structure not by comparing arbitrarily predefined subgroups but by analyzing the data of the total group to ascertain the major differentiations of opinion found within that group. One can then study persons who hold various points of view to determine the nature of these persons with respect to such characteristics as Democrat-Republican, rich-poor, urban-rural, and so forth. This is Tucker's (1955; 1960a; 1960b) vector model for linear scaling. An approximation is obtained by taking the number of votes given by each person to each object and factor-analyzing the intercorrelations between the objects. The data furnished by the group thus define the points of view in the group.

One is not dependent on any arbitrary criterion of average intercorrelation or on correctly anticipating a relevant definition of subgroups.

This approach, using factor analysis to determine the number and nature of the major viewpoints held by members of the group, is suggested as a solution to the difficulty noted above — that a given average may arise in several different ways. A number of studies using this technique have been surveyed by Gulliksen (1962) and Tucker (1963). The data for such a study are frequently in the form of a fixed set of ranks, in which case the matrix or subsections of it will be "double-centered," that is, the sum of the ranks is the same constant for *each rater*, and the sum of the deviation scores (or standard scores), used for the correlation coefficient, is zero for *each item*. Such a matrix should be factored by procedures described by Tucker (1956).

Another question that is frequently raised with respect to questionnaire approaches is the extent to which the persons exhibit appropriate consistency in answering the questions. Both the multiple rank order procedure and paired comparisons give a possible approach to this question. Since Kendall (1948; 1955) has developed a procedure for counting the number of circular triads in a paired comparison schedule and has developed the criteria for judging the randomness or nonrandomness of these circular triads, it is possible now to give another score for each person taking a paired comparison schedule — his total circular triads score. A circular triad is a judgment of the form: A is greater than B, B is greater than C, C is greater than A. One counts the total number of triads that have such circularity and thus obtains an index of the extent to which each person had a consistent opinion regarding rank ordering or, conversely, was confusing the objects being scaled.

This confusion of the objects might be due to carelessness of the subject; or it might be due to the fact that the objects are really very much alike and hence cannot be successfully and consistently discriminated, even though the person was very careful; or it might be due to the fact that the person does not have a very stable preference system for making these judgments. In any case, the total number of circular triads is a valuable score. It could be used, for instance, for distinguishing some of the subjects whose responses are extremely out of line with others, or it could be used as an additional measure in itself. The varying stability of a preference system, or the varying carefulness among subjects, can be measured by using the total circular triads score.

The question raised in beginning this study of international attitudes, then, was this: "Could the recently developed theoretical, experimental, and analytical methods in psychological scaling be used with profit in comparing the attitudes of different national groups with respect to such topics as occupational prestige, nationality preferences, reasons for work, and goals of life?"

THE QUESTIONNAIRES

We are using four preference schedules. One questionnaire deals with the social status of occupations and asks, "Which occupation has the better social standing?" It presents for comparison 31 different occupations. A second questionnaire concerns attitudes toward work, and the subject is required to indicate his degree of "agreement" in responding to statements about "reasons for work." A third questionnaire deals with nationality preferences ("Which nationality do you prefer?") and asks for comparisons of 31 different nationalities. A fourth questionnaire deals with more remote goals of life. The items were

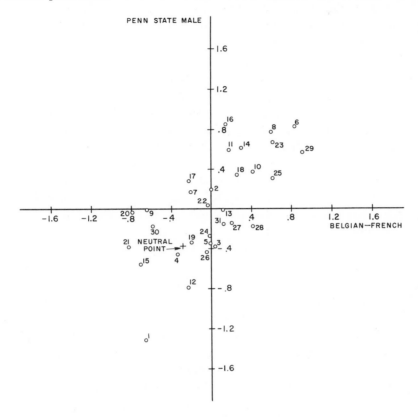

FIGURE 3.5. *Comparison of scale values of Reasons for Work: Penn State and Belgian-French. (The number near each point is the number of an item in the schedule. The items are shown in Table 3.5)*

selected from a schedule used in a study conducted some years ago under the direction of Ralph Tyler (Dunkel, 1947). It contained items indicating that major purposes of life were, for example: "Gaining personal immortality in heaven," "Having power, control over people and things," or "Serving the community of which I am a part."

We shall refer to these questionnaires as the Occupations, Reasons for Work, Nationalities, and Goals of Life Schedules. The Goals of Life Schedule contains only 12 items and was set up as a complete paired comparisons schedule. The Occupations, Reasons for Work, and Nationalities Schedules each contain 31 items and were designed in a balanced incomplete block form.

In paired comparisons, the judgment required is very simple. One presents a pair of objects and asks a question such as, "Which has greater social prestige?" or "Which is brighter?" The judgment is easy, but the method is laborious because many judgments are required of the subject.

The other extreme is simply to ask the person to rank the objects. This has the disadvantage that one does not get any indication of the degree of intransitivity, that is, the number of circular triads that the person would exhibit; and so one cannot determine the degree to which the person may have a stable or an unstable set of preferences.

The method used here is to present the 31 objects in 31 sets of six. The subject is asked to rank the objects in each set of six. If the items are properly chosen for the sets, it is possible to get all possible paired comparisons. An IBM 650 program is available for analyzing data collected in this way, either with 31 objects in 31 sets of six or with 21 objects in 21 sets of five each. A Fortran program is now available for the IBM 7090 and for the CDC 1604 that will analyze any multiple rank order design from 7 stimuli in 7 blocks of 3 each to 81 stimuli in 90 blocks of 9 each. Table 3.2 represents a sample page of a questionnaire with a 6-31 design. The complete set of items used for each questionnaire is shown in the tables of scale values (Tables 3.4 to 3.7).

The questionnaires were administered in Belgium, Italy, the United States, France, and Germany. More specifically, all four schedules were given to about 200 Flemish-speaking students in Belgium by Leopold Knops of the University of Louvain and to another French-speaking Belgian group by Gerard DeMontpellier of Louvain. Three schedules (all but Goals of Life) were administered to about 275 young men in military service in Norway by Eivind Baade and Rolf Gerhardt. Four were given to about 400 Italian students by Fabio Metelli of the University of Padua. In addition, the Nationalities Schedule was administered to about 200 university students in Germany by Heinrich Roth of the Hochschule for Internationale Paedagogische Forschung, and the Occupations Schedule was given to about 1200 French students by Reuchlin and Larcebeau of the Institut National d'Orientation Professionnelle. In the United States, the four questionnaires were given to 682 students at the University of Texas by H. Paul Kelley and 534 students at Pennsylvania State University by Douglas N. Jackson. Table 3.3 summarizes the information about the groups studied.

THE SCALE VALUES

Average scale values have been computed for data groups from France, Germany, Belgium, Texas, Pennsylvania, and Norway. As will be shown in detail later on, a striking characteristic about these scale values or averages is the agreement from one group to another. The scale values are shown in Tables 3.4 to 3.7.

There is considerable agreement among the different groups on the relative prestige of occupations, as is shown in Table 3.4. Physician, Lawyer, and

University Professor are in the first four for all groups, while Shoemaker, Janitor, and Barber are among the lower seven for all groups.

In the Reasons for Work Schedule (Table 3.5) we find the following two statements among the lowest four for all groups:

"If you see a worker loaf you should tell the supervisor."
"We work only because we have to."

Among the top seven statements for all groups are:

"There is a great deal of satisfaction when one can be creative in one's job."
"Work is a pleasure when you have good working conditions and good work comrades."
"A considerate management and understanding work comrades make the work much lighter to perform."
"There is a great deal of satisfaction in doing work that will help others."

These statements can be characterized, perhaps, as indicating a direct interest

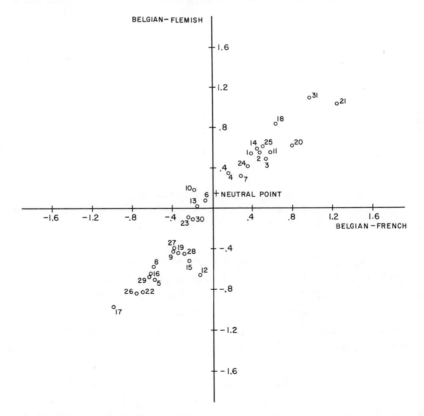

FIGURE 3.6. *Comparison of scale values of Occupations: Belgian-Flemish and Belgian-French. (The number near each point is the number of an item in the schedule. The items are shown in Table 3.4)*

in the characteristics of the job itself rather than an interest in the monetary reward of the job or in what that monetary reward will obtain.

In studying the nationalities (Table 3.6), we find that each national group rates itself the highest. The Norwegians rank Danes relatively higher than do other groups, but give the Swedes about the same ranking as do each of the

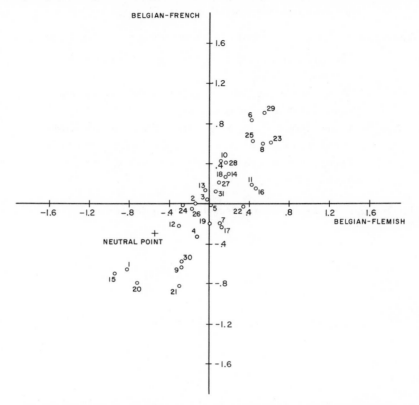

FIGURE 3.7. *Comparison of scale values of Reasons for Work: Belgian-French and Belgian-Flemish. (The number near each point is the number of an item in the schedule. The items are shown in Table 3.5)*

other national groups. Comparing the Norwegian and the two Belgian groups, we find that the Belgians give a relatively higher rank to the Portuguese, Spanish, and South American, while the Norwegians give a relatively higher rank to the British and Dutch. All four of the American groups (male and female groups for the University of Texas and for Penn State) agree in including American, British, Canadian, Swedish, and Swiss among the six highest nationalities.

The nationalities preference scale values may be matched with the scale values found by Professor Thurstone in his earlier study (1928a). These are shown in Figure 3.2 and show marked agreement over a period of about 30 years.

Regarding the goals of life (Table 3.7), we find general agreement that

"Leading a moral life as dictated by God" ranks high for all groups, and "Power, control over people and things" ranks at or near the bottom for all groups. The most striking difference is that the top two goals for the French-speaking Belgian group are "Self-sacrifice for sake of a better world" and "Serving the community of which I am a part," while these two statements have a

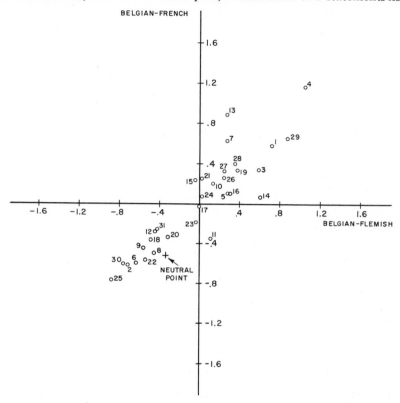

FIGURE 3.8. *Comparison of scale values of Nationalities: Belgian-French and Belgian-Flemish. (The number near each point is the number of an item in the schedule. The items are shown in Table 3.6)*

definitely lower rank for all of the other groups, the first one being below the median for all other groups.

For the Goals of Life questionnaire the neutral point was, in general, at the bottom of the scale; the 12 statements in the scale were on the favorable side in all but two instances. The statement generally rating the lowest was "Power, control over people and things." It was below the neutral point only for the female group from the University of Texas. The other statement below the neutral point was "Doing the best I can for myself," as judged by the French-speaking group in Belgium.

Another interesting comparison exists with regard to the scale value of the neutral point. The largest differences between the various groups occurred with the Occupations Schedule. For the Norwegians, only five of the occupations were disliked, that is, had scale values below the neutral point. These were the occupations of Butcher, Coal Miner, Janitor, Mail Carrier, and Shoemaker. These five were below the neutral point for all other groups also; but the French and the Belgian groups had 17 or 18 occupations below the neutral point,

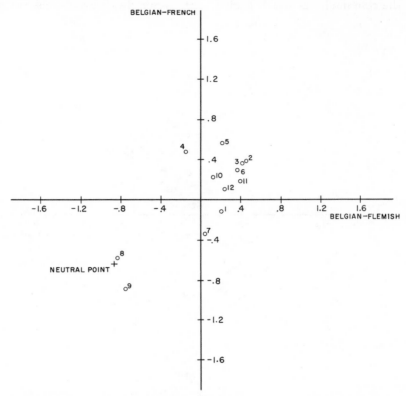

FIGURE 3.9. *Comparison of scale values of Goals of Life: Belgian-French and Belgian-Flemish. (The number near each point is the number of an item in the schedule. The items are shown in Table 3.7)*

including Policeman and Soldier as well as trades such as Barber, Carpenter, and Plumber.

In the Reasons for Work schedule there were no marked differences in the position of the neutral point. Of 31 statements, the number with scale values below the neutral point ranged from a high of only seven, for two of the groups, to a low of three for three of the groups.

For the nationalities, the neutral point was near the bottom of the scale for all groups, that is, we find a positive "liking" for most of the nationalities listed. For the Texas, Pennsylvania, German, and Norwegian groups, only one or two of the 31 nationalities in the schedule are below the neutral point — the Russians twice, the Chinese twice, the Arabs twice, and the Czechs once. For the French-speaking Belgian group, however, five were below the neutral point (Russian, Arab, Bulgarian, Persian, and Turk). For the Flemish-speaking Belgian group, there were 10 nationalities below the neutral point. They include, in addition

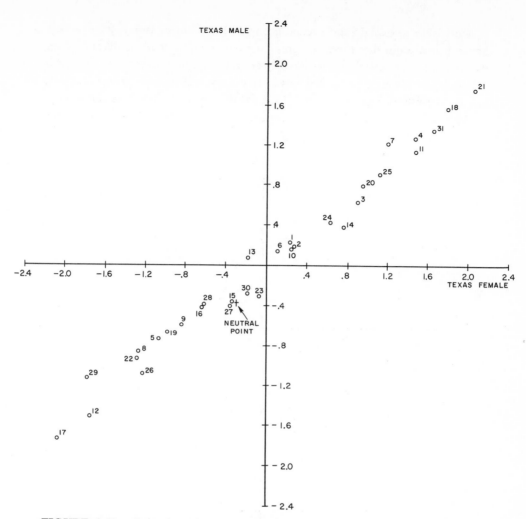

FIGURE 3.10. *Comparison of scale values of Occupations: Texas Male and Texas Female. (The number near each point is the number of an item in the schedule. The items are shown in Table 3.4)*

to the five mentioned above, the Chinese, Czechs, Egyptians, Israelis, and Yugoslavs.

In comparing results for the different groups it has been conventional to use correlation coefficients. Some illustrative correlations of scale values for different groups are shown in Table 3.8. These correlations range from 0.63 to 0.99. The correlation coefficient, however, is an over-all measure and does not distinguish, for example, a low correlation, due to a general lack of relationship, from a low correlation, due primarily to one or two aberrant points.

It would seem that an interesting way of comparing different national groups would be to plot scale values for one group on the ordinate against scale values for another group on the abscissa. A good many of the scale values may fall along a diagonal line that indicates corresponding rank orderings in the two groups. This line will then serve as a reference line for comparing the groups.

If one wishes to explain the French group to the Flemish group, for example, he might point out that there was great agreement on those items that fall along the reference line, but that a nationality or an occupation that falls in the upper left or in the lower right corner was judged very high by one group and very low by the other. Figures 3.3 to 3.13 show such plots for some of the groups.

Figures 3.3 and 3.4 show scale values for occupations obtained from the

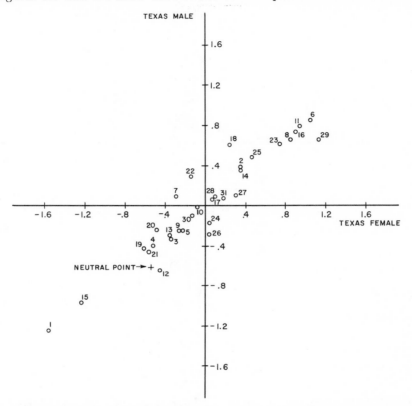

FIGURE 3.11. *Comparison of scale values of Reasons for Work: Texas Male and Texas Female. (The number near each point is the number of an item in the schedule. The items are shown in Table 3.5)*

French-speaking group in Belgium plotted against corresponding values for French and Norwegians. Figure 3.5 shows Reasons for Work for the same Belgian group versus the Penn State (male). Figures 3.6 to 3.9 show scale values for two subgroups in one country — the Belgian-Flemish versus the Belgian-French — for items from the four schedules (Occupations, Reasons for Work, Nationalities, and Goals of Life). Figures 3.10 to 3.13 show scale values on these same four questionnaires for male and female groups from the University of Texas.

These graphs show the close agreement that is possible in comparing two groups with similar backgrounds. Close agreement is also shown in Figures 3.6 to 3.9 for two different national groups in one country — the Belgian-Flemish vs. the Belgian-French.

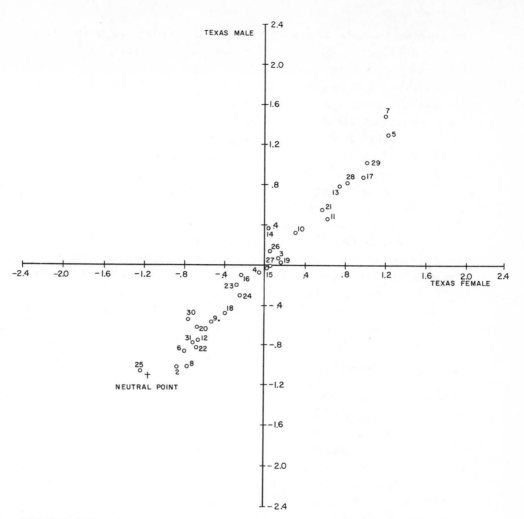

FIGURE 3.12. *Comparison of scale values of Nationalities: Texas Male and Texas Female. (The number near each point is the number of an item in the schedule. The items are shown in Table 3.6)*

One contrast occurs in comparing the Norwegians and the Belgians: Missionary ranks relatively much higher for the Belgians, and Soldier ranks higher or the Norwegians (see Figure 3.4). The Norwegians tested were young men,f 18 to 20 years of age, who were undergoing military training before possibly undertaking further university or technical studies. The Belgians were students finishing secondary schools.

The most striking contrast occurs in comparing the occupation prestige ratings for the group in France with those of the Belgian (French-speaking) group (see Figure 3.3). For the Belgian-French group, Missionary and Clergyman (Prêtre) are ranked third and fifth from the top; they are rated about the same as University Professor, Lawyer, and Author. For the group in France, Missionary ranked sixth from the bottom and Clergyman next to the lowest;

they are rated about the same as Grocer, Miner. Shoemaker, and Janitor. These differences in occupational ratings can perhaps be accounted for by differences in the backgrounds of the two groups. Mme. Larcebeau, who administered the questionnaires in France, states that the questionnaire was given in the public schools only, to pupils who were 14 to 15 years of age and who were in the last class of elementary school. Most pupils in this group were terminating their education at this level. About one-sixth of the children in France attend private schools, where the education is mainly confessional. If children in these parochial schools had answered the questionnaire, the average opinions about Priests and Missionaries undoubtedly would have been different. For Belgium, the questionnaires were given mainly in confessional schools, at the end of secondary school, to 17- to 19-year-old subjects.

The low average rating for Priest and Missionary by the group in France, however, may not arise from a set of uniformly low ratings. Likewise, a high average rating for these two occupations (such as that from the French-speaking Belgian group) may not arise from a set of uniformly high ratings. There may be various points of view exhibited by persons within the group. The next section deals with an approach to this type of problem.

THE FACTOR ANALYSES

In order to determine the different points of view that exist among the judges, we have, as an approximation to the vector model, used a factor analysis of the "votes for" scores on all of the questionnaires combined. Three of the questionnaires have 31 items plus one for the neutral point, plus another for the total circular triads score. In all, we have 33 items each for the Occupations, Work, and Nationalities Schedules and 14 items (12 + 2) for the Goals of Life Schedule, giving a total of 113 items. This gives us a 113 × 113 matrix to be factored.

The factor analyses and orthogonal equimax rotations have been completed for data from Belgium and Texas. The complete sets of factor loadings are given in Tables 3.9 and 3.10 at the end of this chapter. The factor analysis of the 113 items gave 27 factors for the Belgian data and 29 factors for the Texas data. Although some further rotations may be desirable, the composition of the different factors is reasonably clearly indicated by the results of the orthogonal rotation.

One rather striking finding was that there was relatively little tendency for factors to have loadings on more than one of the schedules. It was thought initially that preferences for certain occupations might be associated with certain goal preferences or with certain reasons-for-work preferences. For example, the preference for the goal of immortality or for serving God might be correlated with the belief that a clergyman or missionary had higher status. It turned out, in general, that this was not true if attention was confined to the items with high loadings. When the items with relatively small loadings were considered as well, however, there were a few instances in which a factor that was primarily characterized by items from one questionnaire also had items from another questionnaire. For example, it was found that certain goals of life reflecting a desire for service were associated in the same Texas factor (18) with the reason-for-work statement, "There is a great deal of satisfaction in doing work that will help others."

The factor that was most striking in having items from the various questionnaires on it was a factor of Total Circular Triads (TCT). The tendency of some individuals to produce a large number and others to produce a small number of circular triads was found for all four questionnaires in the Belgian, but not in the Texas group. For the Belgian data, the loadings of the TCT scores for the four schedules were as follows: Work, 3.54; Goals, 3.10; Nationalities, 3.07; and Occupations, 2.82. This factor also had the highest loading found for the occupation Janitor (factor loading, 1.88) and a negative loading for the nationality French (factor loading, −2.80). (See Table 3.14.)

The four neutral points did not appear in any clear manner in the factor structure.

All items with loadings of 2.0 or more are given in Tables 3.11 to 3.14. Where an item has no loading as high as 2.0, it is listed in the factor where it had its highest loading. Since factors tend to be composed of items from the same schedule, the results are presented separately for each schedule.

In the nationality preference structure we found eight factors for the Texans and seven for the Belgians, as shown in Table 3.11. Five of these were the same for the two groups: A Slavic or East European grouping, which included the Czechs, Yugoslavs, Poles, and Hungarians; a Scandinavian or North European group, which included the Danes, Swedes, the Norwegians; a Latin group, composed of the Italians, Portuguese, South Americans, and Spanish; a West European group (British, French, and American); and an Oriental group of the Chinese and Japanese.

For the Texas data, Egyptians, Arabs, and Persians formed one cluster, while Israelis, Turks, and Greeks formed another. In the Belgian data, these six nationalities formed a single broad East Mediterranean cluster. For the Belgian data, the Germans, Austrians, and Swiss formed a group, while for the Texas data, the Germans were grouped with the Russians.

Items in the Goals of Life Schedule appeared on four factors. Variables with factor loadings of 2.0 or more on these four factors are listed in Table 3.12. A previous factor analysis of the goals of life by Tucker (1956) had given a four-factor structure for a group of students at Princeton University. One factor was concerned with religion, one with a stoic acceptance of life, one with service to others, and one with selfish power acquisition. A similar structure for the goals of life was found in the Belgian and in the Texas groups. For both groups, one factor was concerned with service to others, and a second with stoic acceptance; a third factor initially appeared as a bipolar contrast between religious devotion and power over others. When the vector of average scale values was added to the structure, however, this bipolar factor appeared as two essentially orthogonal factors, giving the four-factor structure for the Goals of Life Schedule.

For the Occupations Schedule, variables with factor loadings of 2.0 or more on each of the "occupations" factors are listed in Table 3.13. Five factors are

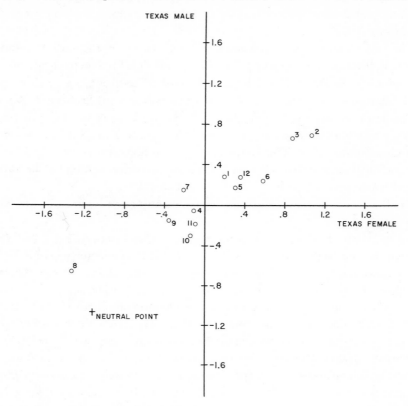

FIGURE 3.13. *Comparison of scale values of Goals of Life: Texas Male and Texas Female. (The number near each point is the number of an item in the schedule. The items are shown in Table 3.7)*

essentially similar for the Texas and Belgian groups. One of these factors was the *religious*, characterized by Priest and Missionary in both groups. Other occupations on this factor had very much lower loadings. Another clear factor for both groups was the *artistic*, characterized by highest loadings for Author, Actor, and Artist for both groups. Another grouping includes Politician, Banker, Businessman, and Lawyer for both groups. This perhaps represents a professional grouping with emphasis on financial aspects. A fourth occupations factor is characterized in both groups by outdoor occupations, emphasizing government employees. Soldier, Policeman, and Mail Carrier appeared in this group for both the Texas and Belgian data. For the Belgian data, this factor also included non-government occupations: Electrician, Carpenter, Coal Miner, and Farmer. A fifth factor which appeared in both sets of data is the small tradesman — Butcher and Grocer were on this factor. For the Belgian data, this factor also included numerous other trades, such as Tailor and Carpenter.

For the Texas group, the service occupations clustered in a separate factor including Electrician, Carpenter, and Plumber, while these occupations were grouped with the government workers in the Belgian analysis. For the Belgian data, the educational occupations formed a separate cluster (School Principal, University Professor, and Elementary School Teacher); these were combined with the religious group in the Texas data.

It is interesting to note that Physician, which consistently had the highest average scale value for occupations, appears with only moderate loadings on three factors (1, 4, and 3) for the Belgian data and on two factors (3 and 12) for the Texas data.

One factor related to occupations for the Texas data seems to be a residual mixture which includes Typographer, Bookkeeper, and University Professor. The Belgian occupations data also showed another residual group including Farmer and the Irish.

Table 3.14 shows the factors arising from the Reasons for Work Schedule, giving all items with loadings of 2.0 or more on these factors. There were eight for the Belgian data and nine for the Texas data. Of these, six seem to be reasonably duplicated in both sets of data. The other factors in this area were not as clearly overlapping. One of these overlapping factors included the following four statements:

> "The purpose of life is to work."
> "Hard work never hurt anyone."
> "Work is usually a pleasure."
> "Hard work is a virtue."

All of these seem to be statements that regard work as good in itself, without regard to what the work produces, the working conditions, personal satisfactions, or monetary rewards.

Another factor included the following two statements:

> "Hard work, efficiency, and conscientiousness are not
> always properly rewarded."
> "Most jobs do not make proper use of workers' skills
> and imagination."

Both of these statements might be characterized as "pessimistic." These two statements formed a factor in both the Texas and Belgian studies.

For both the Texans and Belgians, we found what Lazarsfeld characterized as a retirement or security mentality:

> "One of the chief satisfactions of work is to provide
> a good pension for one's self."
> "The most important thing to look for in a job is the
> security it offers."

These statements might be characterized as looking to retirement for satisfaction, rather than directing attention to satisfaction with characteristics of the job. They have relatively low scale values for the total group.

Another factor emphasized the importance of working well. It included the following statements, for both the Belgian and Texas groups:

> "A nation can get on its feet only when all of its citizens work as hard as they can."
>
> "All work must be painstakingly done, else it reflects upon the honor of the worker."
>
> "One should work so well that no supervision is needed."
>
> "A considerate management and understanding work comrades make the work much lighter to perform."

For both the Texas and Belgian data, we found one factor emphasizing satisfaction in the job itself. For both sets of data this cluster included the statements:

> "One of the great pleasures in life is to have a satisfying job which is almost like a hobby."
>
> "There is a great deal of satisfaction when one can be creative in one's job."
>
> "Work is a pleasure when you have good working conditions and good work comrades."

Another grouping seems to emphasize the importance of satisfaction, whether in or out of the job; however, the match between the two sets of data is not clear here. Only one statement ranked high on both sets of data:

> "It is not in one's daily work that one finds one's creativeness, but in the hobbies and activities outside of it."

Another factor seems to include statements referring to the importance of striving in work, but includes one set of statements for the Belgian group and a different set for the Texas group. Another factor included the following statement for both sets of data, "We work only because we have to," (an item that had a very low scale value) together with the total circular triads for work. An indifference to positive reasons for work is associated with a lack of consistent discrimination among the questionnaire items. Two items emphasizing care for tools appeared together in the Texas, but not in the Belgian data.

In the Detroit Area Study conducted by the University of Michigan (1956), a similar emphasis was found on "satisfactions of the job itself" among a group of factory workers and their wives, with "job security" rating relatively low. Correspondingly, Palmer (1957) in a study of attitudes toward work in an industrial community (Norristown, Pa.) found three-fifths of the workers liked the "nature of the job" itself primarily, while the remainder liked the job for wages, working conditions, character of their associates, and employers.

The striking thing about the questionnaire on reasons for work seems to be that there is considerable agreement from one nation to another. This agreement should not be judged in terms of correlation, however, this being too crude and too global a measure. One needs to establish some criterion regarding how large a difference in scale values is an important difference, and then to specify the number of items and which items exceed such a difference.

It is to be noted that the Priest-Missionary cluster formed a religious factor, regardless of whether or not the Priest-Missionary was rated high or low. This factor appeared in the data from France, Belgium, and Texas, even though the scale value ratings were very different. One may find, apparently, uniformities in factor structure when there are very large differences in scale values. When one looks beyond the total scale values to the detail of the factor structure, again there are very marked similarities from one national group to another. Fairly comparable factors were found among the occupations for the French, the Belgian, and the Texas groups and among the other items for the Belgian and the Texas groups. There were a few differences regarding clustering, but the major groups were the same.

The psychological scaling methods, together with factor analysis, provide a useful approach to attitude measurement problems as indicated by these preliminary results in international attitude comparisons.

TABLE 3.1. *Illustrative Preference Rankings Given to Four Objects by Three Persons**

Judges	Objects			
	A	B	C	D
X	2	1	3	4
Y	2	4	1	3
Z	2	3	4	1
Mean	2	2⅔	2⅔	2⅔

* Adapted from Tucker, L. R, Dimensions of Preference. *Research Memorandum* 60-7. Princeton, N. J.: Educational Testing Service, 1960. (Multilithed report)

TABLE 3.2. *Sample Page from Reasons for Work Schedule*

(1) Here is a list of six statements regarding work. Rank these statements by writing the number "1" in front of the statement with which you agree most, writing the number "2" in front of the statement with which you agree next most, and so on until you write the number "6" in front of the statement with which you agree least.

☐ It is more fun to work if there is competition to see who can get the most done.
☐ One of the chief satisfactions of work is to provide a good pension for one's self.
☐ There is no sense in doing a job if you are not happy in it.
☐ It is not in one's daily work that one finds one's creativeness but in the hobbies and activities outside of it.
☐ Hard work never hurt anyone.
☐ There is a great deal of satisfaction in doing work that will help others.

TABLE 3.2. (*Continued*)

(2) Here is another list of six statements regarding work. Rank these statements by writing the number "1" in front of the statement with which you agree most, writing the number "2" in front of the statement with which you agree next most, and so on until you write the number "6" in front of the statement with which you agree least.

☐ All work must be painstakingly done, else it reflects upon the honor of the worker.

☐ Hard work never hurt anyone.

☐ The purpose of work is to give us money enough so that we can have good leisure time activities and pleasures.

☐ One of the great pleasures in life is to have a satisfying job, which is almost like a hobby.

☐ Work is much more satisfying if one is working for one's self.

☐ There is a great deal of satisfaction when one can be creative in one's job.

TABLE 3.3. *Summary Description of Groups Studied*

	Group	N	Sex	Nationality	Language	Description
1	Belgian-French	142	M and F	Belgian	French	17- to 19-year-old students completing secondary schools
4	University of Texas	323	M	American	English	
3	University of Texas	359	F	American	English	
2	Belgian-Flemish	195	M and F	Belgian	Flemish	17- to 19-year-old students completing secondary schools
7	Norwegian	275	M	Norwegian	Norwegian	18- to 20-year-olds in military service
10	Italian	400	M and F	Italian	Italian	Students
9	German	189	M and F	German	German	Students
8	French	1200	M	French	French	14- to 15-year-olds in last class of elementary public schools
5	Pennsylvania State University	324	F	American	English	
6	Pennsylvania State University	210	M	American	English	

TABLE 3.4. *Scale Values for Occupations (based on normal curve transformation)*

Occupations	Belg.-Fr. M and F, N = 142	Belg.-Flem. M and F, N = 195	Univ. of Texas Female, N = 359	Univ. of Texas Male, N = 323	Penn State Female, N = 324	Penn State Male, N = 210	Norwegian Male, N = 275	French Male, N = 987
1. Actor	0.394	0.533	0.242	0.229	0.269	0.213	0.010	0.328
2. Artist	0.484	0.548	0.282	0.171	0.457	0.303	-0.004	0.423
3. Author	0.549	0.481	0.901	0.624	0.922	0.547	0.246	0.228
4. Banker	0.158	0.342	1.478	1.258	1.003	0.843	0.285	0.400
5. Barber	-0.569	-0.713	-1.067	-0.761	-0.961	-0.553	-0.552	-0.282
6. Bookkeeper	-0.066	0.068	0.114	0.130	0.077	0.054	-0.047	0.345
7. Businessman	0.290	0.311	1.214	1.209	1.018	0.937	0.329	0.291
8. Butcher	-0.591	-0.576	-1.272	-0.889	-1.055	-0.682	-0.665	-0.299
9. Carpenter	-0.394	-0.431	-0.843	-0.603	-0.602	-0.355	-0.227	-0.190
10. Civil service employee	-0.180	0.175	0.252	0.149	0.423	0.165	0.194	0.157
11. Clergyman	0.587	0.552	1.489	1.129	1.032	0.535	0.373	-0.766
12. Coal miner	-0.124	-0.666	-1.747	-1.530	-1.458	-1.080	-0.742	-0.386
13. Electrician	-0.151	0.023	-0.186	0.063	0.078	0.033	0.115	0.298
14. Elementary school teacher	0.451	0.588	0.770	0.378	0.819	0.517	0.378	0.482
15. Farmer	-0.226	-0.515	-0.336	-0.381	-0.526	-0.483	0.074	-0.476
16. Grocer	-0.612	-0.643	-0.640	-0.444	-0.819	-0.511	-0.199	-0.309

TABLE 3.4. (Continued)

Occupations	Belg.-Fr. M and F N = 142	Belg.-Flem. M and F N = 195	Univ. of Texas Female N = 359	Univ. of Texas Male N = 323	Penn State Female N = 324	Penn State Male N = 210	Norwegian Male N = 275	French Male N = 987
17. Janitor	−0.984	−0.976	−2.083	−1.764	−1.858	−1.257	−0.612	−0.827
18. Lawyer	0.616	0.833	1.804	1.560	1.701	1.104	0.760	0.484
19. Mail carrier	−0.349	−0.444	−0.987	−0.680	−0.847	−0.463	−0.699	−0.252
20. Missionary	0.789	0.621	0.956	0.790	0.599	0.294	0.108	−0.381
21. Physician	1.250	1.025	2.063	1.748	1.824	1.222	0.982	0.703
22. Plumber	−0.686	−0.825	−1.289	−0.965	−1.029	−0.649	−0.363	−0.308
23. Policeman	−0.240	−0.094	−0.069	−0.322	−0.255	−0.082	0.155	0.225
24. Politician	0.358	0.411	0.635	0.424	0.450	0.340	0.244	0.024
25. School principal	0.500	0.618	1.126	0.909	1.057	0.866	0.812	0.570
26. Shoemaker	−0.762	−0.844	−1.231	−1.087	−1.125	−0.925	−0.815	−0.724
27. Soldier	−0.377	−0.400	−0.355	−0.428	−0.276	−0.284	0.656	−0.250
28. Tailor	−0.285	−0.452	−0.608	−0.419	−0.548	−0.454	−0.436	−0.245
29. Truck driver	−0.633	−0.679	−1.776	−1.143	−1.402	−0.745	−0.505	−0.056
30. Typographer	−0.195	−0.108	−0.193	−0.304	−0.243	−0.299	−0.223	0.073
31. University professor	0.967	1.087	1.667	1.344	1.424	1.096	0.941	0.632
32. Neutral point	0.027	0.150	−0.310	−0.396	−0.381	−0.247	−0.575	0.095

TABLE 3.5. *Scale Values for Reasons for Work (based on normal curve transformation)*

Reasons for Work	Belg.-Fr. M and F N = 142	Belg.-Flem. M and F N = 195	Univ. of Texas Female N = 359	Univ. of Texas Male N = 323	Penn State Female N = 324	Penn State Male N = 210	Norwegian Male N = 275
1. If you see a worker loaf, you should tell the supervisor.	−0.658	−0.810	−1.553	−1.248	−1.432	−1.316	−0.912
2. It is more fun to work if there is competition to see who can get the most done.	0.003	−0.145	0.336	0.382	0.138	0.187	0.020
3. You get your job done better if you lend a hand or loan tools to other workers when needed.	0.043	−0.009	−0.337	−0.340	−0.401	−0.388	−0.147
4. If you are a good worker, you will get to be boss some day.	−0.331	−0.120	−0.521	−0.405	−0.681	−0.473	−0.003
5. A worker's most important responsibility is to take care of his tools or machine.	−0.007	0.017	−0.217	−0.251	−0.317	−0.357	−0.005
6. There is a great deal of satisfaction when one can be creative in one's job.	0.834	0.425	1.036	0.840	1.042	0.821	0.791
7. Work is much more satisfying if one is working for one's self.	−0.197	0.111	−0.288	0.077	−0.173	0.158	0.048
8. Work is a pleasure when you have good working conditions and good work comrades.	0.601	0.527	0.851	0.651	0.842	0.768	0.739
9. One of the chief satisfactions of work is to provide a good pension for one's self.	−0.642	−0.270	−0.255	−0.250	−0.121	−0.022	−0.532
10. Hard work, efficiency, and conscientiousness are not always properly rewarded.	0.424	0.117	−0.077	−0.020	0.408	0.366	0.206
11. The way to get ahead is by work well done.	0.179	0.418	0.936	0.785	0.785	0.585	0.748
12. The purpose of life is to work.	−0.231	−0.302	−0.452	−0.635	−0.596	−0.800	−0.414
13. Most jobs do not make proper use of workers' skills and imagination.	0.127	−0.033	−0.360	−0.294	−0.026	−0.009	0.004
14. There is no sense in doing a job if you are not happy in it.	0.290	0.186	0.354	0.347	0.581	0.598	0.014
15. We work only because we have to work.	−0.701	−0.926	−1.224	−0.966	−0.852	−0.565	−0.974
16. One of the great pleasures in life is to have a satisfying job, which is almost like a hobby.	0.149	0.470	0.901	0.718	0.854	0.837	0.510

TABLE 3.5. *(Continued)*

Reasons for Work	Belg.-Fr. M and F N = 142	Belg.-Flem. M and F N = 195	Univ. of Texas Female N = 359	Univ. of Texas Male N = 323	Penn State Female N = 324	Penn State Male N = 210	Norwegian Male N = 275
17. The most important thing to look for in a job is the security it offers.	−0.229	0.128	0.082	0.065	0.195	0.277	0.143
18. One should try to do a job better than others do it.	0.259	0.156	0.238	0.590	0.192	0.340	0.332
19. It is not in one's daily work that one finds one's creativeness but in the hobbies and activities outside of it.	−0.202	0.008	−0.606	−0.430	−0.511	−0.342	−0.537
20. The purpose of work is to give us money enough so that we can have good leisure-time activities and pleasures.	−0.800	−0.710	−0.477	−0.235	−0.392	−0.051	−0.602
21. The harder you work, the more money you can earn.	−0.827	−0.290	−0.563	−0.455	−0.617	−0.390	−0.237
22. It is far better to use one's brains than one's muscles in one's work.	−0.032	0.351	−0.144	0.238	−0.253	0.043	−0.262
23. A considerate management and understanding work comrades make the work much lighter to perform.	0.610	0.622	0.739	0.595	0.720	0.658	0.707
24. Hard work never hurt anyone.	−0.010	−0.257	0.045	−0.168	0.031	−0.288	−0.241
25. One should work so well that no supervision is needed.	0.617	0.444	0.459	0.480	0.358	0.302	0.624
26. Work is usually a pleasure.	−0.048	−0.171	0.039	−0.270	−0.266	−0.448	0.127
27. A nation can get on its feet only when all of its citizens work as hard as they can.	0.214	0.100	0.309	0.093	0.057	−0.154	0.026
28. All work must be painstakingly done, else it reflects upon the honor of the worker.	0.406	0.166	0.103	0.089	−0.037	−0.181	0.268
29. There is a great deal of satisfaction in doing work that will help others.	0.906	0.544	1.127	0.651	1.010	0.560	0.476
30. Employers can pay higher wages only when their workers work harder for them and produce more.	−0.576	−0.269	−0.132	−0.095	−0.198	−0.177	−0.193
31. Hard work is a virtue.	0.117	0.074	0.189	0.069	0.095	−0.157	−0.168
32. Neutral point.	−0.286	−0.551	−0.539	−0.608	−0.436	−0.383	−0.553

TABLE 3.6. *Scale Values for Nationalities (based on normal curve transformation)*

Nationalities	Belg.-Fr. M and F N = 142	Belg.-Flem. M and F N = 195	Univ. of Texas Female N = 395	Univ. of Texas Male N = 323	Penn State Female N = 324	Penn State Male N = 210	Norwegian Male N = 275	German Male N = 189
1. Americans	0.570	0.724	2.190	2.260	1.926	1.759	0.716	0.698
2. Arabs	−0.619	−0.717	−0.876	−1.026	−0.963	−0.938	−1.070	−0.558
3. Austrians	0.328	0.591	0.129	0.067	0.054	0.051	0.272	0.699
4. Belgians	1.158	1.050	−0.060	−0.085	−0.031	0.047	0.381	−0.006
5. British	0.101	0.289	1.225	1.294	0.860	0.840	0.978	0.223
6. Bulgarians	−0.595	−0.629	−0.796	−0.866	−0.712	−0.635	−0.452	−0.658
7. Canadians	0.620	0.286	1.203	1.476	1.106	1.240	0.759	0.473
8. Chinese	−0.502	−0.445	−0.782	−1.017	−0.705	−0.963	−0.905	−0.623
9. Czechs	−0.446	−0.552	−0.529	−0.574	−0.606	−0.434	−0.361	−0.995
10. Danes	0.186	0.140	0.308	0.323	0.325	0.410	1.190	0.232
11. Dutch	−0.356	0.121	0.616	0.462	0.583	0.424	0.598	0.354
12. Egyptians	−0.293	−0.437	−0.653	−0.759	−0.602	−0.718	−0.714	−0.644
13. French	0.885	0.283	0.742	0.775	0.803	0.562	0.391	0.156
14. Germans	0.057	0.610	0.031	0.357	0.067	0.445	0.018	1.326
15. Greeks	0.228	−0.041	0.023	−0.033	−0.057	0.014	−0.216	0.288
16. Hungarians	0.098	0.299	−0.242	−0.103	−0.228	−0.199	0.106	0.294

TABLE 3.6. (Continued)

Nationalities	Belg.-Fr. M and F N = 142	Belg.-Flem. M and F N = 195	Univ. of Texas Female N = 395	Male N = 323	Penn State Female N = 324	Male N = 210	Norwegian Male N = 275	German Male N = 189
17. Irish	−0.019	−0.003	0.981	0.870	0.669	0.502	0.421	0.302
18. Israelis	−0.371	−0.482	−0.395	−0.483	−0.018	−0.294	−0.068	−0.607
19. Italians	0.327	0.385	0.159	0.024	0.100	0.039	0.120	0.086
20. Japanese	−0.336	−0.309	−0.674	−0.618	−0.507	−0.529	−0.463	0.368
21. Norwegians	0.246	0.022	0.570	0.551	0.684	0.597	1.369	0.487
22. Persians	−0.573	−0.533	−0.681	−0.844	−0.592	−0.643	−0.770	−0.795
23. Poles	−0.192	−0.038	−0.284	−0.205	−0.263	−0.061	−0.232	−0.602
24. Portuguese	0.070	0.034	−0.252	−0.313	−0.354	−0.341	−0.389	−0.049
25. Russians	−0.771	−0.870	−1.242	−1.060	−0.986	−0.687	−0.674	−0.382
26. South Americans	0.246	0.247	0.047	0.138	0.138	0.025	−0.130	−0.152
27. Spanish	0.319	0.246	0.046	−0.011	0.070	−0.132	−0.411	0.142
28. Swedes	0.393	0.361	0.822	0.825	0.853	0.831	0.590	0.749
29. Swiss	0.641	0.878	1.025	1.018	0.856	0.807	0.635	0.593
30. Turks	−0.606	−0.747	−0.769	−0.543	−0.839	−0.528	−0.562	−0.090
31. Yugoslavs	−0.272	−0.420	−0.711	−0.787	−0.634	−0.542	−0.331	−0.531
32. Neutral point	−0.528	−0.340	−1.171	−1.111	−0.938	−0.949	−0.796	−0.774

TABLE 3.7. Scale Values for Goals of Life (based on normal curve transformation)

Goals of Life	Belg.-Fr. M and F N = 142	Belg.-Flem. M and F N = 195	Univ. of Texas Female N = 359	Univ. of Texas Male N = 323	Penn State Female N = 324	Penn State Male N = 210
1. Gaining personal immortality in heaven	−0.115	0.215	0.194	0.269	−0.289	−0.158
2. Devotion to God; doing God's will	0.381	0.464	1.056	0.705	0.234	0.131
3. Leading a moral life as dictated by God	0.361	0.424	0.870	0.663	0.330	0.207
4. Self-sacrifice for the sake of a better world	0.468	−0.134	−0.110	−0.061	−0.224	−0.223
5. Serving the community of which I am a part	0.555	0.231	0.311	0.169	0.243	0.155
6. Promoting the most deep and lasting pleasures for others as I can	0.286	0.367	0.586	0.226	0.567	0.105
7. Making a place for myself in the world; getting ahead	−0.335	0.064	−0.213	0.151	0.158	0.296
8. Power; control over people and things	−0.582	−0.822	−1.332	−0.664	−0.796	−0.298
9. Doing the best I can for myself	−0.892	−0.735	−0.358	−0.155	−0.016	0.139
10. Finding my place in life and accepting it	0.225	0.130	−0.135	−0.307	0.105	0.002
11. Being able to "take it"; brave and uncomplaining acceptance of what circumstances bring	0.180	0.395	−0.101	−0.199	0.136	0.045
12. Handling the specific problems of life as they arise	0.104	0.250	0.363	0.268	0.531	0.472
13. Neutral point	−0.634	−0.848	−1.130	−1.065	−0.977	−0.873

TABLE 3.8. *Correlations between Scale Values for Different National Groups*

National Groups	r	Schedule
Belgian-Flemish vs. French	0.721	Occupations
*Belgian-French vs. French	0.627	Occupations
*Belgian-French vs. Norwegian	0.793	Occupations
*Belgian-French vs. Penn State Male	0.682	Reasons for Work
*Belgian-Flemish vs. Belgian-French	0.951	Occupations
*Belgian-Flemish vs. Belgian-French	0.827	Reasons for Work
*Belgian-Flemish vs. Belgian-French	0.898	Nationalities
*Belgian-Flemish vs. Belgian-French	0.817	Goals of Life
*Texas Male vs. Texas Female	0.988	Occupations
*Texas Male vs. Texas Female	0.952	Reasons for Work
*Texas Male vs. Texas Female	0.890	Nationalities
*Texas Male vs. Texas Female	0.930	Goals of Life
Texas Male vs. Norwegian Male	0.852	Occupations
Texas Male vs. Norwegian Male	0.881	Reasons for Work
Texas Male vs. Norwegian Male	0.856	Nationalities
Texas Male vs. Penn State Male	0.764	Goals of Life
Texas Female vs. Penn State Female	0.811	Goals of Life

* Graphs are shown for these sets of scale values (Figures 3.3 to 3.13).

TABLE 3.9. *Covariance Factor Loadings (Texas data) A. Factors 1–15; Variables 1–58*

Variable	h²	1	2	3	4	5	6	7	8	9	10	11	12	13	14	15
																Factor
1	9.55	-0.52	-0.37	-0.48	-0.02	0.12	-0.53	-0.15	-0.54	0.16	0.40	0.12	-0.75	0.09	-0.73	1.93
2	38.62	5.48	-0.31	0.77	-0.67	-0.05	-0.10	-0.17	0.16	0.06	0.11	0.10	2.23	0.24	-0.14	-0.45
3	38.52	6.00	-0.09	0.40	0.09	0.13	-0.08	-0.22	0.04	0.04	-0.44	-0.02	0.28	0.08	-0.00	-0.01
4	33.14	5.25	-0.21	1.23	0.06	0.07	0.16	-0.27	-0.35	0.13	0.28	0.44	1.08	0.17	0.34	-0.38
5	20.79	1.33	0.43	1.05	0.12	-0.09	0.12	-0.13	-0.20	-0.40	0.17	0.25	3.07	0.30	0.01	-1.10
6	5.74	-0.44	0.03	0.83	0.03	-0.34	-0.24	0.25	0.11	-0.00	0.03	-0.05	0.07	0.20	-0.30	0.66
7	10.54	0.27	-0.03	0.55	-0.20	0.15	-0.20	-0.04	0.11	-0.18	-0.21	0.10	1.07	0.04	0.06	-0.63
8	18.45	0.94	0.00	0.57	0.21	-0.01	-0.53	0.09	-0.42	0.26	-0.02	-0.30	2.37	0.30	-0.30	-0.55
9	6.48	-0.44	-0.18	0.33	0.04	-0.05	-0.08	0.14	-0.27	0.05	-0.03	-0.03	0.18	-0.07	-0.05	0.62
10	10.30	-0.17	-0.10	0.14	0.40	-0.11	0.05	0.20	0.13	-0.12	-0.18	0.45	0.62	-0.15	0.25	0.22
11	15.47	-0.15	-0.17	1.22	0.03	-0.14	-0.30	-0.30	0.05	0.76	0.11	-0.02	0.85	-0.41	-0.49	0.23
12	31.37	0.91	-0.21	4.93	0.26	-0.20	0.63	-0.26	0.21	0.01	0.11	-0.09	0.97	-0.69	-0.18	-0.90
13	3.05	-0.12	-0.15	-0.28	0.25	0.10	-0.09	-0.12	-0.56	-0.05	0.32	0.47	-0.25	0.19	-0.30	-0.33
14	15.00	-0.07	0.02	0.26	-0.02	0.30	-0.26	-0.15	-0.17	0.07	0.15	-0.10	0.45	-0.17	-0.19	-0.06
15	18.57	0.01	0.04	3.29	-0.18	-0.23	-0.23	-0.00	-0.10	0.16	-0.30	-0.21	0.42	0.09	0.65	0.83
16	12.78	-0.85	-0.15	1.26	0.70	-0.25	-0.23	0.05	-0.50	-0.15	-0.13	0.28	1.26	0.31	-0.14	0.53
17	9.92	-0.33	-0.33	0.60	-0.39	-0.23	-0.41	0.31	0.33	-0.15	-0.39	-0.02	0.99	0.27	-0.25	-0.07
18	2.68	-0.31	-0.21	0.15	-0.03	-0.03	-0.18	-0.04	-0.30	0.04	-0.17	0.06	-0.55	-0.09	-0.37	0.71
19	19.71	-1.50	-0.12	1.65	0.30	-0.01	-0.03	0.17	-0.11	-0.20	0.18	0.21	2.41	0.27	-0.07	-0.84
20	10.92	-0.55	-0.37	0.69	-0.18	0.02	-0.04	-0.29	-0.39	0.30	-0.17	0.60	-0.35	-0.21	0.07	0.60
21	40.52	0.98	-0.63	5.55	0.66	0.22	1.37	0.01	0.06	0.45	0.18	0.09	0.15	-1.34	0.14	-0.60
22	20.04	1.37	0.22	2.04	0.18	-0.07	0.06	0.36	0.12	-0.21	-0.13	-0.26	2.25	0.07	-0.06	-0.45
23	7.11	-0.45	-0.02	0.14	-0.09	-0.02	-0.14	0.07	0.18	-0.04	-0.07	-0.11	-0.06	0.00	-0.07	0.30
24	13.26	-0.21	-0.07	1.03	-0.04	-0.13	-0.05	0.22	0.40	-0.21	-0.30	-0.12	0.39	0.17	-0.00	-0.36
25	28.80	2.37	-0.33	0.29	-0.33	-0.12	-0.15	0.14	0.76	0.29	-0.13	-0.32	4.31	0.61	-0.53	-0.27
26	17.15	0.57	-0.28	2.74	-0.27	-0.23	-0.12	-0.26	0.31	-0.34	-0.28	-0.48	1.35	0.09	-0.31	-0.41
27	4.02	-0.09	-0.00	0.19	-0.10	-0.08	-0.17	-0.04	-0.27	0.06	-0.28	0.06	0.20	-0.10	0.16	0.54
28	17.92	-0.06	0.42	0.91	0.16	0.19	-0.13	0.02	-0.99	-0.23	-0.18	-0.54	0.87	-0.06	-1.04	-1.45
29	6.50	0.64	-0.03	0.50	-0.13	-0.13	0.10	-0.04	-0.08	-0.18	-0.01	0.05	0.68	-0.01	-0.05	0.35
30	9.56	0.05	-0.11	0.23	-0.06	0.12	-0.12	-0.10	0.73	0.32	0.46	-0.21	0.33	-0.09	-0.45	0.59
31	9.32	0.70	-0.05	0.64	-0.23	0.38	-0.13	-0.12	1.03	0.16	0.06	-0.40	0.71	-0.07	-0.01	0.13
32	21.09	1.98	-0.15	2.63	-0.13	0.45	0.25	-0.01	0.30	-0.29	-0.17	0.15	1.53	0.83	-0.54	-0.18
33	14.54	2.27	-0.17	-0.32	-0.05	-0.15	-0.01	0.21	0.24	-0.39	0.36	-0.07	1.28	0.46	-0.32	-1.37
34	32.87	-0.35	0.08	-0.03	0.33	-0.02	-0.46	-0.16	-1.53	0.04	1.19	0.04	-0.74	0.19	-1.00	4.95
35	7.05	-0.30	-0.03	-0.16	0.11	0.55	-0.05	0.16	0.28	-0.33	-0.16	-0.18	-0.16	0.06	-0.15	2.09
36	16.72	-0.40	0.42	0.39	-0.35	0.13	0.22	-0.28	3.17	-0.15	0.49	0.32	-0.10	-0.72	0.67	0.59
37	14.02	-0.38	0.04	-0.00	-0.17	0.33	0.25	0.34	1.36	-0.20	0.11	0.57	-0.14	-0.12	0.27	1.16
38	15.02	0.04	-0.29	-0.13	-0.35	-0.80	-0.06	0.08	0.51	0.50	0.04	-0.29	-0.11	-0.10	0.43	0.15
39	16.30	0.04	0.18	-0.25	-0.33	-0.00	-0.35	-0.51	-0.01	0.50	0.46	-0.65	-0.21	-0.39	0.55	-0.69
40	24.62	0.52	-0.30	0.15	0.74	1.90	-0.09	-0.51	2.97	0.86	0.62	-0.03	-0.49	-0.39	1.41	-0.69
41	19.63	0.65	-0.45	-0.53	-0.06	1.12	0.08	-0.07	1.20	0.33	2.65	-0.03	0.78	0.38	0.42	-0.76
42	20.56	-0.12	0.07	-0.36	-0.32	0.41	0.27	-0.02	3.14	-0.14	3.88	-0.21	-0.78	-0.39	1.33	-1.06
43	18.49	-0.07	0.38	0.23	-0.46	0.39	0.28	0.15	0.60	-0.38	0.34	-0.30	-0.32	-0.01	-0.14	0.31
44	36.57	-0.08	0.03	0.23	-0.76	5.58	0.01	0.34	0.73	0.06	0.57	-0.27	0.03	0.08	0.05	0.51
45	21.54	0.00	0.55	0.20	2.33	5.54	0.04	0.42	1.83	-0.49	0.57	-0.28	-0.42	0.07	1.46	-1.28
46	27.01	-0.56	-0.07	-0.15	3.74	1.67	-0.57	-0.22	0.42	0.04	0.28	1.44	-0.22	-0.07	0.85	1.97
47	34.40	-0.36	-0.45	-0.32	-0.68	1.60	-0.23	-0.10	3.70	-0.42	0.46	-0.21	-0.36	0.28	-0.35	0.15
48	27.71	0.47	-0.28	-0.43	0.29	1.46	-0.47	-0.63	1.31	0.69	0.76	-0.38	0.72	-0.25	-0.01	-0.31
49	18.37	0.13	-0.41	0.34	-0.20	1.60	0.03	-0.04	-1.26	0.05	2.51	-0.12	-0.01	0.69	-0.64	2.03
50	25.52	-0.40	-0.36	0.24	0.35	1.60	0.06	-0.09	3.77	-0.36	1.32	-0.02	-0.27	-0.03	1.21	-0.90
51	22.05	-0.10	0.71	-0.25	0.49	0.34	-0.04	-0.36	0.40	-0.42	1.86	-0.20	-0.57	0.41	-0.21	-0.42
52	20.03	-0.46	0.26	-0.05	0.98	0.75	-0.17	-0.18	1.61	-0.10	0.61	-0.45	0.72	0.47	2.48	-0.95
53	11.70	-0.02	-0.17	-0.25	-0.03	0.96	-0.28	-0.21	-0.53	0.31	0.86	-0.45	-0.25	0.02	0.95	1.18
54	23.51	-0.44	-0.29	-0.09	-0.68	-0.57	-0.29	-0.33	-0.57	0.69	1.38	0.06	0.82	1.13	-0.01	0.88
55	20.98	-0.07	-0.26	-0.31	-0.86	-0.75	-0.45	0.26	-0.03	0.05	4.11	-0.12	0.23	0.29	-0.64	0.43
56	25.50	3.75	0.39	-0.61	-0.79	2.77	-0.01	0.21	0.10	-0.14	1.86	-0.64	0.95	0.51	1.42	0.36
57	18.48	-0.23	0.22	0.00	0.31	-0.48	0.35	0.35	2.33	-0.37	0.78	-0.39	0.74	-0.38	2.06	-0.79
58	28.76	-0.26	-0.33	0.22	4.83	-0.40	-0.13	-0.03	-0.21	0.12	-0.82	-0.59	0.27	-0.21	0.42	-0.66

TABLE 3.9 *(continued)* B. Factors 1–15; *Variables* 59–113

| | | Factor | | | | | | | | | | | | | | |
Variable	h^2	1	2	3	4	5	6	7	8	9	10	11	12	13	14	15
59	24.27	0.16	-0.78	0.02	0.51	0.88	0.25	0.03	1.10	0.31	-0.11	0.44	-0.13	-0.24	3.80	-0.64
60	23.07	-0.11	0.41	-0.52	2.89	-1.58	0.08	-0.78	2.36	0.10	-0.63	0.23	-0.03	-0.82	0.22	-0.44
61	19.90	-0.41	0.41	-0.12	2.06	0.28	0.08	-0.08	-0.35	-0.87	-0.49	-0.50	-0.20	-0.59	2.03	-0.56
62	24.14	-0.04	0.07	0.77	1.33	0.01	0.08	0.22	0.16	0.41	-0.21	-0.11	-0.67	0.04	4.27	-0.28
63	30.40	0.08	0.30	0.64	1.33	0.77	0.45	0.06	2.32	0.04	0.49	-0.72	-0.09	-2.47	1.05	-1.06
64	19.04	-0.16	-0.08	-0.11	0.78	0.15	-0.28	0.00	0.02	-0.17	-0.92	0.04	-0.73	0.48	1.38	-0.07
65	36.47	-0.25	-0.09	0.35	5.47	-0.58	-0.08	0.66	0.16	-0.15	-0.06	-0.17	-0.10	-0.53	1.01	0.62
66	3.79	-0.29	-0.17	0.14	0.50	0.65	0.16	-0.19	1.02	-0.06	-0.31	-0.12	-0.06	0.02	0.47	-0.03
67	8.33	-0.10	-0.01	-0.02	0.26	0.06	-0.07	-0.86	0.16	-1.27	-0.01	-0.12	-0.12	-0.01	-0.55	0.66
68	22.22	-0.10	1.87	-0.03	0.02	-0.05	0.08	2.27	-0.12	2.50	0.02	1.46	-0.16	-0.10	-0.01	-0.23
69	15.21	-0.25	0.80	-0.06	0.07	0.15	0.08	-0.06	-0.06	-0.48	-0.17	-0.14	-0.01	-0.23	-0.07	-0.11
70	17.48	-0.37	-0.45	0.39	-0.55	0.57	0.17	1.38	-0.05	1.07	-0.51	1.84	0.08	-0.21	-0.60	-0.43
71	13.22	-0.06	-0.08	0.02	-0.22	-0.04	0.21	1.62	0.40	-0.48	-0.32	1.07	-0.35	0.43	-0.08	-0.17
72	21.79	0.18	1.59	0.17	-0.01	-0.30	-0.04	1.33	-0.35	3.40	0.09	0.57	-0.04	-0.13	-0.82	-0.07
73	6.35	-0.15	-0.28	-0.10	-0.19	-0.09	0.05	2.07	-0.08	0.17	0.10	0.24	0.11	0.04	-0.07	0.18
74	20.97	-0.03	1.72	0.42	0.08	-0.06	0.49	2.07	-0.09	2.39	-0.11	0.97	-0.08	0.05	0.42	-0.29
75	21.55	0.20	-0.51	-0.07	0.05	0.08	-0.46	-0.09	-0.07	0.00	-0.32	0.33	-0.00	-0.25	-0.09	-0.09
76	16.26	0.07	-0.26	-0.22	-0.13	-0.34	-0.11	0.52	0.47	0.29	0.20	0.82	0.03	-0.11	0.24	-0.11
77	21.71	-0.29	0.23	-0.10	0.04	0.04	-0.26	3.82	-0.37	0.49	0.07	0.35	-0.50	-0.12	0.56	-0.08
78	13.38	-0.26	1.03	-0.03	-0.48	0.27	-0.37	2.17	-0.01	1.58	-0.39	-0.12	-0.18	-0.22	-0.14	0.46
79	21.86	0.33	-0.27	0.06	-0.48	-0.48	0.01	-0.10	-0.07	1.16	0.06	-0.32	-0.02	-0.19	0.14	-0.19
80	22.34	0.02	2.15	0.18	0.17	-0.22	-0.05	0.94	-0.28	3.77	-0.21	0.01	-0.41	-0.21	0.21	-0.14
81	40.38	0.66	0.18	-0.07	-0.24	-0.15	0.26	1.42	-0.05	0.23	-0.06	5.81	-0.06	-0.04	0.04	-0.40
82	13.14	0.29	0.53	-0.22	0.37	-0.34	0.18	0.58	-0.30	0.87	0.29	0.38	-0.89	-0.26	0.59	0.05
83	18.95	-0.63	0.05	-0.21	0.63	0.60	-0.32	-0.43	0.25	1.02	-0.43	1.46	-0.26	0.33	-0.42	-0.13
84	22.47	-0.03	2.20	-0.21	-0.50	-0.19	0.61	1.61	0.48	3.12	-0.38	-0.08	0.72	-0.10	-0.40	-0.17
85	15.07	0.44	0.19	0.16	0.00	-0.09	-0.59	0.25	0.92	0.67	-0.03	-0.31	-0.18	-0.20	-0.40	0.23
86	21.59	0.02	2.71	-0.53	-0.22	0.25	-0.07	1.02	-0.23	2.25	-0.06	-0.16	-0.81	-0.83	-0.26	0.19
87	34.48	-0.24	0.36	0.58	-0.03	0.10	-0.30	-0.53	-0.06	0.42	-0.33	1.81	-0.40	0.13	-0.16	-0.26
88	20.05	0.49	-0.22	-0.07	-0.31	0.29	-0.01	4.00	-0.25	0.95	0.15	0.57	-0.25	-0.13	0.06	-0.11
89	10.15	0.09	-0.20	-0.17	-0.15	0.40	-0.14	0.72	-0.12	0.54	-0.00	-0.54	-0.36	0.17	-0.65	-0.13
90	16.61	-0.67	0.26	0.36	-0.48	0.21	-0.23	0.89	-0.21	-0.49	-0.40	0.62	-0.59	-0.12	-0.28	0.10
91	15.23	0.65	3.11	0.01	-0.10	-0.06	-0.30	0.76	0.11	0.81	-0.28	-1.02	-0.56	0.02	0.51	-0.18
92	24.14	-0.70	-0.76	-0.30	-0.24	0.08	-0.47	-0.34	0.12	-0.45	-0.10	3.98	-0.24	0.07	-0.68	-0.20
93	39.32	-0.22	5.57	-0.21	0.31	-0.18	0.36	-0.45	0.08	-0.47	-0.25	-0.08	-0.08	-0.14	0.37	0.19
94	36.96	-0.52	5.46	-0.22	-0.36	-0.60	0.41	-0.26	0.04	1.33	0.52	0.25	1.44	0.38	0.14	-0.40
95	19.98	0.11	0.40	-0.09	0.27	-0.09	-0.13	3.65	-0.17	1.88	0.31	0.98	0.22	-0.06	-0.24	-0.01
96	18.40	-0.47	0.34	0.05	0.15	-0.13	-0.58	3.09	0.28	1.76	-0.40	0.86	0.27	0.00	-0.13	-0.08
97	15.96	-0.11	-0.64	-0.21	0.04	0.32	-0.59	0.18	-0.72	-1.06	-0.23	0.63	0.31	0.30	-0.19	-0.20
98	10.74	-0.17	-0.09	-0.02	-0.16	-0.15	-0.02	0.57	-0.10	-0.11	0.06	0.02	0.25	-0.05	-0.06	-0.10
99	4.38	0.38	0.13	-0.38	-0.17	-0.10	-0.03	-0.90	0.12	1.09	0.06	0.40	-0.39	0.33	-0.40	-0.29
100	30.51	-0.30	0.48	0.91	0.29	0.56	4.89	-0.03	-0.14	-0.04	0.80	0.05	-0.12	0.05	0.37	0.56
101	40.82	-0.31	-0.30	0.17	-0.12	-0.12	5.83	0.30	-0.28	-0.30	-0.53	-0.49	-0.18	-1.53	-0.31	-0.02
102	25.66	-0.16	-0.27	-0.20	-0.42	-0.49	4.77	-0.23	0.35	-0.26	-0.43	-0.40	-0.12	-1.58	0.11	-0.62
103	24.16	-0.39	-0.17	0.04	-0.05	0.23	-0.94	-0.09	-0.30	-0.16	-0.79	-0.35	-0.22	-0.04	0.35	0.39
104	12.86	0.27	-0.11	-0.01	-0.14	-0.33	-0.10	0.21	0.42	-0.27	-0.68	-0.15	0.11	-0.11	0.07	0.29
105	19.63	0.25	-0.38	0.22	-0.22	-0.34	0.29	-0.22	-0.15	0.20	0.37	1.19	-0.24	4.82	-0.21	-0.10
106	26.40	0.14	0.39	-0.25	-0.12	-0.13	-0.97	-0.21	-0.18	-0.50	0.62	-0.40	-0.05	3.88	-0.11	-0.14
107	23.70	0.08	-0.83	-0.31	-0.02	0.57	-0.29	-0.18	0.31	-0.15	-0.08	-0.35	0.25	3.83	-0.21	0.73
108	20.14	-0.07	-0.29	-0.31	-0.05	0.23	-0.78	-0.01	0.25	0.23	-0.18	-0.51	0.83	-0.18	-0.46	-0.16
109	19.76	-0.24	0.05	-0.10	-0.38	-0.05	-0.33	-0.18	-0.86	-0.37	-0.08	-0.40	-0.06	0.45	-0.81	-0.12
110	10.63	0.26	-0.44	0.16	-0.31	-0.18	-0.58	-0.38	0.36	-0.14	0.04	-0.35	-0.48	0.98	-0.01	-0.41
111	19.78	-0.10	-0.26	-0.37	-0.17	-0.10	-0.50	-0.32	-0.09	-0.37	0.18	-0.09	-0.51	0.45	0.48	-0.22
112	1.91	0.10	-0.07	-0.26	-0.17	0.17	-0.06	-0.08	-0.09	-0.14	-0.33	-0.12	-0.17	0.77	0.25	-0.08
113	7.36	-0.32	0.20	-0.23	0.33	0.21	-1.24	-0.03	0.39	0.19	-0.13	-0.12	-0.43	0.73	-0.19	1.09
Sum of Squares		128.86	108.11	106.28	101.63	96.44	94.58	91.00	88.49	82.77	81.54	80.25	79.98	78.22	76.07	71.79

TABLE 3.9 *(continued)* C. Factors 16–29; Variables 1–58

Variable	h^2	\[Factor\] 16	17	18	19	20	21	22	23	24	25	26	27	28	29
1	9.55	-0.09	-0.00	0.23	0.32	-0.19	0.34	0.89	0.72	-0.00	0.28	0.20	0.62	1.08	-0.02
2	38.62	-0.06	-0.13	-0.01	-0.21	-0.33	-0.23	-0.35	0.07	0.47	0.01	-0.24	-1.19	-0.25	-0.01
3	38.52	0.27	-0.09	-0.01	-0.11	0.86	-0.38	-0.92	0.07	-0.05	-0.01	-0.03	0.23	-0.35	-0.04
4	33.14	-0.15	-0.13	-0.31	0.02	0.75	-0.10	-0.47	-0.33	-0.24	-0.10	-0.13	0.03	-0.86	-0.40
5	20.79	-0.42	-0.23	-0.16	0.49	1.50	0.04	0.86	-0.34	-0.11	-0.33	-0.26	1.52	0.60	0.46
6	5.74	-0.12	0.03	-0.27	0.08	0.68	0.05	0.79	-0.06	0.48	-0.01	-0.18	1.52	0.37	-0.39
7	10.54	-0.54	0.32	-0.40	0.08	2.27	-0.09	0.78	0.01	0.14	0.17	0.23	1.34	0.49	-0.02
8	18.45	-0.12	-0.12	-0.05	0.48	1.81	-0.02	0.75	0.09	0.20	-0.20	0.35	2.19	1.13	0.26
9	6.48	0.01	-0.04	-0.05	-0.12	0.26	-0.08	0.35	0.18	0.19	-0.01	0.20	2.20	0.65	0.10
10	10.30	-0.19	0.03	-0.18	-0.47	0.15	-0.15	0.37	0.16	-0.27	-0.14	0.33	0.99	2.72	-0.40
11	15.47	-0.47	-0.18	0.50	0.31	2.55	-0.08	2.06	0.02	-0.63	0.19	0.29	-0.16	0.21	-0.12
12	31.37	-0.10	0.07	0.20	-0.01	0.65	0.25	0.67	0.13	-0.88	-0.22	-0.24	1.17	-0.13	-0.23
13	3.05	-0.10	-0.06	-0.06	-0.06	0.38	0.06	0.26	0.35	-0.13	-0.15	-0.03	0.26	-0.17	-0.25
14	15.00	-0.37	-0.11	0.29	0.57	1.46	0.08	1.18	-0.44	-0.01	0.18	0.15	0.58	3.13	-0.04
15	18.57	0.65	-0.31	0.29	0.20	1.28	-0.08	1.30	-0.29	0.18	-0.40	-0.08	0.80	-0.23	1.09
16	12.78	0.11	-0.20	-0.37	-0.36	0.13	0.42	-0.34	0.58	0.24	-0.02	-0.22	1.32	2.01	-0.78
17	9.92	-0.42	-0.31	-0.38	0.09	0.09	-0.30	0.41	0.07	0.27	-0.12	0.69	2.27	0.99	-0.23
18	2.68	-0.09	0.10	0.15	0.20	0.04	-0.13	0.36	-0.33	0.18	-0.27	0.14	0.49	0.81	-0.11
19	19.71	-0.20	-0.57	-0.28	0.09	1.91	-0.07	0.64	1.65	0.01	-0.35	0.10	1.65	0.85	-0.05
20	10.92	-0.18	-0.48	-0.05	-0.08	0.97	-0.05	2.24	-0.09	0.72	0.62	0.29	-0.44	0.70	-0.40
21	40.52	-0.53	-0.34	0.34	0.60	0.45	0.49	0.91	0.14	-0.74	-0.23	-0.68	-0.04	-0.03	-0.69
22	20.04	-0.29	-0.12	-0.20	-0.77	1.94	0.30	0.95	-0.44	-0.07	-0.14	0.11	1.47	1.09	-0.04
23	7.11	-0.22	0.12	0.17	-0.09	0.26	-0.04	0.49	-0.02	-0.25	-0.08	0.07	0.71	2.39	-0.05
24	13.26	-0.14	-0.02	-0.19	-0.13	0.46	-0.04	3.12	0.39	-0.14	-0.27	-0.28	-0.18	0.48	-0.04
25	28.80	-0.93	-0.20	-0.31	0.01	1.03	-0.23	-0.06	-0.01	-0.50	0.07	0.20	-0.15	-0.69	0.06
26	17.15	0.51	-0.25	0.04	0.21	1.55	-0.59	1.59	-0.45	0.32	-0.21	0.03	0.78	-0.03	0.31
27	4.02	0.42	-0.02	0.22	-0.25	0.05	-0.21	0.05	-0.07	-0.27	-0.00	0.08	1.22	1.21	0.09
28	17.92	0.69	-0.57	0.40	1.36	0.09	-0.12	2.08	0.95	-0.32	0.25	-0.10	-0.54	0.99	0.44
29	6.50	-0.18	0.05	-0.23	0.16	1.03	-0.05	-0.40	-0.09	-0.23	0.15	0.26	0.24	0.38	0.24
30	9.56	-0.17	-0.31	-0.10	0.60	-0.19	0.03	-0.13	0.61	-0.19	-0.09	0.30	0.14	2.21	-0.27
31	9.32	-0.27	0.49	0.03	-0.30	2.56	0.42	0.83	-0.08	-0.16	-0.23	-0.22	0.38	0.07	-0.14
32	21.09	0.48	0.22	-0.01	-0.10	2.10	-0.47	0.27	-0.54	-0.08	-0.15	0.16	0.18	-0.14	0.42
33	14.54	0.90	0.52	-0.03	-0.71	-0.75	-0.52	1.30	-0.66	1.02	-0.09	-0.73	0.96	0.26	-0.03
34	32.87	-0.07	-0.15	-0.36	0.39	-0.08	0.61	-0.02	0.67	0.20	-0.13	0.14	0.16	0.47	0.10
35	7.05	0.49	0.21	0.45	0.65	0.04	-0.12	0.17	-0.13	-0.01	-0.15	-0.71	0.54	-0.47	-0.03
36	16.72	-0.02	0.11	0.09	1.24	0.28	0.47	-0.44	0.95	0.98	-0.56	-0.30	-0.06	-0.64	-0.24
37	14.02	-0.07	-0.39	0.26	0.11	0.30	0.50	-0.42	3.05	0.15	-0.05	0.19	-0.26	-0.24	0.51
38	15.02	-0.02	-0.74	0.08	2.93	0.59	-0.16	0.08	0.95	-0.45	-0.40	-0.09	0.15	-0.30	1.01
39	16.30	-0.74	-0.21	0.20	0.50	-0.57	0.19	-0.10	3.61	0.51	-0.40	-0.37	0.04	-0.18	-0.04
40	24.62	1.34	-0.00	0.72	1.07	0.53	-0.78	-0.49	1.24	-0.33	-0.18	-0.16	1.97	-0.80	0.39
41	19.63	-0.14	0.07	-0.31	0.52	-0.77	-0.53	-0.60	1.26	-0.23	-0.01	-0.23	-0.52	0.11	0.59
42	20.56	-0.06	0.03	-0.19	0.08	0.08	-0.05	-0.40	1.36	1.83	0.30	0.43	-0.32	0.58	-0.24
43	18.49	-0.02	-0.51	-0.66	0.51	0.10	0.26	0.05	0.29	0.58	-0.16	0.33	-0.57	0.45	0.19
44	36.57	-0.15	-0.16	-0.37	-0.72	0.12	0.05	-0.37	0.56	1.26	-0.32	0.17	-0.69	0.12	0.39
45	21.54	-0.05	0.31	0.31	1.91	1.06	-0.38	-0.24	0.99	0.84	-0.14	-0.21	-0.36	-0.06	0.02
46	27.01	-0.47	0.17	-0.69	-0.55	-0.59	0.28	-0.64	-0.27	-0.60	-0.11	-0.27	0.08	-0.89	-0.38
47	34.40	-0.24	0.45	-0.06	-0.78	0.68	0.23	1.30	-0.04	0.64	-0.02	-0.11	0.23	-0.33	-0.21
48	27.71	-0.47	0.31	0.15	0.68	-0.47	0.84	0.23	-0.02	4.29	-0.20	0.79	-0.23	-0.38	0.62
49	18.37	-0.40	-0.25	-0.92	0.09	-0.65	0.01	0.43	0.33	0.56	-0.10	-0.08	-0.68	-0.21	-0.39
50	25.52	-0.20	0.43	-0.39	-0.07	-0.30	-0.75	0.37	0.11	0.89	0.86	-0.42	-0.49	-0.57	-0.56
51	22.05	-0.48	-0.22	-0.22	0.02	0.91	0.29	0.62	1.07	1.55	0.39	-0.08	0.18	0.48	0.29
52	20.03	-0.18	-0.19	0.25	1.82	-0.04	0.38	-0.03	0.50	0.21	-0.12	-0.86	0.00	0.33	0.11
53	11.70	0.20	0.19	0.20	3.95	-0.58	0.02	-0.87	0.87	2.29	-1.10	-0.06	-0.17	-0.36	-0.17
54	23.51	-0.38	-0.30	-0.69	-0.40	-0.42	-0.41	0.25	-0.44	-0.61	0.06	-0.28	0.91	-0.01	-0.17
55	20.98	-0.14	-0.71	0.05	1.46	-0.76	-0.31	0.01	-0.26	1.52	-0.10	-0.22	-0.30	-0.36	-0.33
56	25.50	0.30	0.37	-0.46	0.54	-0.39	-0.69	-0.46	-0.61	1.19	0.59	0.40	0.91	-0.56	-0.52
57	18.48	-0.26	-0.32	-0.32	0.28	-0.47	-0.69	-0.78	1.54	1.19	0.64	0.40	-0.30	-0.01	-0.53
58	28.76	0.62	0.03	0.31	0.98	-0.74	-0.06	0.07	0.75	0.19	0.17	0.11	0.43	-0.29	-0.54

TABLE 3.9 *(continued) D. Factors 16–29; Variables 59–113*

Factor

Variable	h²	16	17	18	19	20	21	22	23	24	25	26	27	28	29
59	24.27	-0.89	-0.76	0.11	1.32	-0.50	-0.21	0.55	-0.09	1.01	0.56	-0.13	0.17	0.01	1.02
60	23.07	-1.06	-0.26	0.47	0.97	-0.17	-0.34	0.17	-0.02	0.38	0.69	0.43	0.49	0.55	0.55
61	19.90	-0.21	-0.39	0.55	1.21	1.15	0.33	-0.59	1.76	0.23	1.39	-0.03	-0.14	-0.19	-0.40
62	24.14	0.47	0.32	0.21	-0.07	0.10	-0.41	-0.18	1.03	-0.03	-0.64	-0.29	-0.05	-0.06	-0.76
63	30.40	0.31	-0.11	2.82	-0.07	0.24	-0.56	-0.86	1.20	-0.54	0.38	-0.85	-0.29	-0.03	-0.01
64	19.04	-0.26	0.73	-0.51	2.83	-0.41	-0.35	-0.06	1.27	0.81	0.89	0.42	-0.29	0.02	-1.50
65	36.47	-0.15	0.48	0.85	0.62	0.39	-0.13	-0.57	-0.38	0.17	-0.92	-0.24	-0.58	0.60	-0.41
66	3.79	0.32	0.05	-0.11	-0.02	-0.04	-0.37	-0.49	0.42	0.77	0.13	-0.08	-0.20	-0.30	-0.34
67	8.33	1.00	0.92	-0.10	-0.02	-0.44	1.65	0.32	0.10	-0.05	0.33	-0.07	0.21	-0.08	0.23
68	22.22	0.31	1.07	-0.15	-0.10	0.39	0.49	-0.23	0.09	0.30	1.47	-0.02	-0.18	0.10	1.03
69	15.21	0.32	-0.34	-0.09	-0.21	0.13	3.59	-0.50	0.25	-0.31	0.66	-0.07	-0.04	-0.24	-0.21
70	17.48	0.18	1.51	-0.12	1.00	1.03	0.29	-1.90	-0.37	-0.10	0.36	0.13	0.11	0.03	0.79
71	13.22	-0.45	1.38	-0.09	0.40	-0.52	-0.66	0.12	0.06	-0.24	1.00	0.04	0.79	0.03	1.94
72	21.79	-0.22	1.03	-0.32	-0.22	-0.11	-0.70	-0.19	-0.21	0.12	1.25	-0.16	-0.31	0.12	1.04
73	6.35	-0.45	1.27	-0.03	-0.14	0.07	0.37	-0.06	0.21	-0.13	0.13	-0.08	-0.10	-0.25	1.93
74	20.97	-0.43	-0.72	-0.47	-0.21	-0.27	0.28	-0.61	0.29	0.01	1.58	-0.11	-0.28	0.19	1.45
75	21.55	4.21	-0.06	0.20	-0.02	-0.31	-0.93	0.71	0.16	0.29	0.12	0.57	0.02	-0.37	-0.95
76	16.26	-0.16	3.64	0.17	-0.07	-0.26	-0.71	0.08	-0.49	-0.25	-0.04	0.07	0.17	0.17	0.58
77	21.71	-1.23	1.13	0.08	0.08	-0.20	-0.11	0.10	0.02	-0.15	0.46	0.14	0.70	0.01	1.51
78	13.38	-0.73	-0.86	-0.23	-0.05	-0.34	-0.32	0.16	0.01	0.38	0.80	-0.00	0.22	-0.26	1.41
79	21.86	0.14	-0.58	0.49	-0.21	0.45	4.27	-0.18	0.37	0.62	-0.04	-0.25	-0.37	-0.27	-0.10
80	22.34	0.54	0.21	-0.07	0.16	-0.20	-0.83	0.06	-0.20	0.42	0.57	0.36	-0.07	0.09	-0.12
81	40.38	0.61	0.47	-0.12	0.03	-0.07	-1.50	-0.13	-0.12	0.03	0.85	-0.18	-0.24	0.27	0.65
82	13.14	0.38	0.38	-0.12	-0.37	0.14	1.44	0.46	-0.55	0.34	2.47	0.17	-0.23	-0.35	0.26
83	18.95	-0.03	2.91	-0.04	-0.68	0.03	-0.38	-0.06	0.21	-0.55	0.98	-0.05	-0.10	-0.05	1.39
84	22.47	-0.52	0.93	-0.47	-0.50	0.22	-0.24	-0.22	-0.21	0.13	0.83	-0.13	0.14	-0.24	0.62
85	15.07	0.54	0.00	-0.45	0.07	0.02	0.13	-0.05	-0.43	-0.04	3.44	0.01	-0.06	-0.18	-0.22
86	21.59	0.24	-0.17	0.64	0.18	0.73	1.08	0.41	-0.22	-0.44	0.38	0.13	-0.39	-0.42	-1.71
87	34.48	5.06	-1.26	-0.16	-0.23	-0.32	-0.34	-0.24	0.41	0.21	1.20	0.34	-0.29	0.33	0.45
88	20.05	-0.44	0.68	-0.10	-0.34	-0.01	-0.11	-0.32	-0.31	-0.11	0.87	-0.09	-0.10	0.14	0.80
89	10.15	0.03	-0.02	-0.11	0.14	-0.14	2.56	-0.11	0.05	-0.37	0.41	0.21	-0.06	-0.13	0.65
90	16.61	-0.98	3.51	0.14	0.19	0.19	-0.10	-0.30	-0.04	0.60	0.30	-0.39	-0.02	0.19	0.35
91	15.23	-0.49	0.10	-0.26	0.13	-0.27	0.24	0.32	-0.44	0.55	-0.45	-0.04	0.08	-0.26	0.53
92	24.14	1.70	-0.87	-0.46	-0.31	-0.47	0.34	0.68	-0.24	-0.74	-0.87	-0.24	-0.20	-0.10	-0.01
93	39.32	0.60	-0.87	-0.67	-0.46	-0.07	0.87	-1.00	-0.23	-0.12	0.84	0.45	-0.38	0.12	-0.38
94	36.96	1.13	-0.62	-0.28	-0.14	-0.09	0.11	0.20	-0.22	-0.53	0.03	-0.52	0.12	0.08	-1.19
95	19.98	-0.09	0.54	-0.42	0.09	0.26	0.30	0.07	-0.15	-0.07	0.37	-0.11	-0.11	-0.25	0.66
96	18.40	0.29	0.90	-0.17	0.06	-0.33	0.57	-0.17	-0.19	-0.46	1.32	-0.28	-0.05	0.08	0.85
97	15.96	-0.10	0.28	0.02	0.01	-0.34	-0.59	0.16	0.71	-0.07	2.79	0.19	0.32	0.33	1.82
98	10.74	2.69	0.02	0.10	0.23	0.12	-0.05	-0.10	-0.14	0.05	-0.43	0.05	-0.45	-0.29	1.41
99	4.38	-0.15	-0.16	-0.47	-0.30	0.22	0.02	0.04	0.10	1.05	-0.06	0.20	0.20	0.29	-0.26
100	30.51	-0.45	-0.12	-0.32	-0.37	-0.61	0.45	-0.25	-0.98	-0.34	-0.01	-1.01	-0.54	0.29	-0.22
101	40.82	-0.37	-0.23	1.32	-0.09	0.29	-0.42	-0.22	0.16	-0.49	-0.07	-1.05	0.00	-0.16	-0.46
102	25.66	-0.10	-0.15	0.29	-0.19	0.39	0.12	-0.18	0.37	0.24	-0.47	0.14	0.09	0.04	-0.53
103	24.16	0.06	0.05	4.04	-0.69	0.05	0.57	0.50	0.58	-0.04	0.55	-0.23	-0.25	-0.13	-0.61
104	12.86	-0.38	-0.15	2.95	0.24	0.57	0.23	0.16	0.24	-1.02	-0.28	1.35	-0.00	-0.13	0.34
105	19.63	-0.45	0.36	4.20	0.10	-0.66	0.14	-0.02	-0.20	0.50	-0.19	-0.14	-0.02	0.01	0.02
106	26.40	-0.16	-0.44	-0.06	0.38	-0.18	-0.09	-0.12	0.11	-0.04	-0.21	-0.63	-0.53	-0.02	0.16
107	23.70	-0.51	-0.10	-1.10	0.65	-0.68	-0.44	-0.04	-0.39	-0.14	0.19	-0.73	0.37	-0.84	0.03
108	20.14	0.23	0.51	-0.95	0.05	0.11	-0.05	0.29	-0.48	-0.21	-0.14	1.44	-0.04	0.14	-0.03
109	19.76	0.22	-0.30	-0.38	-0.14	-0.52	-0.04	-0.68	0.25	-1.15	-0.15	3.99	-0.12	0.30	-0.35
110	10.63	0.18	-0.27	0.85	0.14	-0.78	-0.00	-0.12	0.29	0.07	0.20	2.55	0.08	0.23	-0.01
111	19.78	0.42	-0.11	0.30	0.18	-0.15	-0.18	0.62	0.05	-0.58	0.16	3.90	0.59	-0.52	0.24
112	1.91	0.36	0.07	0.43	-0.34	-0.12	-0.33	-0.20	-0.13	0.38	0.06	-0.00	0.34	-0.17	-0.18
113	7.36	0.42	-0.57	-0.04	-0.56	-0.07	0.60	-0.17	-0.40	0.38	-0.69	0.77	-0.17	0.67	0.47
Sum of Squares		67.92	67.77	66.72	64.93	64.34	60.83	57.66	56.33	56.13	55.49	54.20	53.58	53.36	48.63

TABLE 3.10. *Covariance Factor Loadings (Belgian data) A. Factors 1–15; Variables 1–58*

Variable	h^2	1	2	3	4	5	6	7	8	9	10	11	12	13	14	15
1	15.92	-0.31	0.10	-0.64	-0.79	0.20	-0.59	1.04	-0.27	-0.54	-0.07	0.75	-0.55	-0.16	2.82	-0.71
2	30.67	0.06	-0.13	1.69	4.92	-0.22	0.16	0.62	-0.14	0.81	-0.10	-0.17	-0.09	0.32	-0.86	-0.06
3	45.30	1.17	-0.36	0.25	6.22	-0.42	0.49	-0.75	-0.64	1.15	-0.11	-0.10	-0.37	0.46	0.11	0.05
4	40.55	1.50	-0.44	0.29	5.64	-0.63	-0.29	-0.60	0.34	1.42	-0.12	0.68	-0.13	0.18	-0.23	-0.29
5	36.81	-0.71	0.04	5.22	1.00	0.22	0.11	-1.47	0.09	1.45	-0.19	-0.03	-0.12	-0.19	-0.40	-0.28
6	9.40	-0.45	-0.05	0.52	0.20	-0.04	0.18	0.71	-0.25	-0.12	-0.45	0.47	-0.18	-0.46	-0.19	-0.06
7	19.55	-0.95	0.65	2.55	0.84	-0.25	-0.01	-0.61	-0.19	2.07	-0.20	-0.56	0.19	0.11	0.11	-0.41
8	27.37	-0.81	-0.51	4.14	1.27	-0.02	0.96	-0.53	-0.03	1.63	-0.27	-0.28	-0.36	0.04	-0.46	-0.52
9	16.08	0.31	0.01	0.57	-0.75	0.40	0.42	-0.18	-0.35	0.10	0.19	0.02	-0.34	0.20	-0.53	0.23
10	19.86	-0.72	-0.08	-0.88	-0.24	1.08	-0.52	-0.18	-0.20	0.51	0.34	-0.24	-0.43	-0.31	0.41	0.46
11	23.61	-0.28	-0.09	3.19	0.16	-0.65	0.45	2.59	0.20	2.09	-0.32	-0.17	0.03	0.75	0.70	-0.15
12	78.02	7.93	-0.11	-0.02	1.52	-0.59	0.11	-0.69	-0.63	0.69	2.47	0.35	0.70	0.59	-0.20	0.48
13	41.46	3.37	-0.44	-1.69	-0.49	-0.46	-0.46	-0.51	-0.94	-1.08	-1.20	-0.29	-0.15	-0.83	-0.04	-0.16
14	16.43	-0.43	0.00	0.01	-0.05	0.62	0.49	3.71	1.28	1.19	0.29	-1.11	-0.28	-0.29	-0.54	0.66
15	20.99	0.49	0.72	0.12	0.74	0.11	-0.37	2.60	0.14	4.04	-0.09	-0.63	0.15	-0.43	0.52	0.19
16	30.00	1.39	0.17	-1.23	-0.92	-0.37	-0.31	0.87	0.45	0.15	-0.60	-0.32	0.44	-0.23	0.29	-0.03
17	13.14	-0.42	-0.13	0.20	-0.58	0.95	-0.08	2.87	-0.09	-0.37	-0.14	-0.24	-0.19	-0.36	-0.10	-0.50
18	10.80	-0.83	-0.18	-0.38	-0.01	-0.23	-0.57	0.49	-0.25	-0.05	0.28	0.48	0.53	-0.02	0.63	-0.38
19	29.21	0.79	-0.28	3.75	2.43	0.35	0.61	1.41	-0.25	2.05	-0.10	-0.28	0.04	-0.27	1.88	0.09
20	16.98	0.55	-0.29	-1.55	-0.17	-0.04	-0.93	-0.23	-0.00	0.84	-0.24	0.56	0.28	-0.58	0.52	0.35
21	80.03	8.50	-0.43	-0.53	1.22	0.28	-0.19	2.78	0.08	0.83	1.39	0.03	-0.07	-0.26	-0.52	-0.22
22	23.40	2.55	-0.17	2.17	1.72	0.38	0.30	0.12	0.42	2.16	0.12	-0.11	-0.25	-0.55	-0.64	-0.14
23	10.60	-0.47	0.87	-0.03	-0.65	0.33	0.44	0.52	0.48	0.12	0.16	-0.53	0.67	0.43	-0.07	-0.14
24	23.61	-0.02	-0.20	0.62	-0.74	-0.57	-0.48	1.51	0.42	1.66	-0.36	0.46	1.00	0.82	1.65	-0.04
25	44.87	0.60	0.33	5.41	1.50	-0.58	-0.23	2.76	-0.73	1.48	-0.84	0.59	0.59	-0.13	-1.05	-0.98
26	27.10	0.58	-0.03	1.69	1.12	-0.16	-0.07	-0.75	-0.14	-0.84	-0.09	-0.26	1.00	-0.52	-0.64	0.32
27	10.38	0.35	-0.34	-0.79	-0.51	0.46	-0.23	-0.08	0.08	-0.02	0.05	-0.00	-0.14	-0.43	0.68	0.14
28	36.73	0.27	0.37	-0.15	-0.32	0.42	-0.22	1.41	0.22	0.36	-0.54	-0.63	-0.12	0.02	1.02	-0.07
29	9.54	0.28	0.02	0.23	0.52	0.22	-0.19	5.64	0.11	-0.27	-0.37	-0.23	0.16	0.09	0.11	-0.19
30	24.81	-0.55	-0.14	-0.88	-0.23	0.25	-0.17	0.25	-0.18	-0.31	-0.54	-0.36	-0.13	0.14	-0.84	-0.25
31	19.83	-0.46	-0.14	0.71	1.18	0.42	0.21	0.23	0.33	-0.32	0.40	0.06	-0.10	-0.09	0.64	-0.54
32	34.82	1.21	-0.28	2.84	2.03	0.42	0.23	4.04	0.20	1.83	-0.35	-0.13	-0.10	0.19	-0.56	-0.15
33	13.13	-0.03	0.07	-2.28	1.23	-0.37	-0.35	0.23	0.20	4.25	-1.29	0.20	-0.63	-0.09	-0.56	-0.08
34	41.99	-0.89	0.22	-0.28	-0.30	-0.01	-0.42	-0.89	0.54	1.39	-0.01	0.44	-1.04	0.33	0.21	-0.44
35	12.07	0.76	-0.11	-0.28	-1.03	0.61	-0.23	0.60	-0.86	-0.02	-0.49	0.18	0.94	-0.23	3.54	-0.15
36	22.50	-0.02	-0.35	-0.01	0.69	-0.44	-0.29	0.59	-0.02	0.36	-0.53	-0.24	0.28	-0.13	-0.09	-0.09
37	17.47	0.28	-0.49	-0.27	-0.24	0.98	-0.33	-0.18	0.19	-0.27	1.02	-0.45	0.83	-0.66	1.30	0.51
38	15.56	-0.80	-0.91	-0.59	-0.22	1.24	-0.36	-0.08	0.10	0.18	0.41	-0.26	0.83	0.03	1.27	0.54
39	15.14	-0.04	0.29	-0.63	-0.85	0.89	-0.13	0.34	-0.26	0.05	0.42	-0.10	1.03	-0.50	-0.61	0.34
40	29.98	0.56	-0.59	-0.27	0.27	-0.28	-0.27	0.83	-0.54	-0.76	0.30	-0.57	1.03	-0.43	-0.86	-0.51
41	19.91	0.03	-0.04	0.43	0.22	-0.74	-0.20	-0.11	0.28	-0.25	0.18	-0.79	-0.47	0.02	-0.09	-0.03
42	20.52	-0.28	-0.10	0.72	-0.34	-0.15	-0.12	-0.62	-0.35	-0.06	0.14	-0.22	0.68	0.09	-0.03	-0.35
43	25.98	-0.54	-0.25	0.08	-0.43	-0.30	-0.54	-0.63	0.60	-0.09	-0.33	0.32	2.55	0.14	-0.97	-0.21
44	25.19	-0.12	0.46	0.49	-0.04	-0.82	-0.70	0.66	0.26	0.39	-0.34	0.08	0.64	1.32	0.49	-0.18
45	19.83	-0.47	-0.45	0.60	-0.56	-0.71	-0.49	-0.20	0.01	-0.29	-1.18	-0.13	0.40	0.17	-0.38	-0.28
46	41.75	-0.04	-0.35	0.18	-0.84	1.11	-0.39	-0.42	-0.09	-0.03	-0.13	-0.44	-0.01	-0.36	-0.52	-0.11
47	20.11	0.25	-0.07	-0.35	0.44	5.78	-0.46	0.22	0.05	-0.07	-0.04	-0.01	-0.07	-0.01	0.57	0.71
48	24.74	-0.16	0.11	-0.43	0.68	0.19	-0.08	-0.02	0.44	-0.38	-0.14	-0.01	-0.26	-0.69	0.29	-0.44
49	19.41	-0.14	0.18	0.26	0.11	-0.77	-0.06	-0.14	0.36	0.24	-0.34	-0.15	-0.35	0.50	-0.53	-0.42
50	33.67	-0.09	0.59	0.46	0.03	-0.53	-0.01	-0.42	-0.06	0.55	-0.72	0.30	0.65	0.49	0.93	-0.29
51	23.11	-0.22	0.15	0.06	-0.43	-0.30	-0.02	0.27	0.02	-0.02	0.59	-0.33	0.04	0.08	-1.22	-1.13
52	22.66	-0.07	-0.13	0.15	-0.61	1.66	-0.48	-0.08	-0.37	0.20	0.65	0.85	-1.27	0.25	-0.16	0.01
53	17.22	0.06	0.16	-0.14	0.53	-0.71	0.11	0.07	0.34	0.48	0.52	-0.03	1.48	-0.31	-0.09	0.10
54	22.45	-1.49	0.74	-0.01	0.48	0.34	0.35	-0.13	-0.71	0.55	0.72	-0.47	1.20	0.69	0.02	0.20
55	21.57	-0.57	-0.28	-0.23	0.25	-0.44	-0.35	-0.04	-0.82	-0.19	0.59	-0.14	2.60	0.57	0.72	0.62
56	21.54	-0.82	-0.19	-0.04	0.62	0.11	0.40	0.59	-0.12	0.48	0.65	-1.74	1.20	0.69	1.27	0.04
57	22.12	-0.05	-0.28	-0.04	0.02	-0.29	0.35	-0.07	0.06	0.35	0.52	0.35	2.60	0.57	0.90	-0.31
58	36.30	-0.17	-0.19	-0.28	0.45	4.07	0.40	-0.22	0.06	-0.12	0.72	0.25	2.57	-0.92	0.81	0.41

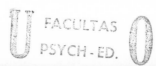

TABLE 3.10 (*continued*) *B. Factors 1–15; Variables 59–113*

		Factor														
Variable	h^2	1	2	3	4	5	6	7	8	9	10	11	12	13	14	15
59	22.64	0.58	0.05	-0.09	-0.21	0.97	0.12	0.16	-0.02	-0.02	0.18	0.72	3.31	-0.26	0.16	-0.45
60	34.01	-0.31	0.06	-0.08	-0.43	5.17	-0.37	0.21	-0.12	-0.24	0.36	0.16	0.10	-0.15	-0.37	-0.29
61	25.32	0.66	-0.03	0.61	-0.10	1.36	-0.14	-0.13	-0.25	-0.28	0.07	-0.60	4.39	-0.23	-0.39	0.60
62	16.44	0.33	-0.06	-0.55	0.15	1.42	0.23	-0.17	-0.30	-0.04	-0.16	0.44	2.39	-0.47	-0.78	0.09
63	29.93	0.96	-0.71	-0.59	-0.10	1.37	0.02	0.05	0.41	-0.06	1.33	0.48	2.60	0.25	-0.45	-0.33
64	16.84	-0.67	0.11	-0.10	-0.12	0.29	0.19	-0.11	0.16	-0.23	0.16	0.10	1.71	0.53	0.06	-0.06
65	39.31	0.37	0.81	0.56	-0.00	4.64	-0.08	0.72	-0.28	-1.33	0.69	-0.34	2.68	-0.07	0.57	-0.06
66	8.28	0.16	-0.61	-0.04	-0.15	0.16	-0.33	-0.20	-0.11	0.25	-0.09	0.69	0.84	-0.20	0.11	-0.17
67	17.67	-0.48	0.11	-0.54	-0.44	0.37	-0.67	0.51	-1.03	0.39	-0.35	0.83	-0.60	0.09	3.07	0.57
68	50.94	-0.08	4.10	1.53	-0.32	-1.10	3.42	0.01	1.60	-0.52	0.04	-0.86	-0.63	0.79	1.30	-0.26
69	20.67	-0.66	-0.40	-0.40	0.14	0.02	0.85	0.30	-0.48	0.09	0.33	3.54	-0.35	-1.32	1.35	0.69
70	31.76	0.26	0.62	0.11	0.48	0.05	0.43	-0.42	1.52	-0.22	-0.04	-0.33	0.36	4.94	-0.32	-0.30
71	35.90	0.35	4.96	-0.34	-0.65	0.12	0.69	0.17	1.24	-0.10	0.96	-0.50	0.83	1.22	-0.94	0.44
72	58.26	-0.99	6.77	-0.04	-0.12	0.28	-0.17	0.60	0.71	0.51	0.12	-1.47	-1.25	0.72	1.03	-0.02
73	15.21	-0.23	-0.36	-0.14	-0.14	0.68	-0.11	-0.20	0.33	0.09	-0.15	-1.12	-0.27	-0.03	-0.65	-0.42
74	30.55	-0.48	1.64	0.88	0.48	-0.45	2.48	0.97	3.17	-0.82	-0.28	-0.41	-0.58	-0.21	-0.55	-0.11
75	42.63	0.43	0.38	-0.54	0.18	0.39	-0.14	-0.28	-1.08	0.30	-0.31	0.85	-0.09	-0.25	-0.10	6.13
76	15.49	-0.06	-0.80	0.14	0.19	0.28	-0.06	0.08	0.68	-0.35	-0.36	0.41	-0.51	-0.34	-0.23	0.64
77	27.91	-0.33	-0.28	0.14	0.33	0.12	-0.13	-0.30	4.69	-0.30	-0.80	0.14	-0.21	1.57	0.12	-0.93
78	58.48	0.19	5.98	-0.97	-0.97	0.90	-0.10	-0.65	-0.80	1.44	0.25	-1.77	0.61	1.65	-0.03	-0.03
79	25.38	0.80	-0.47	-0.46	0.07	0.18	-0.15	-0.11	-0.25	-0.47	-0.30	4.27	-0.17	-0.33	0.12	-1.13
80	37.56	-0.76	3.17	0.15	0.44	1.14	2.09	0.40	0.48	-0.14	-0.49	1.17	-0.27	-0.05	-2.80	-0.01
81	38.07	0.38	0.54	-0.09	0.29	-0.78	0.60	0.74	1.09	-0.52	0.69	-0.48	-0.76	5.09	0.94	1.00
82	22.54	-0.26	-0.58	-0.09	0.37	-0.34	1.76	-0.35	0.83	-0.38	0.18	3.58	-0.42	-0.06	0.02	0.73
83	30.28	0.75	1.13	0.09	-0.05	-0.18	0.80	0.42	0.29	-0.98	0.04	0.02	0.56	0.62	0.10	1.03
84	23.73	0.29	1.64	0.26	-0.67	-0.40	-0.14	0.49	3.32	-0.30	0.47	-0.27	0.02	0.74	-0.56	-0.17
85	22.08	-0.03	-0.20	-0.02	-0.21	-0.33	-0.25	0.54	-0.24	-0.19	0.54	3.93	0.31	0.38	-0.90	-0.64
86	30.40	-0.27	0.75	-0.69	-0.35	-0.28	4.54	-0.32	-0.08	0.09	0.06	0.95	0.72	0.95	-1.63	-0.50
87	32.78	-0.02	-0.07	0.09	-0.28	-0.47	-0.08	-0.13	-0.50	0.39	0.34	1.01	0.35	1.05	-0.30	5.37
88	28.92	-0.29	-0.01	-0.16	-0.16	0.13	-0.06	0.22	4.81	0.46	0.00	0.28	0.01	0.63	-0.76	-0.78
89	10.98	0.27	-0.44	0.24	0.33	0.17	0.74	-0.21	0.34	-0.34	-0.46	2.59	0.12	0.16	0.74	0.30
90	20.91	-0.11	0.79	-0.11	0.05	-0.61	0.12	0.31	0.34	-0.20	-0.79	-0.65	0.66	0.79	-0.13	-0.82
91	18.90	-0.14	-0.11	-0.28	-0.17	-0.09	3.71	-0.50	0.64	0.30	-0.28	0.95	0.24	0.69	-0.61	-0.61
92	26.74	-0.97	-0.36	-0.01	-0.77	-0.23	-0.94	2.18	-0.33	-0.09	0.05	-0.23	-0.67	0.29	-0.38	2.13
93	37.94	-0.21	1.02	0.97	0.09	-0.71	5.22	0.22	0.08	-0.63	-0.38	-0.20	-0.10	-0.83	1.50	1.37
94	32.48	-0.12	-0.18	-0.19	-0.08	0.25	5.21	-0.63	-0.48	0.18	0.21	1.49	-0.06	0.66	-0.64	-0.15
95	26.00	-0.14	0.89	-0.34	-0.32	0.16	0.28	0.13	4.42	0.42	-0.59	-0.07	0.10	1.76	-0.41	-0.73
96	26.47	-0.42	2.48	-0.43	0.31	0.38	0.52	-0.58	2.01	-0.17	-0.11	0.24	-0.14	3.49	-0.04	-0.04
97	13.12	-0.88	-0.07	0.12	-0.05	0.03	0.30	0.24	1.10	-0.02	-0.21	2.22	-0.05	-0.54	0.88	0.62
98	16.59	0.17	-0.65	0.12	0.06	-0.34	0.18	-0.45	-0.69	-0.03	-0.69	0.88	-0.04	-0.14	-0.07	-0.09
99	9.52	-0.64	1.56	0.37	-0.16	-0.22	0.57	-0.21	0.58	0.45	-0.51	0.30	-0.25	1.26	0.92	-0.09
100	19.70	0.30	0.11	-0.40	0.30	-0.60	-0.27	-0.07	0.52	-0.43	4.06	0.04	0.29	0.37	0.45	-0.44
101	43.70	1.15	0.09	0.33	-0.07	0.23	0.15	0.52	-0.76	0.24	5.92	0.34	-0.33	0.05	-0.31	-0.69
102	25.55	0.78	0.37	-0.19	-0.35	0.31	-0.03	-0.31	-0.69	0.14	4.74	0.17	-0.43	-0.20	-0.25	0.26
103	25.18	0.08	0.06	-0.47	-0.29	0.57	-0.45	0.72	-0.13	0.15	1.07	0.33	1.05	-0.16	-0.07	0.52
104	13.61	-0.06	-0.12	-0.27	-0.24	-0.39	-0.05	-0.13	-0.03	-0.43	0.15	-0.42	-0.05	-0.35	-0.31	0.14
105	11.56	-0.12	-0.28	0.16	-0.16	-0.22	-0.04	-0.02	0.06	-0.33	-0.51	-0.33	0.44	0.02	-0.10	-0.16
106	28.49	-1.01	0.19	0.67	0.30	-0.03	0.09	0.52	0.70	-0.18	0.41	-0.79	-1.19	0.67	0.17	-0.37
107	16.08	-0.58	-0.02	0.33	-0.39	-0.41	0.09	-0.27	0.06	0.07	-1.16	-0.78	-0.37	-0.83	0.43	-0.35
108	12.39	-0.08	-0.07	0.46	0.09	-0.08	0.45	-0.21	-0.69	-0.21	-0.98	-0.38	-0.43	-0.38	-0.15	-0.14
109	14.31	-0.44	-0.04	-0.48	-0.02	-0.36	0.31	0.15	0.23	-0.24	-0.40	-0.10	-0.31	-0.36	-0.14	-0.40
110	12.04	-0.01	0.06	-0.05	-0.06	0.35	0.44	-0.11	-0.12	-0.09	-0.16	-0.25	-0.18	-0.07	-0.11	-0.22
111	12.04	-0.01	0.06	0.13	0.10	0.13	-0.57	-0.17	-0.19	-0.29	-0.08	0.16	-0.88	0.62	-0.08	-0.21
112	5.21	-0.12	-0.39	0.13	0.25	0.21	-0.12	-0.30	-0.10	-0.01	-0.31	-0.06	-0.21	-0.12	-0.06	-0.03
113	19.66	-0.70	0.29	0.13	-0.24	0.31	-0.19	0.07	-0.22	-0.41	-0.54	0.65	0.01	0.61	3.10	-1.14
Sum of Squares		187.95	163.84	153.81	138.79	133.02	132.47	131.10	119.00	110.39	108.96	103.42	103.04	99.14	97.81	95.27

TABLE 3.10 (continued) C. Factors 16–27; Variables 1–58

Variable	h^2	Factor											
		16	17	18	19	20	21	22	23	24	25	26	27
1	15.92	0.43	0.73	1.13	0.88	0.28	-0.62	-0.44	-0.03	0.04	-0.10	0.06	0.35
2	30.67	-0.28	-0.11	0.55	-0.50	-0.14	0.04	0.29	-0.55	0.19	-0.63	0.09	-0.24
3	45.30	-0.31	-0.28	-0.31	-0.18	0.44	0.15	0.73	-0.57	0.16	0.26	0.25	-0.67
4	40.55	-0.30	-0.03	-0.59	-0.34	0.15	0.85	-0.00	-0.54	0.17	0.35	-0.02	-0.88
5	36.81	1.14	0.28	0.02	0.61	-0.18	-0.42	-0.07	0.74	-0.03	-0.74	-0.26	-0.51
6	9.40	-0.09	0.19	0.82	2.31	0.64	-0.31	-0.01	0.34	-0.22	-0.07	0.45	-0.79
7	19.55	0.80	-0.44	-0.47	1.01	-0.28	-0.29	0.39	0.53	0.03	0.20	-0.03	-1.67
8	27.37	0.22	-0.01	0.15	0.66	0.80	-0.33	-0.16	1.05	-0.03	-0.15	-0.33	-0.67
9	16.08	-1.12	-0.40	0.31	3.49	-0.33	-0.27	-0.21	-0.28	-0.27	0.11	-0.19	0.29
10	19.86	0.12	0.42	0.12	2.63	-0.49	-0.80	-0.15	-0.13	-0.29	-0.30	-0.23	0.79
11	23.61	1.35	0.20	-0.82	0.81	-0.70	-0.22	0.77	-0.05	-0.17	0.06	0.47	-1.44
12	78.02	0.15	0.37	-0.61	-0.12	0.38	-0.16	0.17	-1.46	-0.38	-0.05	-0.73	-0.06
13	41.46	-0.80	0.14	-0.03	1.28	1.66	-0.16	-0.40	0.57	-0.25	0.75	0.42	-0.85
14	16.43	0.61	0.48	0.05	1.84	-0.66	-0.29	-0.03	-0.25	0.38	-0.56	-0.03	-0.88
15	20.99	0.29	-0.38	-0.05	0.55	0.21	-0.13	-0.44	-0.30	0.28	0.12	0.08	0.23
16	30.00	-0.98	-0.31	0.05	2.41	0.35	0.12	-0.86	-0.30	-0.45	0.19	-0.29	2.71
17	13.14	-0.51	-0.02	0.28	3.14	-0.15	0.18	-0.41	-0.53	-0.05	0.22	0.04	0.83
18	10.80	0.11	-0.05	-0.04	1.49	-0.10	0.08	-0.58	-0.13	-0.50	-0.37	0.20	0.12
19	29.21	-0.23	-0.17	0.51	-0.55	-0.57	-0.62	0.85	-0.13	-0.52	-0.07	0.18	-0.76
20	16.98	-0.26	0.22	0.41	1.71	0.01	-0.06	-0.37	-0.66	0.13	0.35	0.49	-0.04
21	80.03	-0.29	-0.22	-0.72	-0.03	0.11	0.05	0.04	-0.62	0.13	-0.08	-0.40	0.49
22	23.40	-0.75	0.01	-0.11	0.74	-0.13	0.32	0.21	-0.44	0.07	-0.63	-0.10	-0.94
23	10.60	-0.19	0.14	0.25	2.32	-0.07	-0.34	-0.24	-0.39	0.29	-0.46	-0.17	0.44
24	23.61	-0.15	-0.66	0.17	0.30	-0.32	-1.27	-0.48	-0.88	1.27	-0.18	-0.17	-0.71
25	44.87	-1.22	-0.49	-0.38	-1.09	0.17	0.16	0.20	0.91	0.21	-0.60	1.13	-0.70
26	27.10	-0.28	-0.13	-0.38	-0.82	0.08	0.21	0.09	0.19	0.11	-0.18	0.28	-0.42
27	10.38	-0.68	-0.06	-0.14	2.32	0.11	-0.11	0.46	0.35	-0.38	-0.17	-0.17	0.40
28	36.73	0.58	-0.22	-0.12	-0.72	-0.57	-0.20	-0.29	-0.07	-0.29	0.45	-0.09	-0.03
29	9.54	-0.30	0.03	0.48	2.66	0.02	-0.16	-0.04	0.28	-0.58	0.12	0.26	-0.48
30	24.81	0.54	-0.20	0.42	1.01	0.44	0.22	-0.72	1.42	-0.57	-0.20	-0.50	0.94
31	9.15	0.55	-0.04	-0.79	1.12	-0.23	-0.08	0.09	-0.04	-0.23	-0.03	-0.23	-0.32
32	34.82	-0.35	-0.03	-0.16	-0.58	-0.49	-0.34	0.58	-0.09	0.38	0.11	0.11	-0.47
33	13.13	-0.09	-0.50	0.48	0.48	0.14	0.24	-0.27	0.47	0.29	-0.89	0.18	-0.10
34	41.99	1.17	0.61	4.29	0.03	-1.03	-1.49	-0.72	0.93	0.17	-0.54	-0.22	-0.32
35	12.07	-0.76	-0.26	1.87	-0.42	0.13	-0.07	-1.09	0.70	0.98	0.62	-0.99	-0.02
36	22.50	-0.56	0.43	0.45	-0.07	0.75	0.08	0.74	-0.18	4.30	0.81	-0.28	-0.06
37	17.47	-0.06	-0.40	-0.87	-0.31	1.44	0.90	1.71	-1.83	0.13	0.85	-0.39	-0.16
38	15.56	0.96	-0.08	0.90	-0.24	-1.32	1.61	1.00	0.08	-0.05	-0.13	-0.16	-1.19
39	15.14	1.85	-0.00	-0.58	0.39	1.58	-0.50	0.20	0.02	1.38	-0.73	-0.08	-0.69
40	29.98	-2.03	0.52	1.01	-0.02	2.23	3.04	1.72	-0.60	1.67	-1.23	-0.04	-0.33
41	19.91	1.90	-0.28	-0.67	0.78	1.00	0.44	2.35	1.24	1.11	-0.39	-0.28	-0.50
42	20.52	0.87	0.32	2.28	-0.01	1.60	2.26	1.74	-1.02	1.82	0.05	0.52	-0.38
43	25.98	3.68	0.37	0.45	0.09	0.43	0.71	1.42	0.19	-0.66	-1.12	0.44	-0.44
44	25.19	0.41	-0.13	-0.10	-0.10	4.31	1.46	1.20	-0.04	0.64	0.22	0.10	0.75
45	19.83	1.57	-0.84	-0.03	0.32	-0.58	1.64	0.49	0.10	0.62	-0.33	0.56	-0.73
46	41.75	0.60	-0.31	0.38	0.20	0.16	-0.22	-0.88	0.74	-0.63	0.10	0.88	-0.88
47	20.11	0.45	-0.25	0.14	-0.13	3.62	0.79	1.43	-0.50	0.61	0.04	0.51	1.23
48	24.74	0.99	-0.24	-0.38	0.36	0.83	4.35	1.14	0.30	0.10	-0.39	0.48	0.31
49	19.41	0.74	0.28	3.50	0.54	0.53	0.42	0.45	0.09	-0.06	0.16	0.28	1.03
50	33.67	1.26	0.22	-0.41	-0.27	-0.05	2.69	4.26	0.12	-0.93	-0.98	0.51	-0.50
51	23.11	3.57	-0.97	0.88	-0.19	0.21	1.04	1.11	0.21	0.76	-1.47	-0.99	-0.65
52	22.66	0.35	0.08	0.03	-0.13	-0.33	0.69	0.09	0.36	3.75	0.63	-1.12	-0.36
53	17.22	0.41	0.22	0.73	-0.14	1.27	0.69	3.58	0.92	-0.45	-0.19	-0.05	-0.23
54	22.45	1.20	0.07	3.09	0.74	-0.83	0.40	1.09	0.92	0.32	-1.18	0.56	0.23
55	21.57	0.88	0.21	1.66	-0.04	-2.58	0.36	0.54	0.35	0.73	-1.92	0.36	0.32
56	21.54	1.41	0.21	-0.09	-0.63	1.08	0.74	1.10	0.76	2.58	-1.44	-0.05	-0.21
57	22.12	0.58	0.56	-0.86	-0.20	1.69	1.03	2.04	-1.23	1.46	-0.17	-0.39	-0.46
58	36.30	-2.52	-0.23	0.34	0.14	-0.85	-0.44	-0.49	-0.61	1.07	-0.11	-0.39	0.95

TABLE 3.10 *(continued) D. Factors 16–27; Variables 59–113*

Variable	h^2	16	17	18	19	20	21	22	23	24	25	26	27
59	22.64	0.38	-0.21	-0.68	-0.22	1.37	0.91	0.17	-1.28	1.41	1.36	-0.46	0.57
60	34.01	-0.49	0.54	-1.00	0.19	-0.32	0.78	-0.74	-1.02	1.40	0.20	0.03	0.69
61	25.32	-0.96	-0.03	-0.34	-0.61	0.25	-0.03	-0.17	0.10	0.73	0.30	-0.24	-0.29
62	16.44	-0.54	0.29	-0.48	0.22	1.70	-0.28	-0.31	-0.25	1.71	0.07	0.47	-0.33
63	29.93	-0.71	0.02	-1.12	0.07	1.40	1.93	1.46	-1.75	1.06	-1.40	-1.07	0.41
64	16.84	0.21	0.14	2.58	0.41	-0.79	-0.07	0.47	0.31	0.31	-1.69	-0.87	-0.61
65	39.31	-0.50	-0.60	-0.10	-0.01	-0.74	-0.15	0.35	-0.15	-0.52	1.06	-1.62	-0.93
66	8.28	-0.47	-0.04	0.29	-0.00	1.42	1.23	0.27	-0.04	0.69	0.46	-0.51	1.21
67	17.67	-0.09	0.54	1.28	-0.09	-0.61	-0.95	0.11	-0.01	0.32	-0.77	0.17	0.13
68	50.94	-0.17	-1.97	0.77	-1.18	-0.58	1.91	-0.88	-0.16	0.79	-0.14	-0.03	-1.05
69	20.67	0.28	0.87	-0.04	0.19	-0.10	0.28	-0.72	0.37	0.41	-0.54	-0.04	-0.02
70	31.76	0.55	1.11	0.16	-0.02	-0.12	-0.32	-0.18	-0.60	-0.17	0.87	-0.08	-0.82
71	35.90	-0.38	0.68	0.78	0.77	-0.15	-0.10	-0.49	-0.36	-0.37	0.56	-0.73	-0.98
72	58.26	-0.92	-1.28	-0.88	-0.43	-0.37	0.49	0.14	0.45	-0.78	-0.38	-0.21	-0.04
73	15.21	0.43	3.46	0.56	-0.01	-0.14	-0.42	-0.17	-0.03	-0.15	-0.11	-0.06	-0.18
74	30.55	-0.12	-0.28	-0.20	-0.68	0.89	0.65	-1.41	0.23	1.21	-0.33	-0.64	1.32
75	42.63	-0.51	0.51	0.38	0.21	-0.28	-0.37	-0.28	-0.47	0.19	-0.53	0.21	-0.27
76	15.49	-0.51	3.41	0.00	-0.09	0.04	0.41	-0.18	0.39	-0.04	0.23	-0.17	-0.58
77	27.91	0.09	0.76	0.24	-0.35	0.04	0.37	-0.17	0.23	-0.22	0.37	0.27	-0.36
78	58.48	0.19	-0.46	-0.54	-0.32	-0.73	-2.01	-0.05	-0.16	-0.31	-1.60	1.23	-0.09
79	25.38	-0.64	-0.12	0.59	-0.30	-0.07	0.35	-0.17	-0.78	0.68	0.02	-0.51	-0.70
80	37.56	0.40	0.40	1.40	0.79	0.52	-0.05	-0.66	0.74	-0.31	1.04	-0.90	0.10
81	38.07	-0.38	-0.04	-0.85	-0.69	0.08	0.82	1.09	0.44	-0.05	-1.01	-0.31	0.95
82	22.54	-0.32	-0.82	-0.67	0.38	-0.61	0.61	-0.36	0.30	-0.19	-0.95	-0.70	-0.72
83	30.28	1.12	3.62	-0.21	0.34	-1.73	-0.50	0.51	-2.18	0.06	0.58	0.48	1.17
84	23.73	0.67	0.35	-0.91	0.11	0.04	-0.55	1.03	-0.79	-0.25	-0.40	-0.18	2.02
85	22.08	0.15	0.69	-0.80	0.12	-0.19	-0.18	-0.25	-0.43	-0.15	-0.15	-0.51	1.58
86	30.40	-0.92	0.35	-0.12	1.00	-0.25	-0.48	0.60	0.21	-0.11	-0.23	0.26	-0.68
87	32.78	-0.19	0.04	-0.15	-0.10	0.57	-0.30	-0.16	0.06	-0.12	-0.02	-0.38	0.31
88	28.92	-0.64	1.17	-0.35	-0.12	0.20	0.61	-0.09	0.64	-0.02	0.23	-0.72	0.62
89	10.98	0.51	0.55	0.07	-0.39	0.27	-0.59	0.25	0.61	-0.47	-0.29	-0.28	0.06
90	20.91	0.40	3.75	-0.90	-0.46	-0.47	-0.29	0.08	-0.61	-0.18	-0.15	-0.14	0.86
91	18.90	-0.53	0.25	-0.26	-0.17	0.78	-0.70	0.06	0.19	-0.31	-0.32	0.30	0.40
92	26.74	-1.15	2.03	-0.30	-0.36	0.51	1.90	-1.00	1.61	0.08	-0.75	-0.32	0.02
93	37.94	-0.23	-0.45	-0.39	-0.71	-0.14	0.87	-0.54	-0.01	0.23	-0.31	0.60	-0.42
94	32.48	-0.28	0.27	-0.17	0.76	0.06	0.12	-0.03	-0.27	-0.50	0.28	-0.27	-0.36
95	26.00	-0.10	0.62	0.10	0.11	-0.07	0.11	-0.06	-0.07	-0.08	0.01	0.64	-0.36
96	26.47	-0.10	0.36	-0.20	0.54	-0.39	-0.54	0.16	-0.99	-0.24	0.58	0.25	-0.60
97	13.12	-0.88	1.31	-0.03	0.27	0.36	-0.23	0.01	1.73	-0.02	-0.61	-0.46	-0.39
98	16.59	-0.88	3.36	0.80	0.11	0.09	-0.19	0.45	-0.19	0.22	0.39	-0.25	-0.15
99	9.52	0.15	-0.36	0.43	-0.29	-0.19	-0.21	-0.33	0.27	0.27	-1.02	0.72	-0.42
100	19.70	0.06	-0.55	-0.48	-0.34	-0.53	0.05	0.34	0.29	0.02	-0.32	-0.23	-0.31
101	43.70	-0.02	0.17	-0.28	0.03	0.27	-0.25	-0.54	-1.78	-0.40	0.99	-0.52	-0.42
102	25.55	-0.07	0.01	-0.11	0.20	0.06	-0.12	-0.02	-0.82	-0.12	0.58	-0.10	0.07
103	25.18	-1.17	-0.28	0.33	0.09	0.37	-0.61	-1.07	-0.93	0.42	3.95	-0.43	1.04
104	13.61	-0.37	0.31	-0.30	0.32	-0.22	-0.02	-0.20	-0.20	0.58	3.29	-0.93	0.33
105	11.56	0.64	0.64	-0.59	-0.58	-0.44	0.43	0.54	0.31	0.37	2.17	1.60	-0.27
106	28.49	-0.96	-0.87	0.17	-0.33	-0.91	-0.25	1.07	3.85	0.98	-0.56	1.49	-0.03
107	16.08	-0.34	-0.11	0.46	-0.01	-0.20	-0.27	-0.06	3.36	0.17	-0.17	-0.03	0.59
108	12.39	-1.31	0.09	1.11	0.27	-0.27	-0.16	-0.02	2.30	-0.25	-0.47	0.64	0.72
109	14.31	-0.24	-0.09	-0.32	-0.37	-0.14	0.71	-0.34	-0.08	-0.49	0.40	3.38	0.45
110	16.12	-0.67	0.02	-0.10	0.16	-0.16	-0.41	0.37	-0.36	-0.64	0.49	3.74	-0.06
111	12.04	0.30	0.20	0.29	-0.49	0.22	0.07	0.12	1.48	0.43	-0.11	2.68	-0.20
112	5.21	-0.19	0.22	0.22	0.07	-0.43	-0.08	0.07	0.64	-0.28	-0.48	0.46	1.84
113	19.66	0.29	-0.39	1.64	0.43	-0.45	-0.64	-0.55	1.39	-0.08	-0.64	-0.13	-0.53
Sum of Squares		91.86	91.85	91.79	90.61	90.13	88.94	88.43	88.01	78.64	75.27	62.76	60.02

TABLE 3.11. *Factors in the Nationalities Schedule (31 items — Numbers 68–98)*

Belgian Data		Loading	Texas Data		Loading
Item			Item		
Factor 2: West European			**Factor 9: West European**		
72	*British	6.77	80	*French	3.77
78	Dutch	5.98	72	*British	3.40
71	Belgian	4.96	84	Irish	3.12
68	*Americans	4.10	68	*Americans	2.50
80	*French	3.17	74	Canadians	2.39
96	Swiss	2.48	86	Italians	2.25
Factor 6: Latin			**Factor 2: Latin**		
93	*South Americans	5.22	93	*South Americans	5.57
94	*Spanish	5.21	94	*Spanish	5.46
86	*Italians	4.54	91	*Portuguese	3.11
91	*Portuguese	3.71	86	*Italians	2.71
68	Americans	3.42	80	*French	2.15
74	Canadian	2.48	84	Irish	2.20
80	*French	2.09			
Factor 8: North European			**Factor 7: North European**		
88	*Norwegians	4.81	88	*Norwegians	4.00
77	*Danes	4.69	77	*Danes	3.82
95	*Swedes	4.42	95	*Swedes	3.65
84	Irish	3.32	96	*Swiss	3.09
74	*Canadians	3.17	68	Americans	2.27
96	*Swiss	2.01	78	Dutch	2.17
			74	*Canadians	2.07
			71	Belgian	(1.62)
Factor 11: East Mediterranean and Arab			**Factor 21: Arab**		
79	*1 Egyptians	4.27	79	*1 Egyptians	4.27
85	*2 Israelis	3.93	69	*1 Arabs	3.59
82	*2 Greeks	3.58	89	*1 Persians	2.56
69	*1 Arabs	3.54			
89	*1 Persians	2.59	**Factor 25: East Mediterranean**		
97	*2 Turks	2.22	85	*2 Israelis	3.44
			97	*2 Turks	2.79
			82	*2 Greeks	2.47
Factor 15: Oriental			**Factor 16: Oriental**		
75	*Chinese	6.13	87	*Japanese	5.06
87	*Japanese	5.37	75	*Chinese	4.21
92	Russians	2.13			

* Indicates items having high loadings on the factor for both groups.

TABLE 3.11. *(Continued)*

Item	Belgian Data	Loading	Item	Texas Data	Loading
	Factor 17: East European			*Factor 17: East European*	
90	*Poles	3.75	76	*Czechs	3.64
83	*Hungarians	3.62	90	*Poles	3.51
73	Bulgarians	3.46	83	*Hungarians	2.91
76	*Czechs	3.41	98	*Yugoslavs	2.69
98	*Yugoslavs	3.36	73	Bulgarians	(1.27)
92	Russians	2.03			
	Factor 13: Central European			*Factor 11: Central European*	
81	*Germans	5.09	81	*Germans	5.81
70	Austrians	4.94	92	Russians	3.98
96	Swiss	3.49	70	Austrians	(1.84)

TABLE 3.12. *Factors in Goals of Life Schedule (12 items — Numbers 100–111)*

Item	Belgian Data	Loading	Item	Texas Data	Loading
	Factor 10: Religious			*Factor 6: Religious*	
101	*Doing God's will	5.92	101	*Doing God's will	5.83
102	*Leading moral life dictated by God	4.74	100	*Personal immortality	4.89
100	*Personal immortality	4.06	102	*Leading moral life dictated by God	4.77
12	Clergyman	2.47			
	Factor 25: Service			*Factor 18: Service*	
103	*Sacrifice for better world	3.95	105	*Pleasures for others	4.20
104	*Serve own community	3.29	103	*Sacrifice for better world	4.04
105	*Pleasures for others	2.17	104	*Serve own community	2.95
			63	There is a great deal of satisfaction in doing work that helps others	2.82
	Factor 23: Selfish			*Factor 13: Selfish*	
106	*Get ahead	3.85	106	*Get ahead	4.82
107	*Power; control	3.36	107	*Power; control	3.88
108	*Do best for self	2.30	108	*Do best for self	3.83
			63	There is a great deal of satisfaction in doing work that helps others	−2.47

* Indicates items having high loadings on the factor for both groups.

TABLE 3.12. *(Continued)*

Item	Belgian Data	Loading	Item	Texas Data	Loading
	Factor 26: Stoic			*Factor 26: Stoic*	
110	*"Take it" any time	3.74	109	*Find place, accept it	3.99
109	*Find place, accept it	3.38	111	*Handle problems as they arise	3.90
111	*Handle problems as they arise	2.68	110	*"Take it" any time	2.55

TABLE 3.13. *Factors in Occupations Schedule (31 items — Numbers 2–32)*

Item	Belgian Data	Loading	Item	Texas Data	Loading
	Factor 1: Religious			*Factor 3: Religious*	
21	*Missionary	8.50	21	*Missionary	5.55
12	*Clergyman	7.93	12	*Clergyman	4.93
13	Coal Miner	3.37	15	Elem. School Teacher	3.29
22	*Physician	2.55	26	School Principal	2.74
			32	University Professor	2.63
			22	*Physician	2.04
	Factor 4: Artistic			*Factor 1: Artistic*	
3	*Artist	6.22	3	*Artist	6.00
4	*Author	5.64	2	*Actor	5.48
2	*Actor	4.92	4	*Author	5.25
19	Lawyer	2.43	25	Politician	2.37
32	Physician	2.03	33	Neutral Point	2.27
	Factor 3: Politician, Banker			*Factor 12: Politician, Banker*	
25	*Politician	5.41	25	*Politician	4.31
5	*Banker	5.22	5	*Banker	3.07
8	*Businessman	4.14	19	*Lawyer	2.41
19	*Lawyer	3.75	8	*Businessman	2.37
11	Civil Service Employee	3.19	22	*Physician	2.25
32	University Professor	2.84	2	Actor	2.23
7	Bookkeeper	2.55			
22	*Physician	2.17			
33	Neutral Point	2.28			

* Indicates items having high loadings on the factor for both groups.

TABLE 3.13.   *(Continued)*

Belgian Data		Loading		Texas Data		Loading
Item		*Loading*		*Item*		*Loading*

Factor 7: Soldier, Policeman, Outdoor and Construction Workers				*Factor 22: Soldier, Policeman, Outdoor Workers (Government Employees)*		
28	*Soldier	5.64		24	*Policeman	3.12
30	*Truck Driver	4.04		20	*Mail Carrier	2.24
13	Coal Miner	3.71		28	*Soldier	2.08
16	*Farmer	2.87		11	Civil Service Employee	2.06
20	*Mail Carrier	2.78				
24	*Policeman	2.76		*Factor 28: Outdoor and Construction Workers*		
14	*Electrician	2.60		14	*Electrician	3.13
10	*Carpenter	2.59		10	*Carpenter	2.72
				23	Plumber	2.39
				30	*Truck Driver	2.21
				16	*Farmer	2.01
				13	Coal Miner	(1.17)

Factor 19: Food Dealers and Small Businessmen				*Factor 27: Food Dealers and Small Businessmen*		
9	*Butcher	3.49		17	*Grocer	2.27
17	*Grocer	3.14		9	*Butcher	2.20
29	Tailor	2.66		8	Businessman	2.19
10	Carpenter	2.63		6	Barber	(1.52)
16	Farmer	2.41		27	Shoemaker	(1.22)
23	Plumber	2.32		29	Tailor	(1.90)
27	Shoemaker	2.32				
6	Barber	2.31				

Factor 9: Teachers				*Factor 20: Book Handlers*		
26	School Principal	4.54		31	Typographer	2.56
32	University Professor	4.25		7	Bookkeeper	2.27
15	Elem. School Teacher	4.04		32	University Professor	2.10
22	Physician	2.16				
11	Civil Service Employee	2.09		See *Teachers* in *Religious* above.		
7	Bookkeeper	2.07				
19	Lawyer	2.05				
31	Typographer	(1.83)				

Factor 27: Farmer		
16	Farmer	2.71
84	Irish	2.02

* Indicates items having high loadings on the factor for both groups.

TABLE 3.14. *Factors in Reasons for Work Schedule (31 items — Numbers 35–65)*

	Belgian Data	Loading		Texas Data	Loading
Item			Item		
	Factor 5: Work Is a Virtue			*Factor 4: Work Is a Virtue*	
46	*Purpose of life is work	5.78	65	*Work is a virtue	5.47
60	*Work is a pleasure	5.17	58	*Work never hurt one	4.83
65	*Work is a virtue	4.64	46	*Purpose of life is work	3.74
58	*Work never hurt one	4.07	60	*Work is a pleasure	2.89
			45	Get ahead by good work	2.33
			61	Nation helped by work	2.06
	Factor 20: Work Not Rewarded			*Factor 5: Work Not Rewarded*	
44	*Work not rewarded	4.31	44	*Work not rewarded	5.58
47	*Workers' skills not used	3.62	47	*Workers' skills not used	5.54
40	Be creative in job	2.23	56	Use brains more than	2.77
55	Harder work gets more	−2.58		muscles	
	money				
	Factor 16: Security			*Factor 10: Security*	
43	*Work for pension	3.68	54	Work–money–leisure	4.11
51	*Job gives security	3.57		activities	
39	Care for tools	(1.85)	43	*Work for pension	3.88
58	Work never hurt one	−2.52	51	*Job gives security	3.70
80	French	−2.13	41	Work for self	2.65
40	Be creative in job	−2.03	49	Have to work	2.51
	Factor 12: Work Well			*Factor 14: Work Well*	
61	*Nation helped by work	4.39	62	*Do painstaking work	4.27
59	*No supervision needed	3.31	59	*No supervision needed	3.80
65	Work is a virtue	2.68	52	Do job better than others	2.48
57	*Good management and	2.60	57	*Good management and	2.06
	work comrades			work comrades	
63	Do work that helps others	2.60	61	*Nation helped by work	2.03
58	Work never hurt one	2.57			
45	Get ahead by good work	2.55			
62	*Do painstaking work	2.39			
	Factor 21: Want Satisfactions in Job			*Factor 8: Want Satisfactions in Job*	
48	Be happy in job	4.35	50	*Have satisfying job, like	3.77
40	*Be creative in job	3.04		hobby	
50	*Have satisfying job, like	2.69	36	Like competition	3.17
	hobby		42	*Good work conditions	3.14
42	*Good work conditions	2.27		and comrades	
	and comrades		40	*Be creative in job	2.97
38	Good worker gets to be	(1.61)	60	Work is a pleasure	2.36
	boss		57	Good management and	2.33
78	Dutch	−2.01		work comrades	
			63	Do work that helps others	2.32

* Indicates items having high loadings on the factor for both groups.

TABLE 3.14. *(Continued)*

Belgian Data			Texas Data		
Item		Loading	Item		Loading

Factor 22: *Want Satisfactions — In or Out of Job*			Factor 24: *Want Satisfactions — In or Out of Job*		
50	Have satisfying job, like hobby	4.26	48	Be happy in job	4.29
53	*Creativeness outside of job	3.58	53	*Creativeness outside of job	2.29
41	Best to work for self	2.35			
57	Good management and work comrades	2.04			
37	Loan tools	(1.71)			

Factor 24: *Striving in Work*			Factor 19: *Striving in Work*		
36	Like competition	4.30	55	Harder work gets more money	3.95
52	Do job better than others	3.75	38	Good worker gets to be boss	2.93
56	Use brains more than muscles	2.58	64	Higher wages if work harder	2.83

Factor 18: *Work-Money-Leisure TCT*			Factor 15: *Have to Work TCT*		
34	*TCT work	4.29	34	*TCT work	4.95
49	*Have to work	3.50	35	See worker loaf—report	2.09
54	Work–money–leisure	3.09	49	*Have to work	2.03
64	Higher wages if work harder	2.58			
43	Work for pension	2.28			
35	See worker loaf—report	(1.87)			

Care for Tools			Factor 23: *Care for Tools*		
	Did not appear as a factor. However, see Factor 16 (Item 39) and Factor 22 (Item 37).		39	Care for tools	3.61
			37	Loan tools	3.05

Factor 14: *Total Circular Triads*		
34	TCT work	3.54
113	TCT Goals of Life	3.10
67	TCT Nationalities	3.07
1	TCT Occupations	2.82
18	Janitor	(1.88)
80	French	−2.80

* Indicates items having high loadings on the factor for both groups.

4

THE EXTENSION OF FACTOR ANALYSIS TO THREE-DIMENSIONAL MATRICES

Ledyard R Tucker
University of Illinois

4 THE EXTENSION OF FACTOR ANALYSIS TO THREE-DIMENSIONAL MATRICES[1]

Data from psychological experiments frequently may be classified and cross-classified in many ways. For example, each person in a group of individuals may be measured on each trait in a group of traits by each of a number of methods. This is the situation considered by Campbell and Fiske (1959) in their developments as to multitrait and multimethod matrices. Osgood, Suci, and Tannenbaum (1957) have considered a different type of triple cross-classification in the development of the *semantic differential*. In this case, ratings were obtained from a number of individuals as to the meaning of a number of concepts in terms of a number of bipolar scales defined by opposite adjectives. Still another example occurs when individuals are measured by a battery of measures on a number of occasions. These examples have involved three-way cross-classifications. Higher-order situations can be envisaged also, such as the Osgood, Suci, and Tannenbaum semantic differential experiment repeated on several occasions. Two-way, cross-classifications have been common, usually involving a group of individuals and a battery of measures.

One way of stating the purpose of factor analysis is that it is a method for searching for relations in a body of data. In the past, the factor-analytic model and procedures have been limited to the two-way, cross-classification data. On several occasions, experimenters have applied the two-way factor analysis to data obtained from three-way, cross-classification data as, for example, the analyses reported by Osgood, Suci, and Tannenbaum (1957). The author has been attempting to extend the factor-analytic model and procedures to be appropriate for the search for relations in data classified in three or more ways. The purpose of this effort is to be able to investigate the relations in the observed data rather than in two-way classification data derived from the observed data. One of the systems derived in this effort will be described in this paper.

Table 4.1 presents three-way classification data for a fictitious problem. The values in this table represent the ratings of 12 individuals on 9 traits by each of 5 raters. This data could be assembled into a box or parallelepiped by stacking the two-way matrices for the several raters behind one another. Thus, there would be a vertical dimension for the individuals, a horizontal dimension for the traits, and a depth dimension for the raters. This might be called a three-dimensional data matrix.

A problem in terminology and semantics arises with the use of the word *dimension* to represent a way of classification of the data. There is a second meaning of the word *dimension* in common use in factor analysis: to represent

[1] The research discussed in this paper was jointly supported by the Office of Naval Research under Contract Nonr-1834(39) and the University of Illinois. Reproduction, translation, publication, use and disposal in whole or in part by or for the United States government is permitted.

TABLE 4.1. *Input Data for Fictitious Problem*

Rater (k)	Individual (i)	1j	2j	3j	4j	5j	6j	7j	8j	9j
1k	1i	−0.452	−0.113	0.830	−0.873	−1.295	−0.324	0.409	2.113	0.528
	2i	0.226	0.057	0.480	−0.093	−0.412	−0.103	0.162	0.735	0.184
	3i	0.356	0.089	0.755	−0.227	−0.809	−0.202	0.173	1.154	0.289
	4i	1.145	0.288	0.690	1.567	1.989	0.497	1.112	0.234	0.059
	5i	2.060	0.516	0.805	1.105	0.151	0.038	−0.152	−0.454	−0.114
	6i	−0.243	−0.063	−0.560	−0.880	−1.516	−0.379	−1.198	−0.880	−0.220
	7i	0.243	0.063	0.560	0.880	1.516	0.379	1.198	0.880	0.220
	8i	−2.060	−0.516	−0.805	−1.105	−0.151	−0.038	0.152	0.454	0.114
	9i	0.919	0.228	0.116	−0.459	−1.838	−0.459	−1.264	−0.689	−0.172
	10i	−0.112	−0.027	−0.193	1.108	2.329	0.582	1.028	−0.273	−0.068
	11i	−0.469	−0.119	−1.042	−0.788	−1.107	−0.277	−1.362	−1.616	−0.404
	12i	−1.611	−0.403	−1.636	−0.234	1.144	0.286	−0.257	−1.658	−0.415
2k	1i	−0.625	−0.156	0.686	−0.596	−0.569	−0.142	0.716	2.000	0.500
	2i	0.446	0.112	0.701	0.127	−0.192	−0.048	0.382	0.955	0.239
	3i	−0.315	−0.079	0.309	−0.448	−0.579	−0.145	0.178	0.934	0.234
	4i	1.318	0.331	0.834	1.290	1.262	0.316	0.805	0.348	0.087
	5i	1.507	0.377	0.642	0.553	−0.402	−0.101	−0.315	−0.227	−0.057
	6i	0.197	0.048	−0.121	−0.440	−1.076	−0.269	−0.758	−0.440	−0.110
	7i	−0.197	−0.048	0.121	0.440	1.076	0.269	0.758	0.440	0.110
	8i	−1.507	−0.377	−0.642	−0.553	0.402	0.101	0.315	0.227	0.057
	9i	0.192	0.047	−0.191	−0.736	−1.664	−0.416	−1.120	−0.576	−0.144
	10i	0.119	0.030	−0.187	0.888	1.658	0.415	0.583	−0.493	−0.123
	11i	−0.249	−0.063	−0.822	−0.568	−0.886	−0.222	−1.141	−1.396	−0.349
	12i	−0.885	−0.221	−1.329	0.043	0.971	0.243	−0.401	−1.772	−0.443
3k	1i	−0.798	−0.199	0.543	−0.320	0.158	0.040	1.022	1.886	0.472
	2i	0.666	0.167	0.921	0.347	0.029	0.007	0.603	1.176	0.294
	3i	−0.987	−0.247	−0.137	−0.668	−0.349	−0.087	0.182	0.713	0.178
	4i	1.491	0.374	0.977	1.013	0.535	0.134	0.499	0.462	0.116
	5i	0.955	0.238	0.478	0.000	−0.955	−0.239	−0.478	0.000	0.000
	6i	0.637	0.159	0.319	0.000	−0.637	−0.159	−0.319	0.000	0.000
	7i	−0.637	−0.159	−0.319	0.000	0.637	0.159	0.319	0.000	0.000
	8i	−0.955	−0.238	−0.478	0.000	0.955	0.239	0.478	0.000	0.000
	9i	−0.535	−0.135	−0.498	−1.013	−1.491	−0.373	−0.977	−0.462	−0.116
	10i	0.349	0.088	−0.182	0.668	0.987	0.247	0.137	−0.713	−0.178
	11i	−0.029	−0.008	−0.602	−0.347	−0.666	−0.167	−0.921	−1.176	−0.294
	12i	−0.158	−0.040	−1.021	0.320	0.798	0.200	−0.544	−1.886	−0.472
4k	1i	−0.971	−0.242	0.399	−0.043	0.885	0.221	1.329	1.772	0.443
	2i	0.886	0.222	1.141	0.568	0.249	0.062	0.823	1.396	0.349
	3i	−1.658	−0.415	−0.583	−0.888	−0.118	−0.030	0.188	0.493	0.123
	4i	1.664	0.417	1.120	0.736	−0.192	−0.048	0.192	0.576	0.144
	5i	0.402	0.100	0.315	−0.553	−1.503	−0.376	−0.638	0.227	0.057

TABLE 4.1. *Input Data for Fictitious Problem.* *(Continued)*

Rater	Individual				Trait (j)					
(k)	(i)	$1j$	$2j$	$3j$	$4j$	$5j$	$6j$	$7j$	$8j$	$9j$
	$6i$	1.076	0.269	0.758	0.440	−0.197	−0.049	0.122	0.440	0.110
	$7i$	−1.076	−0.269	−0.758	−0.440	0.197	0.049	−0.122	−0.440	−0.110
	$8i$	−0.402	−0.100	−0.315	0.553	1.503	0.376	0.638	−0.227	−0.057
	$9i$	−1.262	−0.317	−0.805	−1.290	−1.318	−0.330	−0.833	−0.348	−0.087
	$10i$	0.579	0.145	−0.177	0.448	0.315	0.079	−0.310	−0.934	−0.234
	$11i$	0.192	0.047	−0.381	−0.127	−0.446	−0.112	−0.701	−0.955	−0.239
	$12i$	0.569	0.142	−0.714	0.596	0.625	0.156	−0.688	−2.000	−0.500
$5k$	$1i$	−1.144	−0.285	0.256	0.234	1.612	0.403	1.635	1.658	0.415
	$2i$	1.107	0.278	1.361	0.788	0.469	0.117	1.043	1.616	0.404
	$3i$	−2.329	−0.582	−1.029	−1.108	0.112	0.028	0.193	0.273	0.068
	$4i$	1.838	0.460	1.264	0.459	−0.919	−0.230	−0.115	0.689	0.172
	$5i$	−0.151	−0.039	0.151	−1.105	−2.060	−0.515	−0.803	0.454	0.114
	$6i$	1.516	0.380	1.198	0.880	0.243	0.061	0.562	0.880	0.220
	$7i$	−1.516	−0.380	−1.198	−0.880	−0.243	−0.061	−0.562	−0.880	−0.220
	$8i$	0.151	0.039	−0.151	1.105	2.060	0.515	0.803	−0.454	−0.114
	$9i$	−1.989	−0.498	−1.112	−1.567	−1.145	−0.286	−0.690	−0.234	−0.059
	$10i$	0.809	0.202	−0.171	0.227	−0.356	−0.089	−0.755	−1.154	−0.289
	$11i$	0.412	0.103	−0.161	0.093	−0.226	−0.057	−0.481	−0.735	−0.184
	$12i$	1.295	0.324	−0.407	0.873	0.452	0.113	−0.831	−2.113	−0.528

each factor derived from the data. Thus, confusion might arise in describing the results from a two-way matrix that involves 10 factors, if *dimension* were used in both of its meanings; one might say that a two-dimensional matrix yielded a 10-dimensional factorial structure. In order to avoid such confusion, we prefer to use some other term to designate a way of classification of data and suggest the term "mode" or "mode of classification." In more precise terminology, a mode would be a set of indices by which data might be classified. A cross-classification would result from a Cartesian product of two or more modes. The data in Table 4.1 would be a three-mode, or triple-mode, matrix.

Section I in the Mathematical Outline at the end of this chapter presents some notes on notation to be used in the subsequent developments. There are three types of subscript indices, or three types of modes — one type being used to designate classifications on the observed data, a second type to designate classifications on derived coefficients, and a third type to designate classifications on transformed derived coefficients. Consider the modes for the observed data. For our example, the mode I will be used to index the classification by individuals, the mode J will be used to index the classification by traits, and the mode K will be used to index the classification by raters. Elements in these modes will be designated by the lower case letters i, j, and k. Alternate elements in these modes will be designated by primed lower case letters. The number of elements in each mode is designated by the capital letter designating the mode. Another notational point is the postfixing of index numbers by the lower case letter for the mode involved. Thus: $1k$ is to be read as the first k, $2k$ is to be read as the second k, and so forth. These notations have been employed in Table 4.1. An element of the observed data is designated by x_{ijk}, using triple subscripts corresponding to the three observational modes. The triple-mode matrix may be designated by **X**.

Figure 4.1 presents the numerical values from which the observations in our fictitious example were determined. This figure is a pictorial representation of the model being employed. A more precise statement of the model is given in Equation 4.1 in Section II of the Mathematical Outline. This model involves

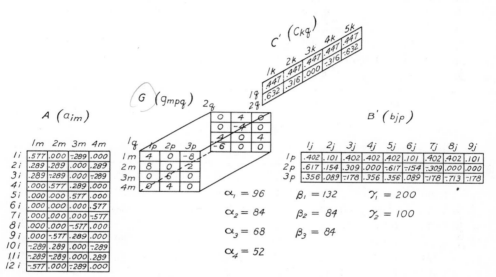

FIGURE 4.1. *The intrinsic structure*

three double-mode matrices, **A**, **B**, and **C**, plus one triple-mode matrix **G**. Each of the double-mode matrices contains dependency coefficients relating observational mode elements to derivational mode elements as indicated in Section I of the Mathematical Outline. The derivational modes are designated as M, P, and Q and correspond respectively to the observational modes I, J, and K. The triple-mode matrix **G** involves only the derivational modes. The elements in these matrices in the model are combined as products and summed over all indices of the derivational modes as indicated in Equation 4.1. The hat is indicated over the $\hat{x}_{ijk}$ to indicate that these are values determined from the model as distinct from possible observed values. This permits consideration of the model as yielding values that approximate the observed values. Differences between x_{ijk} and $\hat{x}_{ijk}$ could be considered as discrepancies of approximations.

Consider Equation 4.2; this equation is obtained from Equation 4.1 by rearrangement of the summations and factoring out constants for these summations. A new coefficient is defined in Equation 4.3, n^{m}_{ipq}, where the superscript

The Extension of Factor Analysis to Three-Dimensional Matrices / **113**

TABLE 4.2. *Matrices* $\mathbf{N}^m$ *and* $\mathbf{S}^{mp}$

$$AG = \mathbf{N}^m$$

		1p	2p	3p			1p	2p	3p
1q	1i	2.308	−1.734	−4.616	2q	1i	−1.156	2.308	−1.156
	2i	3.468	1.156	−1.734		2i	−1.734	0.000	0.000
	3i	−1.156	−1.156	−2.890		3i	1.734	2.312	0.000
	4i	4.616	1.734	1.154		4i	1.156	−2.308	1.156
	5i	0.000	3.462	0.000		5i	2.308	0.000	2.308
	6i	0.000	2.308	0.000		6i	−3.462	0.000	0.000
	7i	0.000	−2.308	0.000		7i	3.462	0.000	0.000
	8i	0.000	−3.462	0.000		8i	−2.308	0.000	−2.308
	9i	−4.616	1.734	−1.154		9i	1.156	2.308	1.156
	10i	1.156	−1.156	2.890		10i	1.734	−2.312	0.000
	11i	−3.468	1.156	1.734		11i	−1.734	0.000	0.000
	12i	−2.308	−1.734	4.616		12i	−1.156	−2.308	−1.156

$$AGB' = \mathbf{S}^{mp}$$

		1j	2j	3j	4j	5j	6j	7j	8j	9j
1q	1i	−1.785	−0.445	1.214	−0.715	0.354	0.089	2.287	4.219	1.055
	2i	1.490	0.374	2.060	0.777	0.064	0.018	1.347	2.630	0.658
	3i	−2.207	−0.552	−0.307	−1.494	−0.780	−0.195	0.408	1.596	0.399
	4i	3.336	0.836	2.186	2.266	1.197	0.302	1.115	1.033	0.258
	5i	2.136	0.533	1.070	0.000	−2.136	−0.533	−1.068	0.000	0.000
	6i	1.424	0.355	0.713	0.000	−1.424	−0.355	−0.712	0.000	0.000
	7i	−1.424	−0.355	−0.713	0.000	1.424	0.355	0.712	0.000	0.000
	8i	−2.136	−0.533	−1.070	0.000	2.136	0.533	1.068	0.000	0.000
	9i	−1.197	−0.302	−1.114	−2.266	−3.336	−0.836	−2.185	−1.033	−0.258
	10i	0.780	0.196	−0.407	1.494	2.207	0.552	0.306	−1.596	−0.399
	11i	−0.064	−0.018	−1.346	−0.777	−1.490	−0.374	−2.060	−2.630	−0.658
	12i	−0.354	−0.089	−2.285	0.715	1.785	0.445	−1.217	−4.219	−1.055
2q	1i	0.548	0.136	0.454	−0.876	−2.300	−0.575	−0.970	0.360	0.090
	2i	−0.697	−0.175	−0.697	−0.697	−0.697	−0.175	−0.697	−0.697	−0.174
	3i	2.124	0.531	1.411	0.697	−0.729	−0.181	−0.016	0.697	0.174
	4i	−0.548	−0.136	−0.454	0.876	2.300	0.575	0.970	−0.360	−0.090
	5i	1.749	0.439	0.517	1.749	1.749	0.439	0.516	−0.718	−0.180
	6i	−1.392	−0.350	−1.391	−1.392	−1.392	−0.350	−1.392	−1.392	−0.348
	7i	1.392	0.350	1.391	1.392	1.392	0.350	1.392	1.392	0.348
	8i	−1.749	−0.439	−0.517	−1.749	−1.749	−0.439	−0.516	0.718	0.180
	9i	2.300	0.575	0.972	0.876	−0.548	−0.136	−0.454	−0.360	−0.090
	10i	−0.729	−0.181	−0.017	0.697	2.124	0.531	1.411	0.697	0.174
	11i	−0.697	−0.175	−0.697	−0.697	−0.697	−0.175	−0.697	−0.697	−0.174
	12i	−2.300	−0.575	−0.972	−0.876	0.548	0.136	0.454	0.360	0.090

indicates the mode over which the summation on the right is taken. This equation may be stated in matrix form as in Equation 4.4, where $(\mathbf{N}^m)_q$ is an $I \times P$ matrix for a fixed value of q, and $(\mathbf{G})_q$ is an $M \times P$ matrix for the fixed value of q. These matrices may be termed "frontal planes" of the triple-mode matrices $\mathbf{N}^m$ and $\mathbf{G}$, respectively. The matrices $(\mathbf{N}^m)_q$ are given in the upper section of Table 4.2. Correspondingly, any triple-mode matrix may be considered to have "lateral planes" when viewed from the side and "horizontal planes" when viewed from above. Equation 4.5 is similar to Equation 4.3, and Equation 4.6 is similar to Equation 4.4. The change from Equations 4.3 and 4.4 to Equations 4.5 and 4.6 involves an interchange of the summations over m and p in Equation 4.2, along with the corresponding shift of a_{im} and b_{jp}. The element n^m_{mjq} is similar in form to the element n^m_{ipq}; they are both obtained from the triple-mode matrix $\mathbf{G}$ by a multiplication by one of the double-mode matrices with dependency coefficients.

Another type of combination coefficient is defined in Equations 4.7 and 4.8. These equations define the elements s^{mp}_{ijq} and matrix $\mathbf{S}^{mp}$. A point of interest is that Equation 4.8 states the relation of a frontal plane of $\mathbf{S}^{mp}$, for fixed value of q, to a frontal plane of $\mathbf{G}$ and the matrices $\mathbf{A}$ and $\mathbf{B}$ in terms of regular matrix algebra for double-mode matrices. The matrices $(\mathbf{S}^{mp})_q$ are given in the lower section of Table 4.2. The substitution of Equation 4.7 into Equation 4.2 yields Equation 4.9 and the $\hat{x}_{ijk}$. Equation 4.10 yields a frontal plane, for fixed value of occasion k, as a weighted sum of the frontal plane matrices $(\mathbf{S}^{mp})_q$ where the weights are a vector from matrix $\mathbf{C}$ for the given value of k.

A suggested interpretation of the various derivational modes and of the several matrices is in terms of idealized entities such as idealized individuals, idealized traits, and idealized raters. The derivational modes M, P, and Q correspond to these idealized entities. The matrices $\mathbf{A}$, $\mathbf{B}$, and $\mathbf{C}$ describe the observed entities in terms of the idealized entities. In this interpretation, the matrix $\mathbf{G}$ gives the interactions among the several types of idealized entities. We might call this matrix the central, or core matrix. We should note here an assumed restriction in the traditional double-mode factor analysis, that of the identity of idealized traits and idealized individuals, so that the core matrix is an identity matrix and is dropped from the system. This is not a necessary restriction and elimination. It is indeed possible that separate and distinct transformations or rotations of the axes for idealized traits and idealized individuals would be desirable. The relation between these transformations could be incorporated into a core matrix between the matrix of factor loadings and the matrix of factor scores in order to preserve the identity of observed score approximations. In the cases for triple-mode and high-order matrices, the core matrix cannot be dropped in general and must remain as an integral part of the structure of our model.

As in any mathematical model, the properties of transformations are of great importance. Section III of the Mathematical Outline is devoted to some of the possible transformations for the three-mode, factor-analytic model. In Equations

4.11 and 4.12, a transformation of the double-mode matrix $\mathbf{A}$ is indicated, 'Equation 4.11 in summational notation and Equation 4.12 in matrix notation. The matrix $\mathbf{T}_m$ is a square, nonsingular matrix with cell entries t_{mm*}. Note that the original derivational mode is designated by M and the transformed derivational mode is designated by M^*. Equations 4.13 and 4.14 give the inverse transformations. Note that elements in the inverse matrix, $\mathbf{T}_m^{-1}$, designated by superscripts, are t^{m*m}. Substitution from Equation 4.14 into Equation 4.2 yields Equation 4.15. Equation 4.16 is a definition of a partially transformed core matrix $\mathbf{G}$. The rearrangement of summations in Equation 4.15, substitution from Equation 4.16, and the elimination of the product of a transformation by its inverse yields Equation 4.17. Note that Equation 4.17 is in the identical form of Equation 4.2. We may conclude, then, that Equations 4.11 and 4.16 define compatible transformations on the matrices $\mathbf{A}$ and $\mathbf{G}$.

Equation 4.18 concerns the effects of the foregoing transformation on the $\mathbf{N}^m$ matrix. Matrix $\mathbf{N}^{m*}$ is defined as in Equation 4.3. Substitutions are made from Equations 4.11 and 4.16, and the product of the transformation by its inverse is eliminated, thus arriving at the conclusion that this transformation does not affect the matrix $\mathbf{N}^m$.

TABLE 4.3. *Transformations of Matrices* $\mathbf{B}$ *and* $\mathbf{C}$

| | **B** | | | | $(\beta^{\frac{1}{2}})$ | | | | Λ_p | | $=$ | | **B*** | |
	$1p$	$2p$	$3p$		$1p$	$2p$	$3p$		$1p^*$	$2p^*$	$3p^*$		$1p^*$	$2p^*$	$3p^*$
$1j$	0.402	0.617	0.356	$1p$	$\sqrt{132}$	0	0	$1p$	$\sqrt{1/3}$	$\sqrt{1/3}$	$\sqrt{1/3}$	$1j$	8	0	0
$2j$	0.101	0.154	0.089	$2p$	0	$\sqrt{84}$	0	$2p$	$\sqrt{1/2}$	$-\sqrt{1/2}$	0	$= 2j$	2	0	0
$3j$	0.402	0.309	−0.178	$3p$	0	0	$\sqrt{84}$	$3p$	$\sqrt{1/6}$	$\sqrt{1/6}$	$-\sqrt{2/3}$	$3j$	4	0	4
$4j$	0.402	0.000	0.356									$4j$	4	4	0
$5j$	0.402	−0.617	0.356									$5j$	0	8	0
$6j$	0.101	−0.154	0.089									$6j$	0	2	0
$7j$	0.402	−0.309	−0.178									$7j$	0	4	4
$8j$	0.402	0.000	−0.713									$8j$	0	0	8
$9j$	0.101	0.000	−0.178									$9j$	0	0	2

$$\mathbf{T}_p = (\beta^{\frac{1}{2}})\Lambda_p$$

| | **C** | | | $(\gamma^{\frac{1}{2}})$ | | | Λ_q | | $=$ | **C*** | |
	$1q$	$2q$		$1q$	$2q$		$1q^*$	$2q^*$		$1q^*$	$2q^*$
$1k$	0.447	0.632	$1q$	$\sqrt{200}$	0	$1q$	$\sqrt{1/2}$	$\sqrt{1/2}$	$= 1k$	$4\sqrt{5}$	0
$2k$	0.447	0.316	$2q$	0	$\sqrt{100}$	$2q$	$\sqrt{1/2}$	$-\sqrt{1/2}$	$2k$	$3\sqrt{5}$	$\sqrt{5}$
$3k$	0.447	0.000							$3k$	$2\sqrt{5}$	$2\sqrt{5}$
$4k$	0.447	−0.316							$4k$	$\sqrt{5}$	$3\sqrt{5}$
$5k$	0.447	−0.632							$5k$	0	$4\sqrt{5}$

$$\mathbf{T}_q = (\gamma^{\frac{1}{2}})\Lambda_q$$

Equation 4.19 states the transformation of Equation 4.16 as a matrix inverse transformation on the frontal planes of the core matrix $\mathbf{G}$. Similarly, Equation 4.20 treats the transformation of the $\mathbf{N}^m$ matrix in terms of matrix algebra on the frontal planes of this matrix. Note the use of the superscript $m*$ to the matrix $\mathbf{G}$ in Equation 4.19 to designate the partially transformed core matrix. Equation 4.21 indicates the alternative partial transformation of the core matrix in terms of the mode P. For this transformation, a series of equations parallel to Equations 4.11 through 4.14 would apply to the matrix $\mathbf{B}$ and transformation $\mathbf{T}_p$. Equation 4.22 indicates a double transformation on the core matrix for transformations on both modes M and P.

The upper half of Table 4.3 presents a transformation on the mode P for the illustrative problem. This transformation was constructed as the product of a diagonal matrix of square roots of characteristic roots, to be described, and an orthogonal rotation of axes. The result of transforming the $\mathbf{B}$ matrix is the very simple structure built into the illustration. This feature of the illustrative problem was included to indicate the possibility of investigating empirical matrices for this kind of feature.

Transformations in the depth mode Q have an effect similar to that of those for the other modes, but they must be developed differently in a mathematical sense. Equations 4.23 through 4.32 deal with this case. Equations 4.23 through 4.26 define this transformation and its inverse on the matrix $\mathbf{C}$, which is parallel to Equations 4.11 through 4.14. Equation 4.26 is substituted into Equation 4.10 to obtain Equation 4.27. Equation 4.28 defines $(\mathbf{S}^{mp})_{q*}$ which are frontal planes of a triple-mode matrix with entries s_{ijq*}^{mp}. Substitution into Equation 4.27 yields Equation 4.29, which is recursive in form to Equation 4.10. Equations 4.30 through 4.32 indicate transformations on the matrices $\mathbf{G}$, $\mathbf{N}^m$, and $\mathbf{N}^p$.

The lower section of Table 4.3 illustrates a transformation in the depth mode Q. This transformation, in the present case, is composed of a multiplication of the $\mathbf{C}$ matrix by a diagonal matrix of roots (to be described subsequently) and an orthogonal matrix. In the present example, the raters were set up to form a transition from one type of rater to another type of rater. This is indicated in the matrix $\mathbf{C}^*$ where the loadings on the idealized rater $1q*$ decrease regularly from $4\sqrt{5}$ to 0 while the loadings on idealized rater $2q*$ increase regularly over this same range.

While the developments involved with triple-mode matrices may be stated more precisely in summational notation, the use of this kind of notation is undesirably tedious. In order to convert the statements and equations to a type of matrix notation, a new kind of matrix multiplication is required to treat the transformations in the depth mode Q. An idea was generated from the pictorial representation in Figure 4.1, where the third mode is represented in approximate perspective. We have adopted a symbol, $\leftarrow\!\circ$, termed "an arrow-circle multiplication," to represent a matrix multiplication in the depth mode. Consider Equation 4.33 in Section IV of the Mathematical Outline. This equation is to be compared with Equation 4.10. Both equations are representative of the same process: the sum of the products indicated in Equation 4.9. The elemental process is a dot product between two vectors, one vector being for a constant combination of ij in the triple-mode matrix $\mathbf{S}^{mp}$ and having elements running in depth over the mode Q, the other vector being a column vector from the matrix $\mathbf{C}'$ for a given value of k. The complete $\leftarrow\!\!\ominus$ multiplication involves such vector multiplications for every vector of $\mathbf{S}^{mp}$ defined by every combination ij by every column vector of matrix $\mathbf{C}'$.

A variant of the multiplication defined in the preceding paragraph could be developed if the perspective in the pictorial representation had been drawn with the distance $1q$–$2q$ running off to the left instead of to the right as in Figure 4.1. Such a state could be denoted by the symbol $\ominus\!\!\rightarrow$ which would be read as "circle-arrow multiplication." The multiplication in the second term of Equation 4.33 would become $\mathbf{C}\ominus\!\!\rightarrow\mathbf{S}^{mp}$. Note that in this statement the matrix $\mathbf{C}$ is used rather than its transpose as in Equation 4.33.

Equation 4.34 is derived from Equations 4.33 and 4.8 by two steps. First, in Equation 4.8, the notation for frontal planes is dropped by elimination of the parentheses and the subscript q from the matrix $\mathbf{S}^{mp}$ in the first term and from the matrix $\mathbf{G}$ in the second term. The intention is to infer the matrix multiplication for every frontal plane of $\mathbf{G}$ to obtain the entire matrix $\mathbf{S}^{mp}$. Second, the result of this reinterpretation of Equation 4.8 is substituted into Equation 4.33 to obtain Equation 4.34. In this equation, the arrow-circle multiplication may be interpreted as applying to the entire product $\mathbf{AGB}'$, or to the partial product $\mathbf{GB}'$, or to the matrix $\mathbf{G}$. The arrow-circle multiplication is commutative with frontal plane multiplications.

The dropping of the frontal plane notation yields some simplification of statements of equations; thus, Equation 4.4 becomes Equation 4.35, Equation 4.8 becomes Equation 4.36, Equation 4.19 becomes Equation 4.37, and Equation 4.21 becomes Equation 4.38. Equation 4.39 states the implied double transformation on the matrix $\mathbf{G}$ for transformations in the modes M and P.

Equation 4.40 defines the transformation on the matrix $\mathbf{G}$ for a transformation in the mode Q in terms of the arrow-circle multiplication by $(\mathbf{T}_q^{-1})'$. This is equivalent to Equation 4.30. Equation 4.41 defines a transformation on the matrix $\mathbf{G}$ for transformations in all modes. Equation 4.42 indicates an interesting possibility in the use of the arrow-circle multiplication. This equation is obtained from Equation 4.41 by frontal plane pre-multiplication by $\mathbf{T}_m$, frontal plane post-multiplication by $\mathbf{T}_p'$, and arrow-circle multiplication by $\mathbf{T}_q'$. Due to the commutative relation between frontal plane multiplications and the arrow-circle multiplications, the multiplications by $\mathbf{T}_m$ and $\mathbf{T}_p$ may be considered prior to the arrow-circle multiplication by $(\mathbf{T}_q^{-1})'$ on the right side of Equation 4.41, thus combining with their respective inverse matrices to yield identity matrices which are eliminated. The arrow-circle multiplication by $\mathbf{T}_q'$ is combined with the inverse of this matrix to yield an identity matrix which is also eliminated. These operations produce Equation 4.42.

Equations 4.43 through 4.45 develop the general proposition concerning transformation for all three modes. Equation 4.43 is obtained by substitution from Equation 4.42 into Equation 4.34. The removal of the parentheses in Equation 4.43 and the use of the commutative relation between frontal plane multiplication and the arrow-circle multiplication yields Equation 4.44. Substitution from Equation 4.12, from an equivalent equation for transformation in mode P, and from Equation 4.24 yields Equation 4.45, which is equivalent in form to Equation 4.34. Thus, the transformations in each mode accompanied by inverse transformations by the inverse transformation matrices on the core matrix, $\mathbf{G}$, as in Equation 4.41, do not alter the $\hat{\mathbf{X}}$ matrix.

Our next problem involves the determination of the matrix $\mathbf{G}^{m^*p^*q^*}$ from the matrix $\hat{\mathbf{X}}$, given the matrices $\mathbf{A}^*$, $\mathbf{B}^*$, and $\mathbf{C}^*$. As in Equation 4.46, let $\hat{\mathbf{X}}$ be pre-multiplied in frontal plane multiplication by $(\mathbf{A}^*)'$, post-multiplied in frontal plane multiplication by $\mathbf{B}^*$, and be arrow-circle multiplied by $\mathbf{C}^*$. Both sides of Equation 4.45 are multiplied in the preceding fashion to produce Equation 4.46. Suppose that the transformations to $\mathbf{A}^*$, $\mathbf{B}^*$, and $\mathbf{C}^*$ were such that these are sections of orthonormal matrices as specified in Equations 4.47 through 4.49. These specifications do not limit the generality of our solution because there is general freedom for transformations, as developed in the preceding section. In case the transformed matrices do not fit these specifications, it is always possible to transform the matrices further to fit the specifications and then to transform the solution back to the original matrices. Substitution of the specification Equations 4.47 through 4.49 into Equation 4.46 yields Equation 4.50 which may be stated in summational notation in Equation 4.51. These equations are the solution to the problem.

Our final problem concerns the solution for the matrices of the intrinsic structure, given the matrix $\mathbf{X}$ of observations. The following is an extension of the principal-components-type solution in double-mode factor analysis. For the present development, it is easier to revert to summational notation. Equations 4.52 through 4.54 are translations of Equations 4.47 through 4.49 with the starred notation dropped for convenience. In Equation 4.55, a type of cross-product coefficient is defined between a pair of individuals, i and i'. To obtain this coefficient, corresponding values of $\hat{x}_{ijk}$ and $\hat{x}_{i'jk}$ are obtained, one for individual i and one for individual i' for a given combination of j and k. These two values are multiplied and all such products are summed over all combinations of j and k. Substitutions from Equation 4.1, algebraic manipulations, and substitutions from Equations 4.52 through 4.54 yield Equation 4.59. Actually, the specification that the matrices $\mathbf{A}$, $\mathbf{B}$, and $\mathbf{C}$ be orthonormal is not very restrictive since such matrices may be obtained in many ways. Consequently, it is possible to define a further restriction on these transformations as in Equation 4.60. This restriction is analogous to the restriction in diagonalizing a square, double-mode matrix by orthogonal rotations. Substitution from Equation 4.60 into 4.59 yields Equation 4.61, which may be written in matrix form as Equation 4.62. This equation, combined with the specification in Equation 4.52, is one of the standard forms for characteristic roots and vectors.

TABLE 4.4. *The P Matrices*

Individual	Matrix $\mathbf{P}_i$											
	1i	2i	3i	4i	5i	6i	7i	8i	9i	10i	11i	12i
1i	37.67	16.00	16.00	− 5.67	−11.33	0.00	0.00	11.33	− 5.67	−16.00	−16.00	−26.33
2i	16.00	19.33	− 3.33	14.00	0.00	8.67	− 8.67	0.00	−14.00	− 5.33	−10.67	−16.00
3i	16.00	− 3.33	19.33	−14.00	0.00	− 8.67	8.67	0.00	14.00	−10.67	− 5.33	−16.00
4i	− 5.67	14.00	−14.00	33.67	11.33	0.00	0.00	−11.33	−22.33	14.00	−14.00	− 5.67
5i	−11.33	0.00	0.00	11.33	22.67	0.00	0.00	−22.67	11.33	0.00	0.00	−11.33
6i	0.00	8.67	− 8.67	0.00	0.00	17.33	−17.33	0.00	0.00	8.67	8.67	0.00
7i	0.00	− 8.67	8.67	0.00	0.00	−17.33	17.33	0.00	0.00	8.67	8.67	0.00
8i	11.33	0.00	0.00	−11.33	−22.67	0.00	0.00	22.67	−11.33	0.00	0.00	11.33
9i	− 5.67	−14.00	14.00	−22.33	11.33	0.00	0.00	−11.33	33.67	−14.00	14.00	− 5.67
10i	−16.00	− 5.33	−10.67	14.00	0.00	8.67	8.67	0.00	−14.00	19.33	− 3.33	16.00
11i	−16.00	−10.67	− 5.33	−14.00	0.00	8.67	8.67	0.00	14.00	− 3.33	19.33	16.00
12i	−26.33	−16.00	−16.00	− 5.67	−11.33	0.00	0.00	11.33	− 5.67	16.00	16.00	37.67

TABLE 4.4. The P Matrices. (Continued)

Matrix P_j

Trait	1j	2j	3j	4j	5j	6j	7j	8j	9j
1j	64	16	32	32	0	0	0	0	0
2j	16	4	8	8	0	0	0	0	0
3j	32	8	32	16	0	0	16	32	8
4j	32	8	16	32	32	8	16	0	0
5j	0	0	0	32	64	16	32	0	0
6j	0	0	0	8	16	4	8	0	0
7j	0	0	16	16	32	8	32	32	8
8j	0	0	32	0	0	0	32	64	16
9j	0	0	8	0	0	0	8	16	64

Matrix P_k

Rater	1k	2k	3k	4k	5k
1k	80	60	40	20	0
2k	60	50	40	30	20
3k	40	40	40	40	40
4k	20	30	40	50	60
5k	0	20	40	60	80

Thus, it is concluded that the matrix **A** contains the characteristic vectors of $\hat{\mathbf{P}}_i$, and (α) contains the characteristic roots.

The upper section of Table 4.4 presents the $\mathbf{P}_i$ matrix for the illustrative problem. The matrix **A** in Figure 4.1 contains the characteristic vectors for this matrix, and the listed values of α are the corresponding characteristic roots. All roots not listed are zero.

Equations 4.63 through 4.65 define the matrix $\hat{\mathbf{P}}_j$ and state that the matrix **B** contains the characteristic vectors of this matrix $\hat{\mathbf{P}}_j$ and that the values of β are the corresponding characteristic roots. Equations 4.66 through 4.68 make similar statements for the matrix $\hat{\mathbf{P}}_k$, the matrix **C**, and the values of γ. The matrices $\mathbf{P}_j$ and $\mathbf{P}_k$ are given in Table 4.4. Matrix **B** contains the characteristic vectors of $\mathbf{P}_j$, and the listed values of β in Figure 4.1 are the corresponding characteristic roots. The matrix **C** and the listed values of γ in Figure 4.1 are the characteristic vectors and roots of the matrix $\mathbf{P}_k$.

The foregoing procedure would give an exact fit of $\hat{\mathbf{X}}$ to **X** if all nonzero roots and vectors were obtained. An approximation of $\hat{\mathbf{X}}$ to **X** could be obtained by discarding roots and vectors for each mode for small values of the roots. Such an approximation would not be a least-squares solution but might be adequate in practice. A complete least-squares solution would involve a much more complex computational procedure.

We have presented in this paper a model for an intrinsic structure for triple-mode matrices and have discussed some of the properties of transformations within this model. In essence, this model may be characterized by the transformations from observed entities in each of the modes of classification to idealized entities in corresponding derivational modes of classification. The idealized entities are interrelated through a core matrix. A procedure related to principal components analysis has been described for approximating observed data by the model discussed. Among the unsolved problems is the analogy in the triple-mode analysis of specific factors and communality involved in double-mode factor analysis, one of the problems to which we are giving considerable thought for future developments.

MATHEMATICAL OUTLINE

I.   Some Notes on Notation

    A.   Subscript indices

Classification modes for observed data (observational modes):

$$i, \, i' \; = \; 1i, \; 2i, \; 3i, \; \cdots, I$$

$$j, \, j' \; = \; 1j, \; 2j, \; 3j, \; \cdots, J$$

$$k, \, k' \; = \; 1k, \; 2k, \; 3k, \; \cdots, K$$

Classification modes for derived coefficients (derivational modes):

$$m, m' = 1m, 2m, 3m, \cdots, M$$

$$p, p' = 1p, 2p, 3p, \cdots, P$$

$$q, q' = 1q, 2q, 3q, \cdots, Q$$

Classification modes for transformed derived coefficients:

$$m^*, m^{*\prime} = 1m^*, 2m^*, 3m^*, \cdots, M$$

$$p^*, p^{*\prime} = 1p^*, 2p^*, 3p^*, \cdots, P$$

$$q^*, q^{*\prime} = 1q^*, 2q^*, 3q^*, \cdots, Q$$

B. Coefficients

x_{ijk} = measure for ijk triple-classification element for observational modes; forms a triple-mode matrix $\mathbf{X}$.

$\hat{x}_{ijk}$ = approximation to x_{ijk}.

a_{im} = dependency coefficients for im double-classification element giving dependency of observational mode element i on derivational mode element m; forms double-mode matrix $\mathbf{A}$.

b_{jp} = (similar definition as for a_{im}); forms double-mode matrix $\mathbf{B}$.

c_{kq} = (similar definition as for a_{im}); forms double-mode matrix $\mathbf{C}$.

g_{mpq} = measure for mpq triple-classification element for derivational modes; forms triple-mode matrix $\mathbf{G}$.

II. A Three-mode Model

$$\hat{x}_{ijk} = \sum_m \sum_p \sum_q a_{im} b_{jp} c_{kq} g_{mpq} \tag{4.1}$$

$$\hat{x}_{ijk} = \sum_q c_{kq} \sum_p b_{jp} \sum_m a_{im} g_{mpq} \tag{4.2}$$

$$n_{ipq}^{m} = \sum_m a_{im} g_{mpq} \tag{4.3}$$

$$(\mathbf{N}^m)_q = \mathbf{A}(\mathbf{G})_q \tag{4.4}$$

$$n_{mjq}^{p} = \sum_p b_{jp} g_{mpq} \tag{4.5}$$

$$(\mathbf{N}^p)_q = (\mathbf{G})_q \mathbf{B}' \tag{4.6}$$

$$s_{ijq}^{mp} = \sum_p b_{jp} \sum_m a_{im} g_{mpq} = \sum_p b_{jp} n_{ipq}^{m} = \sum_m a_{im} n_{mjq}^{p} \tag{4.7}$$

$$(\mathbf{S}^{mp})_q = \mathbf{A}(\mathbf{G})_q \mathbf{B}' = (\mathbf{N}^m)_q \mathbf{B}' = \mathbf{A}(\mathbf{N}^p)_q \tag{4.8}$$

$$\hat{x}_{ijk} = \sum_q c_{kq} s_{ijq}^{mp} \tag{4.9}$$

$$(\hat{\mathbf{X}})_k = \sum_q c_{kq} (\mathbf{S}^{mp})_q \tag{4.10}$$

III. Transformations of Derivational Modes

$$a_{im*} = \sum_m a_{im} t_{mm*} \tag{4.11}$$

$$\mathbf{A}^* = \mathbf{AT}_m \tag{4.12}$$

$$\mathbf{A} = \mathbf{A}^* \mathbf{T}_m^{-1} \tag{4.13}$$

$$a_{im} = \sum_{m*} a_{im*} t^{m*m} \tag{4.14}$$

$$\hat{x}_{ijk} = \sum_q c_{kq} \sum_p b_{jk} \sum_m \sum_{m*} a_{im*} t^{m*m} g_{mpq} \tag{4.15}$$

$$g_{m*pq} = \sum_m t^{m*m} g_{mpq} \tag{4.16}$$

$$\hat{x}_{ijk} = \sum_q c_{kq} \sum_p b_{jp} \sum_{m*} a_{im*} g_{m*pq} \tag{4.17}$$

$$n_{ipq}^{m*} = \sum_{m*} a_{im*} g_{m*pq} = \sum_m a_{im} g_{mpq} = n_{ipq}^{m} \tag{4.18}$$

$$(\mathbf{G}^m)_q = \mathbf{T}_m^{-1}(\mathbf{G})_q \tag{4.19}$$

$$(\mathbf{N}^{m*})_q = \mathbf{A}^*(\mathbf{G}^{m*})_q = \mathbf{A}(\mathbf{G})_q = (\mathbf{N}^m)_q \tag{4.20}$$

$$(\mathbf{G}^{p*})_q = (\mathbf{G})_q(\mathbf{T}_p^{-1})' \tag{4.21}$$

$$(\mathbf{G}^{m*p*})_q = \mathbf{T}_m^{-1}(\mathbf{G})_q(\mathbf{T}_p^{-1})' \tag{4.22}$$

$$c_{kq*} = \sum_q c_{kq} t_{qq*} \tag{4.23}$$

$$\mathbf{C}^* = \mathbf{CT}_q \tag{4.24}$$

$$\mathbf{C} = \mathbf{C}^* \mathbf{T}_q^{-1} \tag{4.25}$$

$$c_{kq} = \sum_{q*} c_{kq*} t^{q*q} \tag{4.26}$$

$$(\hat{\mathbf{X}})_k = \sum_q \sum_{q*} c_{kq*} t^{q*q}(\mathbf{S}^{mp})_q \tag{4.27}$$

$$(\mathbf{S}^{mp})_{q*} = \sum_q t^{q*q}(\mathbf{S}^{mp})_q \tag{4.28}$$

$$(\hat{\mathbf{X}})_k = \sum_{q*} c_{kq*}(\mathbf{S}^{mp})_{q*} \tag{4.29}$$

$$(\mathbf{G})_{q*} = \sum_q t^{q*q}(\mathbf{G})_q \tag{4.30}$$

$$(\mathbf{N}^m)_{q*} = \sum_q t^{q*q}(\mathbf{N}^m)_q = \mathbf{A}(\mathbf{G})_{q*} \tag{4.31}$$

$$(\mathbf{N}^p)_{q*} = \sum_q t^{q*q}(\mathbf{N}^p)_q = (\mathbf{G})_{q*}\mathbf{B}' \tag{4.32}$$

IV. Suggested Third-Mode Matrix Multiplication

$$\hat{X} = S^{mp} \leftarrow\!\!\circ C' \tag{4.33}$$

$$\hat{X} = AGB' \leftarrow\!\!\circ C' \tag{4.34}$$

$$N^m = AG \tag{4.35}$$

$$S^{mp} = AGB' = N^m B' = AN^p \tag{4.36}$$

$$G^{m*} = T_m^{-1} G \tag{4.37}$$

$$G^{p*} = G(T_p^{-1})' \tag{4.38}$$

$$G^{m*p*} = T_m^{-1} G(T_p^{-1})' = G^{m*}(T_p^{-1})' = T_m^{-1} G^{p*} \tag{4.39}$$

$$G^{q*} = G \leftarrow\!\!\circ (T_q^{-1})' \tag{4.40}$$

$$G^{m*p*q*} = T_m^{-1} G(T_p^{-1})' \leftarrow\!\!\circ (T_q^{-1})' \tag{4.41}$$

$$G = T_m G^{m*p*q*} T_p' \leftarrow\!\!\circ T_q' \tag{4.42}$$

$$\hat{X} = A(T_m G^{m*p*q*} T_p' \leftarrow\!\!\circ T_q')B' \leftarrow\!\!\circ C' \tag{4.43}$$

$$\hat{X} = AT_m G^{m*p*q*} T_p' B' \leftarrow\!\!\circ T_q' C' \tag{4.44}$$

$$\hat{X} = A^* G^{m*p*q*} (B^*)' \leftarrow\!\!\circ (C^*)' \tag{4.45}$$

V. Transformation from $\hat{X}$ to G^{m*p*q*}

$$(A^*)'\hat{X}B^* \leftarrow\!\!\circ C^* = (A^*)'A^* G^{m*p*q*} (B^*)'B^* \leftarrow\!\!\circ (C^*)'C^* \tag{4.46}$$

$$(A^*)'A^* = I \tag{4.47}$$

$$(B^*)'B^* = I \tag{4.48}$$

$$(C^*)'C^* = I \tag{4.49}$$

$$(A^*)'\hat{X}B^* \leftarrow\!\!\circ C^* = G^{m*p*q*} \tag{4.50}$$

$$\sum_i a_{im*} \sum_j b_{jp*} \sum_k c_{kq*} \hat{x}_{ijk} = g_{m*p*q*} \tag{4.51}$$

VI. Resolution into Principal Axes Factors for Each Observational Mode

(Transformations of the derivational modes are assumed, so as to have the properties enumerated in Equations 4.52, 4.53, 4.54, 4.60, 4.64, and 4.67. The starred notation is dropped for convenience.)

$$\delta_{mm'} = \sum_i a_{im} a_{im'} = 1 \text{ for } m = m'$$
$$= 0 \text{ for } m \neq m' \tag{4.52}$$

$$\delta_{pp'} = \sum_j b_{jp} b_{jp'} = 1 \text{ for } p = p'$$
$$= 0 \text{ for } p \neq p' \tag{4.53}$$

The Extension of Factor Analysis to Three-Dimensional Matrices / **125**

$$\delta_{qq'} = \sum_k c_{kq} c_{kq'} = 1 \text{ for } q = q' \tag{4.54}$$
$$= 0 \text{ for } q \neq q'$$

$$\hat{p}_{ii'} = \sum_j \sum_k \hat{x}_{ijk} \hat{x}_{i'jk} \tag{4.55}$$

$$= \sum_j \sum_k \sum_m \sum_p \sum_q a_{im} b_{jp} c_{kq} g_{mpq} \sum_{m'} \sum_{p'} \sum_{q'} a_{i'm'} b_{jp'} c_{kq'} g_{m'p'q'} \tag{4.56}$$

$$= \sum_m a_{im} \sum_{m'} a_{i'm'} \sum_p \sum_q \sum_{p'} \sum_{q'} g_{mpq} g_{m'p'q'} \sum_j b_{jp} b_{jp'} \sum_k c_{kq} c_{kq'} \tag{4.57}$$

$$= \sum_m a_{im} \sum_{m'} a_{i'm'} \sum_p \sum_q \sum_{p'} \sum_{q'} g_{mpq} g_{m'p'q'} \delta_{pp'} \delta_{qq'} \tag{4.58}$$

$$\hat{p}_{ii'} = \sum_m a_{im} \sum_{m'} a_{i'm'} \sum_p \sum_q g_{mpq} g_{m'pq} \tag{4.59}$$

$$\sum_p \sum_q g_{mpq} g_{m'pq} = \alpha_m \text{ for } m = m'$$
$$= 0 \text{ for } m \neq m' \tag{4.60}$$

$$\hat{p}_{ii'} = \sum_m a_{im} a_{i'm} \alpha_m \tag{4.61}$$

$$\hat{\mathbf{P}}_i = \mathbf{A}(\boldsymbol{\alpha})\mathbf{A}' \tag{4.62}$$

$\hat{\mathbf{P}}_i$ = square matrix with elements $\hat{p}_{ii'}$

$(\boldsymbol{\alpha})$ = diagonal matrix with elements α_m

$\mathbf{A}$ contains characteristic vectors of $\hat{\mathbf{P}}_i$

$(\boldsymbol{\alpha})$ contains characteristic roots of $\hat{\mathbf{P}}_i$

$$\hat{p}_{jj'} = \sum_i \sum_k \hat{x}_{ijk} \hat{x}_{ij'k} \tag{4.63}$$

$$\sum_m \sum_q g_{mpq} g_{mp'q} = \beta_p \text{ for } p = p'$$
$$= 0 \text{ for } p \neq p' \tag{4.64}$$

$$\hat{\mathbf{P}}_j = \mathbf{B}(\boldsymbol{\beta})\mathbf{B}' \tag{4.65}$$

$\mathbf{B}$ contains characteristic vectors of $\hat{\mathbf{P}}_j$

$(\boldsymbol{\beta})$ contains characteristic roots of $\hat{\mathbf{P}}_j$

$$\hat{p}_{kk'} = \sum_i \sum_j \hat{x}_{ijk} \hat{x}_{ijk'} \tag{4.66}$$

$$\sum_m \sum_p g_{mpq} g_{mpq'} = \gamma_q \text{ for } q = q'$$
$$= 0 \text{ for } q \neq q' \tag{4.67}$$

$$\hat{\mathbf{P}}_k = \mathbf{C}(\boldsymbol{\gamma})\mathbf{C}' \tag{4.68}$$

$\mathbf{C}$ contains characteristic vectors of $\hat{\mathbf{P}}_k$

$(\boldsymbol{\gamma})$ contains characteristic roots of $\hat{\mathbf{P}}_k$

For the approximation of the structure to observed data, unhatted measures x_{ijk} and matrices $\mathbf{P}_i$, $\mathbf{P}_j$, and $\mathbf{P}_k$ for the observed data are substituted for the hatted measures and matrices in Equations 4.55, 4.62, 4.63, 4.65, 4.66, and 4.68. A limited number of dimensions corresponding to large roots may be used in the approximate structure. The corresponding matrix g_{mpq} may be obtained as in Equation 4.51 with x_{ijk} replacing $\hat{x}_{ijk}$.

5

MATRIX FACTORING
AND TEST THEORY

Paul Horst
University of Washington

5 MATRIX FACTORING AND TEST THEORY

Over the years, many investigators in the field of factor analysis and test theory have been interested in the implications of variation in item difficulty or preference for the various models and objectives with which they were concerned. Ferguson (1941) was one of the first to call attention to the fact that the intercorrelations of objective tests are influenced by the dispersions of item preferences. It has long been known that only if two binary variables have equal means is it possible to have a correlation of unity between the two.

Some investigators have insisted that the ideal test for most purposes is one in which items are all of approximately equal difficulty. Others have insisted that in order to get adequate discrimination the dispersion of item difficulties should be large. Some who have been concerned with the effect of item difficulty on correlation have proposed that when matrices of intercorrelations among binary variables are required, then tetrachorics should be used to neutralize the influence of item difficulty or preference. This proposal seems to be based on the idea that variation in item difficulty is a sort of experimental nuisance that creeps into our data.

Perhaps one of the first developments that explicitly recognized the fundamental role of variation in item preference for measurement theory was the work of Guttman (1955) on scaling theory.[1] The concept of a perfectly scalable set of items was based on the notion that all persons marking an item with a given preference value should also mark all items of greater preference value. Guttman worked out his coefficient of reproducibility to indicate to what extent the items satisfied this condition. From this concept he developed the notion of the simplex, which he extended to more general types of data such as those encountered in learning experiments.

The work of Edwards (1957), which has been concerned with the concept of social desirability in personality-type items, is also intimately concerned with variation in item preference values and the implications of this variation on attempts to measure distinct personality traits. The general notion is that items should be of approximately equal preference value, or that they should be cast in forced-choice format, so that items of equal preference value are paired together.

In general, the phenomenon of variation in item preference values and its implications for measurement theory has not received the systematic treatment it deserves. Certainly one cannot disregard this variation as a sort of nuisance phenomenon to be done away with by various tricks or gimmicks, as one attempts to eliminate experimental error. If one has a perfectly homogeneous set of items with perfect retest reliability, then if they are of exactly equal

[1] This reference includes a bibliography of Guttman's most significant contributions.

difficulty or preference value, one such item is of just as much value for measurement purposes as the entire set. The entire set will separate any particular group into only two parts, since an individual can have only one of two scores.

A perfectly homogeneous and perfectly reliable set of items which is also useful for discrimination among members of a group at a number of different levels must have variation in item preference value. Such a set would result in what we may call the simplex binary matrix. In this matrix, all persons marking an item of given preference value also mark all items of greater preference value. We seem to have a paradox, because we have defined a perfectly homogeneous, perfectly reliable, and optimally discriminating set of items in such a way that the rank of the intercorrelation matrix of the items cannot possibly be unity. As a matter of fact, it is fairly easy to show that the rank of a matrix is exactly equal to the number of distinct preference or difficulty values presented in the set.

This point has been made in much of Guttman's work. Guttman seems to have believed that a set of items which has a unique difficulty value for each item will yield a correlation matrix that can have at most a rank two less than its order, no matter how the diagonals are chosen. DuBois (1960) has shown that such a matrix can have its diagonal values determined, so that the rank of the reduced matrix is $n/2$. The problem of determining diagonal values so as to reduce the rank of the matrix is a part of the currently rather ill-defined and controversial communality problem and does not seem to be germane to our interests of the moment. We may choose to formulate a model in which varying levels of difficulty are regarded as distinct dimensions or factors. But this leads us into more fundamental philosophical difficulties.

It might be argued that difficulties caused by variations in item preferences are due to attempts to measure attributes with groups of dichotomous elements when ideally we should strive for some sort of continuous measure. It is doubtful that this can be a fruitful point of view. If we pressed it far enough, we should have to abandon most of the work in both the practice and theory of measurement since the beginning of objective-type instruments. It is not reason enough, of course, to preserve an approach just because much time and money has already been spent on it. I suspect, however, that the problem goes much deeper than this, and that we require new models to reconcile the concepts of difficulty and dimensionality as they clash head-on in the simplex phenomenon. We cannot resort to tetrachoric correlations for item intercorrelations of unequal preference value when we know that this phenomenon is an essential part of the warp and woof of all tests made up of dichotomously scored items. To abandon such tests would certainly be jettisoning the infant with its bath.

It would seem, therefore, that one useful approach, in lieu of more basic epistemological resolutions, would be to embrace wholeheartedly the preference dispersion phenomenon and to have more systematic devices for taking it into account in our models. One approach to the problem would appear to be the assumption of a latent simplex for a given set of items. By statistical or computational procedures we might then segregate the simplex from the dimensionality of the set.

Let us assume, therefore, that we have a binary data matrix obtained on responses to a set of items. We assume that the columns of this matrix represent individual items and the rows represent persons. These may be personality-type items or they may be any kind of objective-test items. They may all be assumed to measure the same thing or to measure different things. With the advent of the high-speed computer, we are freer now to conduct factor analyses on matrices of item scores and therefore extend the techniques for determining dimensionalities to sets of items. We may now test much more fully the rational and *a priori* approaches that have been used in the past for developing sets of homogeneous items. In any case, since we know that the dimensionality of a system will be accounted for in part by the dispersion of item preferences, we may consider procedures for segregating this part of the dimensionality. We may call the simplex of the system that part which is due to variations in item preferences.

We begin with an $(N x n)$ binary data matrix **M** of item scores. We let "**1**" be a vector all of whose elements are unity. Assuming that a score is the number of items "correctly" marked by a person, the vector **S** of test scores is given by

$$\mathbf{M1} = \mathbf{S} \tag{5.1}$$

We let **P**′ be a row vector of the proportion of individuals answering correctly each of the items. This vector is given by

$$\frac{\mathbf{1'M}}{N} = \mathbf{P'} \tag{5.2}$$

We shall assume further that the items are so arranged as to satisfy the inequality

$$S_i \gtreqless S_{i+1} \tag{5.3}$$

This simply means that the rows of the matrix are arranged so that the lower scores are at the top and the higher scores at the bottom. We also assume that the columns are arranged in such a way as to satisfy

$$P_i \gtreqless P_{i+1} \tag{5.4}$$

Here we mean simply that the easiest or preferred items are arranged in descending order of preference or increasing order of difficulty from left to right.

We next consider an $(N x m)$ binary matrix **L** such that its width or number of columns is equal to or less than the number of items or width of the **M** matrix. We indicate a column of row sums of **L** by

$$\mathbf{L1} = \mathbf{U} \tag{5.5}$$

We shall assume that, as in the case of the **M** matrix, the scores from the **L** matrices are in increasing order of magnitude from top to bottom as indicated by

$$U_i \gtreqless U_{i+1} \tag{5.6}$$

We let ϱ' be the vector of proportions for the columns of $\mathbf{L}$ as indicated by

$$\frac{\mathbf{1'L}}{N} = \varrho' \tag{5.7}$$

Consider now any two columns $\mathbf{L}_{.i}$ and $\mathbf{L}_{.j}$ of the $\mathbf{L}$ matrix where i is equal to or less than j. We assume the vectors have been chosen so that their minor product moment is proportional to the jth element of ϱ as given in Equation 5.7. This condition is indicated by

$$\frac{\mathbf{L}'_{.i}\mathbf{L}_{.j}}{N} = \varrho_j, \quad i \gtrless j \tag{5.8}$$

We impose the further restriction that each element of ϱ' in Equation 5.7 shall be greater than the one following it. This is indicated by the inequality

$$\rho_i > \rho_{i+1} \tag{5.9}$$

The $\mathbf{L}$ matrix then is what we have called a binary simplex matrix. This is a matrix in which each person who marks the keyed answer to a given item also marks the keyed answers to all previous items. This matrix represents a hypothetical set of data on a perfectly reliable homogeneous discriminating set of items.

Let us assume for the moment that the $\mathbf{L}$ matrix is a good representation of whatever characteristics or properties of the $\mathbf{M}$ matrix are due to a dispersion of item difficulties. Our problem, then, is to find a transformation of the $\mathbf{L}$ matrix which will yield the best least squares fit to the $\mathbf{M}$ matrix. First we convert the $\mathbf{L}$ matrix to deviation form as indicated in

$$\mathbf{x} = \left(\mathbf{I} - \frac{\mathbf{11'}}{N}\right)\mathbf{L} \tag{5.10}$$

We also make the transformation of the $\mathbf{M}$ matrix to deviation form, indicated by

$$\mathbf{y} = \left(\mathbf{I} - \frac{\mathbf{11'}}{N}\right)\mathbf{M} \tag{5.11}$$

We can now write the equation for the regression of the $\mathbf{y}$ matrix on the $\mathbf{x}$ matrix as in

$$\mathbf{xB} - \mathbf{y} = \boldsymbol{\varepsilon} \tag{5.12}$$

It is well known that the least squares solution for $\mathbf{B}$ or the solution that minimizes the trace of the product moment of $\boldsymbol{\varepsilon}$ in Equation 5.12 is given by

$$\mathbf{B} = (\mathbf{x'x})^{-1}\mathbf{x'y} \tag{5.13}$$

From Equations 5.12 and 5.13 we have the solution for $\boldsymbol{\varepsilon}$, given by

$$[\mathbf{x}(\mathbf{x'x})^{-1}\mathbf{x'} - \mathbf{I}]\mathbf{y} = \boldsymbol{\varepsilon} \tag{5.14}$$

Assuming now that the $\mathbf{L}$ matrix has been satisfactorily chosen, we may assume that the residual matrix, ε, is free of the effect of item dispersions. We may, therefore, proceed to a factoring of the residual covariance matrix given in

$$\frac{\varepsilon'\varepsilon}{N} = \frac{y'[I - x(x'x)^{-1}x']y}{N} \tag{5.15}$$

Such a factoring may be assumed to yield the dimensionality of a set of items after they have been freed from the effect of the simplex phenomenon.

From Equations 5.10, 5.11, and 5.15 we get the minor product moment of the residual matrix ε in terms of the original $\mathbf{M}$ and $\mathbf{L}$ matrices as given in

$$\varepsilon'\varepsilon = \mathbf{M}'\left(I - \frac{11'}{N}\right)\mathbf{M} - \mathbf{M}'\left(I - \frac{11'}{N}\right)\mathbf{L}\left[\mathbf{L}'\left(I - \frac{11'}{N}\right)\mathbf{L}\right]^{-1}\mathbf{L}'\left(I - \frac{11'}{N}\right)\mathbf{M} \tag{5.16}$$

We now define the matrix $\mathbf{G}$ by

$$\frac{\mathbf{L}'\mathbf{L}}{N} = \mathbf{G} \tag{5.17}$$

Because of Equation 5.8, which defines the $\mathbf{L}$ matrix as a simplex, we can write $\mathbf{G}$ as in

$$\mathbf{G} = \begin{bmatrix} \rho_1 & \rho_2 & \cdots & \rho_m \\ \rho_2 & \rho_2 & \cdots & \rho_m \\ \cdot & \cdot & \cdots & \cdot \\ \rho_m & \rho_m & \cdots & \rho_m \end{bmatrix} \tag{5.18}$$

Here we see that the first row of $\mathbf{G}$ is precisely ϱ' given by Equation 5.7. In succeeding rows all values to the left of the diagonal are equal to the diagonal value, and all those to the right are equal to the corresponding values from Equation 5.7.

It is next useful to define a diagonal matrix as in

$$\mathbf{D} = \begin{bmatrix} \rho_1 - \rho_2 & 0 & \cdots & 0 \\ 0 & \rho_2 - \rho_3 & \cdots & 0 \\ \cdots & \cdots & \cdots & \cdots \\ 0 & 0 & \cdots & \rho_m \end{bmatrix} \tag{5.19}$$

Here it is clear that the first element is obtained by subtracting ρ_2 from ρ_1, the second element by subtracting ρ_3 from ρ_2, and so on. The last element is simply the last element of the ϱ' vector in Equation 5.7. We also define a triangular matrix of the form given in

$$\mathbf{T} = \begin{bmatrix} 1 & 0 & 0 & \cdots & 0 & 0 \\ 1 & 1 & 0 & \cdots & 0 & 0 \\ 1 & 1 & 1 & \cdots & 0 & 0 \\ \cdots & \cdots & \cdots & \cdots & \cdots & \cdots \\ 1 & 1 & 1 & \cdots & 1 & 0 \\ 1 & 1 & 1 & \cdots & 1 & 1 \end{bmatrix} \tag{5.20}$$

Here all elements above the diagonal are zero and all elements in and below the diagonal are unity. It can readily be verified now that $\mathbf{G}$, given by Equation 5.18, can be expressed by

$$\mathbf{G} = \mathbf{T'DT} \qquad (5.21)$$

If next we substitute Equations 5.2, 5.7, and 5.21 in Equation 5.16 we get

$$\frac{\boldsymbol{\varepsilon'\varepsilon}}{\mathcal{N}} = \frac{\mathbf{M'M}}{\mathcal{N}} - \mathbf{PP'} - \frac{\mathbf{M'}}{\mathcal{N}}(\mathbf{L} - \mathbf{1}\boldsymbol{\varrho'})(\mathbf{G} - \boldsymbol{\varrho\varrho'})^{-1}(\mathbf{L'} - \boldsymbol{\varrho}\mathbf{1})\frac{\mathbf{M}}{\mathcal{N}} \qquad (5.22)$$

This equation can be simplified by considering the middle parenthesis on the right. The inverse of this parenthesis can be verified to be as given in

$$(\mathbf{G} - \boldsymbol{\varrho\varrho'})^{-1} = \mathbf{G}^{-1} + \frac{\mathbf{G}^{-1}\boldsymbol{\varrho\varrho'}\mathbf{G}^{-1}}{1 - \boldsymbol{\varrho'}\mathbf{G}^{-1}\boldsymbol{\varrho}} \qquad (5.23)$$

Using Equation 5.21 we can write the inverse of $\mathbf{G}$ as in

$$\mathbf{G}^{-1} = \mathbf{T}^{-1}\mathbf{D}^{-1}\mathbf{T'}^{-1} \qquad (5.24)$$

It can readily be verified now that the inverse of $\mathbf{T}$ is of the form given by

$$\mathbf{T}^{-1} = \begin{bmatrix} 1 & 0 & 0 & \cdots & 0 & 0 \\ -1 & 1 & 0 & \cdots & 0 & 0 \\ 0 & -1 & 1 & \cdots & 0 & 0 \\ \cdots & \cdots & \cdots & \cdots & \cdots & \cdots \\ 0 & 0 & 0 & \cdots & 1 & 0 \\ 0 & 0 & 0 & \cdots & -1 & 1 \end{bmatrix} \qquad (5.25)$$

Here we have simply an identity matrix whose diagonals of unity are bordered from beneath by -1. It may be recognized that this is a convenient form of matrix for transforming another matrix into one whose columns are the differences between successive columns of the matrix. Also, from Equations 5.19 and 5.25 we have

$$\mathbf{T'}^{-1}\boldsymbol{\varrho} = \mathbf{D1} \qquad (5.26)$$

We proceed now to simplify the right side of Equation 5.23. First, we have from Equation 5.24 the result indicated by

$$\mathbf{G}^{-1}\boldsymbol{\varrho} = \mathbf{T}^{-1}\mathbf{D}^{-1}\mathbf{T'}^{-1}\boldsymbol{\varrho} \qquad (5.27)$$

From Equations 5.26 and 5.27 we get

$$\mathbf{G}^{-1}\boldsymbol{\varrho} = \mathbf{T}^{-1}\mathbf{1} \qquad (5.28)$$

But from Equations 5.25 and 5.28 we get

$$\mathbf{G}^{-1}\boldsymbol{\varrho} = \mathbf{e}_1 \qquad (5.29)$$

where $\mathbf{e}_1$ is a column vector all of whose elements are zero except the first, which is unity. From Equation 5.29 we get

$$\boldsymbol{\varrho'}\mathbf{G}^{-1}\boldsymbol{\varrho} = \rho_1 \qquad (5.30)$$

Now, putting together Equations 5.23, 5.24, 5.29, and 5.30, we finally have

$$(\mathbf{G} - \varrho\varrho')^{-1} = \left(\mathbf{T}^{-1}\mathbf{D}^{-1}\mathbf{T}^{-1} + \frac{e_1 e_1'}{1 - \rho_1}\right) \tag{5.31}$$

Substituting Equation 5.31 in 5.22 we get Equation 5.32, the minor product moment or the covariance of the residuals, independent of the simplex due to dispersion of item difficulty.

$$\frac{\varepsilon'\varepsilon}{N} = \frac{\mathbf{M'M}}{N} - \mathbf{PP'} - \frac{\mathbf{M'}}{N}(\mathbf{L} - \mathbf{1}\varrho')\left(\mathbf{T}^{-1}\mathbf{D}^{-1}\mathbf{T}'^{-1} + \frac{e_1 e_1'}{1 - \rho_1}\right)(\mathbf{L'} - \varrho\mathbf{1}')\frac{\mathbf{M}}{N} \tag{5.32}$$

For computational purposes, it is convenient to define additional notation. We define the matrix $\mathbf{K}$ by

$$\mathbf{K} = N\mathbf{M'L} - \mathbf{M'11'L} \tag{5.33}$$

We indicate N^2 times the covariance matrix for $\mathbf{M}$ by

$$N^2\mathbf{C}_M = N\mathbf{M'L} - \mathbf{M11'M} \tag{5.34}$$

From Equations 5.32, 5.33, and 5.34, we get N^2 times the residual covariance matrix given by

$$N\varepsilon'\varepsilon = N^2\mathbf{C}_M - \frac{\mathbf{K}\left(\mathbf{T}^{-1}\mathbf{D}^{-1}\mathbf{T}'^{-1} + \frac{e_1 e_1'}{1 - \rho_1}\right)\mathbf{K'}}{N^2} \tag{5.35}$$

We next define the matrix $\mathbf{W}$ by

$$\mathbf{W} = \mathbf{KT}^{-1} \tag{5.36}$$

This equation simply means that each column vector of $\mathbf{W}$ is obtained by subtracting a vector of $\mathbf{K}$ from the one immediately preceding, as indicated in

$$\mathbf{W}_{.i} = \mathbf{K}_{.i} - \mathbf{K}_{.(i+1)} \tag{5.37}$$

The final vector in the $\mathbf{W}$ matrix is simply the last column of $\mathbf{K}$ as shown in

$$\mathbf{W}_{.n} = \mathbf{K}_{.n} \tag{5.38}$$

We define the matrix $\mathbf{H}$ by

$$\mathbf{H} = \frac{\mathbf{WD}^{-1}\mathbf{W'}}{N^2} \tag{5.39}$$

and the matrix $\mathbf{F}$ by

$$\mathbf{F} = \mathbf{H} + \frac{\mathbf{K}_{.1}\mathbf{K}_{.1}'}{N^2(1 - \rho_1)} \tag{5.40}$$

Then from Equations 5.33 through 5.40 we get

$$N\varepsilon'\varepsilon = N^2\mathbf{C}_M - \mathbf{F} \tag{5.41}$$

We consider next the question of how the $\mathbf{L}$ matrix may be constructed. A number of possibilities are available. We may, for example, consider the frequency distribution of the scores or S values in Equation 5.1 obtained from the data matrix. We may then construct a vector $\mathbf{f}$ made up of the nonzero frequencies such that f_1 is the frequency for the lowest S value and f_n for the largest S value. We can then construct the binary simplex matrix $\mathbf{L}$ so that the ρ values are given by

$$\rho_1 = \frac{\mathbf{f'1}}{N}, \quad \rho_{i+1} = \rho_i - \frac{f_i}{N} \tag{5.42}$$

Thus Equation 5.42 for determining the ρ values amounts to constructing a simplex binary matrix such that its row sums are the same as the row sums for $\mathbf{M}$ in Equation 5.1. We then eliminate all but one column from each set of repeated columns of the resulting matrix. Repeated columns may of course occur, but they will add no predictive information; in fact, they will violate the condition that each ρ value must be greater than the one immediately following it as required by Equation 5.9. If repeated ρ values are permitted, the diagonal matrix given by Equation 5.19 will have zero elements in the diagonal for ρ of equal value. This would result in infinite values where the inverse of $\mathbf{D}$ in Equation 5.19 is required.

Another procedure for determining the $\mathbf{L}$ matrix is simply to require that the ρ_i in Equation 5.7 be respectively the same as the distinct P values in Equation 5.2. This means that the experimental P values are taken as the theoretical simplex values in the least squares solution. One objection to this procedure is that although some of the P's may not be exactly equal they may be very close. Very small values in Equation 5.19 would then occur, which may cause difficulty in solutions involving the inverse of the matrix.

A third method which gets around this objection is to construct the $\mathbf{L}$ matrix so that the ρ_i in Equation 5.7 are equally spaced, as indicated by

$$\rho_i = c + \rho_{i+1} \tag{5.43}$$

In this equation, c is an appropriately determined constant. This method has the advantage that no two ρ_i need be very close together and thus avoids difficulty in the inverse of the diagonal matrix in Equation 5.19. Ordinarily, c should be determined so that ρ_1 and ρ_m will be close, respectively, to P_1, P_n. The effect of varying the size of c requires further investigation.

It is quite possible that more elegant and more theoretically satisfactory methods for constructing the $\mathbf{L}$ matrix can be devised.

A numerical example using the third method for determining the matrix $\mathbf{L}$ is given below. Matrix 5.1 gives the $\mathbf{M}$ and $\mathbf{L}$ matrices. Matrix 5.2 shows the calculations for the $N^2\mathbf{C}_M$ matrix given by Equation 5.34. Matrix 5.3 shows the calculations for the $\mathbf{K}$ and $\mathbf{W}$ matrices given by Equations 5.33 and 5.36, respectively. Matrix 5.4 shows the calculation of the $\mathbf{H}$ matrix given by Equation 5.39. Matrix 5.5 shows the calculation of the $\mathbf{F}$ matrix given by Equation 5.40. Matrix 5.6 shows the $N\varepsilon'\varepsilon$ matrix given by Equation 5.41. It will be noted that the first row and column in this matrix are zero, since the first vectors of $\mathbf{M}$ and $\mathbf{L}$ are the same in this example.

MATRIX 5.1. *The* **M** *and* **L** *matrices*

$$
\mathbf{M} = \begin{bmatrix} 0 & 0 & 0 & 0 \\ 1 & 0 & 1 & 0 \\ 1 & 1 & 0 & 0 \\ 1 & 1 & 0 & 0 \\ 1 & 0 & 1 & 1 \\ 1 & 1 & 1 & 0 \\ 1 & 1 & 0 & 1 \\ 1 & 1 & 1 & 1 \\ 1 & 1 & 1 & 1 \\ 1 & 1 & 1 & 1 \end{bmatrix}
\qquad
\mathbf{L} = \begin{bmatrix} 0 & 0 & 0 \\ 1 & 0 & 0 \\ 1 & 0 & 0 \\ 1 & 1 & 0 \\ 1 & 1 & 0 \\ 1 & 1 & 1 \\ 1 & 1 & 1 \\ 1 & 1 & 1 \\ 1 & 1 & 1 \\ 1 & 1 & 1 \end{bmatrix}
$$

MATRIX 5.2. *Calculations for the* $N^2\mathbf{C}_M$ *matrix*

$$
N\mathbf{M'M} = \begin{bmatrix} 90 & 70 & 60 & 50 \\ 70 & 70 & 40 & 40 \\ 60 & 40 & 60 & 40 \\ 50 & 40 & 40 & 50 \end{bmatrix}
$$

$$
\mathbf{M'11'M} = \begin{bmatrix} 81 & 63 & 54 & 45 \\ 63 & 49 & 42 & 35 \\ 54 & 42 & 36 & 30 \\ 45 & 35 & 30 & 25 \end{bmatrix}
$$

$$
N^2\mathbf{C}_M = N\mathbf{M'M} - \mathbf{M'11'M} = \begin{bmatrix} 9 & 7 & 6 & 5 \\ 7 & 21 & -2 & 5 \\ 6 & -2 & 24 & 10 \\ 5 & 5 & 10 & 25 \end{bmatrix}
$$

MATRIX 5.3. *Calculations for the* **K** *and* **W** *matrices*

$$
N\mathbf{M'L} = \begin{bmatrix} 90 & 70 & 50 \\ 70 & 60 & 50 \\ 60 & 50 & 40 \\ 50 & 50 & 40 \end{bmatrix}
$$

$$
\mathbf{M'11'L} = \begin{bmatrix} 81 & 63 & 45 \\ 63 & 49 & 35 \\ 54 & 42 & 30 \\ 45 & 35 & 25 \end{bmatrix}
$$

$$
\mathbf{K} = N\mathbf{M'L} - \mathbf{M'11'L} = \begin{bmatrix} 9 & 7 & 5 \\ 7 & 11 & 15 \\ 6 & 8 & 10 \\ 5 & 15 & 15 \end{bmatrix}
$$

$$
\mathbf{W} = \mathbf{KT}^{-1} = \begin{bmatrix} 2 & 2 & 5 \\ -4 & -4 & 15 \\ -2 & -2 & 10 \\ -10 & 0 & 15 \end{bmatrix}
$$

MATRIX 5.4. *Calculations for the* **H** *matrix*

$$\mathbf{D} = \begin{bmatrix} 0.2 & 0 & 0 \\ 0 & 0.2 & 0 \\ 0 & 0 & 0.5 \end{bmatrix}$$

$$\mathbf{H} = \frac{\mathbf{WD^{-1}W'}}{N^2} = \begin{bmatrix} 0.9 & 0.7 & 0.6 & 0.5 \\ 0.7 & 6.1 & 3.8 & 6.5 \\ 0.6 & 3.8 & 2.4 & 4.0 \\ 0.5 & 6.5 & 4.0 & 9.5 \end{bmatrix}$$

MATRIX 5.5. *Calculations for the* **F** *matrix*

$$\frac{\mathbf{K'_{.1}K'_{.1}}}{N^2(1 - \rho_1)} = \begin{bmatrix} 8.1 & 6.3 & 5.4 & 4.5 \\ 6.3 & 4.9 & 4.2 & 3.5 \\ 5.4 & 4.2 & 3.6 & 3.0 \\ 4.5 & 3.5 & 3.0 & 2.5 \end{bmatrix}$$

$$\mathbf{F} = \mathbf{H} + \frac{\mathbf{K'_{.1}K_{.1}}}{N^2(1 - \rho_1)} = \begin{bmatrix} 9 & 7 & 6 & 5 \\ 7 & 11 & 8 & 10 \\ 6 & 8 & 6 & 7 \\ 5 & 10 & 7 & 12 \end{bmatrix}$$

MATRIX 5.6. *The* $N\varepsilon'\varepsilon$ *matrix*

$$N\varepsilon'\varepsilon = N^2\mathbf{C}_M - \mathbf{F} = \begin{bmatrix} 0 & 0 & 0 & 0 \\ 0 & 10 & -10 & -5 \\ 0 & -10 & 18 & 5 \\ 0 & -5 & 3 & 13 \end{bmatrix}$$

6

MATHEMATICAL MODELS OF THE DISTRIBUTION OF ATTITUDES UNDER CONTROVERSY

Robert P. Abelson

Yale University

6 MATHEMATICAL MODELS OF THE DISTRIBUTION OF ATTITUDES UNDER CONTROVERSY

INTRODUCTION

Some 35 years ago it was controversial whether attitudes could be measured. Thurstone, in his pioneering efforts with attitude quantification (Thurstone, 1929; Thurstone and Chave, 1929; Thurstone, 1931a), even felt impelled to entitle one of his articles "Attitudes can be measured" (Thurstone, 1928b). This now archaic controversy was soon settled, of course, by showing that it could be done, and, furthermore, that it led to important substantive results. Thurstone, himself, was in fact involved in one of the very earliest systematic attitude change studies, an assessment of the long-range effects of movies on children's attitudes (Peterson and Thurstone, 1933). Since then, attitude research has plunged ahead fruitfully in many areas.

Let us address ourselves today to one such development, namely, the area of attitude controversy in a social group or community, and consider the changes in the distribution of attitudes under the impact of social influence processes.

There have been a number of experimental studies (Goldberg, 1954; Hovland and Pritzker, 1957; Hovland, Harvey, and Sherif, 1957; Fisher and Lubin, 1958; Cohen, 1959; Zimbardo, 1960; Aronson, Turner, and Carlsmith, 1962) of attitude change as a function of the discrepancy between initial attitude position of the recipient of a persuasive communication and the attitude position of the communicator attempting the persuasion. Typically, these studies are of the "mass communication" type in that there are many recipients of a persuasive communication from a single communicator. Attitude changes in the recipients are considered vis-a-vis the communicator, but not in relation to each other, since the recipients are not permitted to interact. There is a gap to be bridged in order to apply the results of these studies to a field situation.

Let us suppose that an attitude continuum can be postulated for a certain issue and that, for all individuals aware of the issue, their positions on this continuum are measurable, at least in principle. Denote the positions of some two individuals by x_i and x_j, and consider the potential changes resulting from a mutual attempt to persuade each other. Assume that changes in x_i and x_j depend only upon x_i and x_j and upon personality constants of the two individuals. That is, suppose that there is some function f such that

$$\Delta_j(x_i) = k_{ij}f(x_i, x_j) \tag{6.1}$$

$$\Delta_i(x_j) = k_{ji}f(x_j, x_i) \tag{6.2}$$

where $\Delta_j(x_i)$ is the change in x_i due to persuasion by individual j, $\Delta_i(x_j)$ is the change in x_j, and k_{ij} and k_{ji} are summary constants dependent upon the personality constants of the two members. Other personality constants might be admitted into the argument of the function f, but we have chosen to make explicit the multiplicative constant k_{ij} for reasons that will become clear later.

The first part of this paper is devoted to the exploration of various reasonable assumptions for the function f applied to a situation in which a large number of individuals attempt repeatedly to influence one another within a social network, that is, a situation of group or community controversy.

The second part of the paper advances a theoretical model going beyond the mathematical models of the first part. This later model is suited to computer simulation rather than to mathematical analysis.

THE SIMPLEST MODEL

In all of the models to follow, we shall consider potential contact between each individual and every other in a finite group of n individuals. These contacts will in any realistic situation not be homogeneous, so that we must deal with the $n \times n$ matrix $\mathbf{A}$ of contact rates between pairs of individuals.

For a single contact between two individuals, the simplest assumption is that each member changes his attitude position toward the other by some constant fraction of the "distance" between them. This assumption is consistent with several laboratory studies (Goldberg, 1954; Hovland and Pritzker, 1957; Cohen, 1959; Zimbardo, 1960) and also with J. R. P. French's theory of social power (French, 1956). For the change in attitude of individual i following contact with individual j, we may write:

$$\Delta_j(x_i) = k(x_j - x_i), \text{ with } k > 0 \tag{6.3}$$

To handle repeated contacts between individuals, it is convenient to use the mathematics of differential rather than difference equations, smoothing the postulated changes continuously over time. The rate a_{ij} of contact then enters the system as a proportionality constant.

$$\frac{d_j x_i}{dt} = k a_{ij}(x_j - x_i) \tag{6.4}$$

Summing over all individuals j yields the net rate of change of x_i.

$$\frac{dx_i}{dt} = k \sum_j a_{ij}(x_j - x_i) = k\left[\sum_j a_{ij}x_j - x_i \sum_j a_{ij} \right] \tag{6.5}$$

In this model, the individual does not influence himself by talking to himself, so that it may as well be assumed that $a_{ii} = 0$. Now form the matrix $\mathbf{A}^*$ with elements:

$$\begin{cases} a_{ij}^* = a_{ij} \text{ for } i \neq j \\ a_{ii}^* = -\sum_j a_{ij} \end{cases} \tag{6.6}$$

The matrix $\mathbf{A}^*$ is simply the matrix $\mathbf{A}$ with negative row sums inserted in the diagonals. Equation 6.5 may now be written:

$$\frac{dx_i}{dt} = k \sum_j a^*_{ij} x_j \qquad (6.7)$$

The term $j = i$ in the summation is now meaningful, incorporating the second member of Equation 6.5.

Equation 6.7, of course, represents a system of n equations, one for each individual i. It is a standard mathematical system with well-known properties. This system may be neatly represented by a single vector equation. The notation $\dot{\mathbf{X}}$ represents a (column) vector of time rates of change of the x_i.

$$\dot{\mathbf{X}} = k\mathbf{A}^*\mathbf{X} \qquad (6.8)$$

Equation 6.8 gives an implicit representation of the system of attitude changes when assumption 6.3 is applied to a social group undertaking (pairwise) discussion of a given issue. Certain features of the matrix $\mathbf{A}^*$ should be noted before proceeding further. Firstly, $\mathbf{A}^*$ is a "singly centered" matrix; that is, the row sums of $\mathbf{A}^*$ must necessarily all be zero. This follows directly from specification (6.6). Secondly, all diagonal entries are nonpositive, and all off-diagonal entries are nonnegative, by the definition of a_{ij}. These special properties are important in the analysis of the system (6.8). Finally, from the definition of a_{ij} as a contact rate, one might presume that $a_{ij} = a_{ji}$. One person may talk more than the other, however, or there may be other such special conditions. The symmetry assumption is thus undesirably restrictive and will not be made (although from a computational standpoint the solution is neater if the matrix $\mathbf{A}$ is symmetrical).

The properties of systems of linear differential equations are in principle readily analyzed. The first order of business is to seek equilibrium points, that is, particular $\mathbf{X}$ vectors such that all time rates of change are zero. The significance of an equilibrium point for the present discussion is that it would represent a *stable distribution of attitude positions*. There would seem to be two reasonable types of possibilities for such a distribution: for highly controversial issues, it is commonsensical and well-documented (cf. Coleman, 1957a) that intragroup antagonisms will occur that will permanently maintain a bimodal attitude distribution. For less "hot," yet still debatable issues, though, it might be reasonable that, after a sufficient period of time involving considerable contact and discussion, everyone would agree.

Setting the vector $\dot{\mathbf{X}}$ in Equation 6.8 equal to zero, we have

$$\mathbf{A}^*\mathbf{X} = 0 \qquad (6.9)$$

If one or more solutions exist for $\mathbf{X}$, they must be characteristic vectors corresponding to zero roots of $\mathbf{A}^*$. Since $\mathbf{A}^*$ is a singly centered matrix, it is not of full rank and must have a zero root. The vector corresponding to the guaranteed zero root has all of its entries equal. Denote this vector by $\overline{\mathbf{X}}$. The question remains as to whether there can be *other* zero roots of $\mathbf{A}^*$ with associated vectors.

If so, there will be other possible equilibrium distributions of attitudes besides universal agreement. If not, then universal agreement is the only equilibrium and the question remains whether this equilibrium is stable or unstable. In systems of linear differential equations (cf. Richardson, 1960, for a readable discussion and an interesting application), stability results when all the real parts of the nonzero characteristic roots of the coefficient matrix $\mathbf{A}^*$ are negative. (With a nonsymmetric $\mathbf{A}^*$, it is possible to obtain complex roots, thus the need for the specification "real parts" above.) Stability means that the system will approach an equilibrium asymptotically, regardless of where it starts.

These questions are answered in the following definitions and theorem. The theorem is a composite, reworded version of two theorems available in the mathematical literature (McKenzie, 1960; Berge, 1962). The definitions use convenient but slightly corrupted terms to refer to a standard concept in graph theory.

Definition. The matrix $\mathbf{A}^*$ is *diffuse* if there exists a complete partition of the index set $\mathcal{J} = (1, 2, \ldots n)$ into mutually exclusive sub-sets P and Q such that: $a_{pq} = 0$ for all p in P and q in Q *and* either all $a_{qp} = 0$ or there exists a q in Q with $a_{qj} = 0$ for all j in $\mathcal{J}$.

Definition. If the matrix $\mathbf{A}^*$ is not diffuse, it is *compact*.[1]

Theorem. Any square matrix $\mathbf{A}^*$ with (i) no negative off-diagonal elements and (ii) all row sums equal to zero cannot have a positive root; if, further, it is (iii) compact, then it has exactly one zero root.

This theorem has the following significance: if the contact matrix $\mathbf{A}^*$ is compact, then universal agreement is the only equilibrium, a stable equilibrium at that.

The meaning of the "compactness" of $\mathbf{A}^*$ emerges more clearly if one pictures the interpersonal contact network in the form of a sociogram or directed graph. Each nonzero a_{ij} indicates that individual j has some influence on individual i, or that there is a "path" from j to i. If there is a path from j to i and a path from i to k, then indirectly there is a path from j to k. A compact network, it turns out, is a network with at least one individual from whom there is a path to all other individuals, directly or indirectly. In the diffuse network corresponding to a diffuse matrix there is no individual who can eventually reach everybody. (Such a network would in graph theory be said to possess no "center," or in Harary's (1959) terminology, to possess more than one "power subgroup.")

The present theorem is almost identical to a theorem given by Harary (1959) in following up French's (1956) model, although the present model embodies features that go beyond those of previous models.[2]

[1] In graph theory (Berge, 1962), the standard term for "compact" would be "quasi-strongly connected." What we call "diffuse" would be "nonquasi-strongly connected." The single words are more graceful.

[2] The French-Harary model has intrigued political scientists (Fagen, 1961), but has left them awaiting further developments. The present paper is, in part, addressed to such further developments.

At any rate, the end result of continued discussion and mutual persuasion in a compact network, according to Equation 6.4, is that all attitudes will converge to some common position $\bar{x}$. There will be, so to speak, a complete loss of "attitude entropy."

Universal agreement at $\bar{x}$ is approached asymptotically. Each characteristic vector of $\mathbf{A}^*$ specifies a linear combination of the x's that approaches zero exponentially with the rate parameter given by the corresponding characteristic root. These characteristic vectors will have some positive coefficients and some negative coefficients — they are "bipolar factors" in the individuals. Thus, each characteristic vector identifies a polarity among certain individuals, which tends to vanish as group discussion proceeds. With a big negative root, the polarity vanishes rapidly. With a small negative root, the polarity vanishes slowly, that is, there is a cleavage in the group that will abate only after the passage of time. Indeed, if a negative root is small enough, the time required may be so long that the projected result of universal agreement is a theoretical, but not practical, consequence of the model. Accordingly, the actual size of the roots is of great interest.[3]

Analytically, the development is as follows: The matrix $\mathbf{A}^*$ can be factored by

$$\mathbf{A}^* = \boldsymbol{\xi}\boldsymbol{\Delta}\boldsymbol{\xi}^{-1} \qquad (6.10)$$

where the columns of the $n \times n$ matrix $\boldsymbol{\xi}$ are the right-hand characteristic vectors of $\mathbf{A}^*$, the rows of $\boldsymbol{\xi}^{-1}$ are the left-hand vectors (equivalent to the right-hand vectors only if $\mathbf{A}^*$ is symmetrical) and $\boldsymbol{\Delta}$ is the diagonal matrix of roots.

From Equation 6.8, defining the model,

$$\dot{\mathbf{X}} = k\mathbf{A}^*\mathbf{X} = k\boldsymbol{\xi}\boldsymbol{\Delta}\boldsymbol{\xi}^{-1}\mathbf{X} \qquad (6.11)$$

Pre-multiplying by $\boldsymbol{\xi}^{-1}$,

$$\boldsymbol{\xi}^{-1}\dot{\mathbf{X}} = k\boldsymbol{\Delta}\boldsymbol{\xi}^{-1}\mathbf{X} \qquad (6.12)$$

We define a new vector of canonical variates

$$\mathbf{Y} = \boldsymbol{\xi}^{-1}\mathbf{X} \qquad (6.13)$$

whence

$$\dot{\mathbf{Y}} = k\boldsymbol{\Delta}\mathbf{Y} \qquad (6.14)$$

The individual entries in this vector are

$$\frac{dy_h}{dt} = k\lambda_h y_h \qquad (6.15)$$

with the solution

$$y_h = y_{ho}e^{k\lambda_h t} \qquad (6.16)$$

where y_{ho} is the initial value of y_h. Recalling the theorem, the several λ_h all have negative real parts save one, which is zero. The negative roots give declining exponentials, the zero root a canonical variate constant in time.

The initial values of the y's are readily related to the initial values of the x's.

[3] A discussion by Simon (1957, p. 144) makes a similar point for a related class of models.

Letting $\mathbf{X}_o$ denote the initial $\mathbf{X}$ vector and $\mathbf{Y}_o$ the initial $\mathbf{Y}$ vector, Equation 6.13 gives

$$\mathbf{Y}_o = \boldsymbol{\xi}^{-1}\mathbf{X}_o \qquad (6.17)$$

One of the entries in $\mathbf{Y}_o$, call it $\bar{y}$, is for the canonical variate with zero root. It is constant over time. If $\boldsymbol{\xi}$ is appropriately normalized, then $\bar{y} = \bar{x}$, the equilibrium attitude position.

It is interesting to consider the relative sizes of the other entries in $\mathbf{Y}_o$ in conjunction with the relative sizes of the corresponding roots. A close correspondence between the absolute values of the y_o's and the λ's would be indicative of an issue with initial positions distributed in accord with initial intragroup cleavages — a "party-line" issue, as it were. A poor correspondence between the y_o's and the λ's would be indicative of an issue "cross-cutting" initial cleavages. A full discussion of this distinction is beyond the scope of this paper, but perhaps the following illustration will clarify the matter.

The procedure will be illustrated on a matrix of contact frequencies gathered by Gullahorn (1952) on an office group of 12 female clerical workers. Tallies were made every 15 minutes over a period of two weeks of who talked to whom. Conversation was considered to be symmetrical. The women were seated in three rows of four women each, and the matrix $\mathbf{A}^*$ of Table 6.1 is arranged with the four Row I women first, the Row II women next, and the Row III women last.

TABLE 6.1. *Contact Frequency Matrix, Twelve Office Women**

	Baldwin	Fahey	Rioux	Murray	Doherty	Rafferty	Hall	Donovan	Casey	Carey	O'Malley	Lenihan
Baldwin	−111	53	23	8	0	5	2	2	0	1	1	16
Fahey	53	−97	26	9	0	2	3	0	2	1	0	1
Rioux	23	26	−135	75	1	4	1	2	2	1	0	0
Murray	8	9	75	−102	0	2	1	3	1	1	1	1
Doherty	0	0	1	0	−90	24	26	18	4	8	7	2
Rafferty	5	2	4	2	24	−136	6	30	20	19	21	3
Hall	2	3	1	1	26	6	−107	51	7	5	3	2
Donovan	2	0	2	3	18	30	51	−118	3	7	1	1
Casey	0	2	2	1	4	20	7	3	−147	46	42	20
Carey	1	1	1	1	8	19	5	7	46	−188	69	30
O'Malley	1	0	0	1	7	21	3	1	42	69	−198	53
Lenihan	16	1	0	1	2	3	2	1	20	30	53	−129

* From Gullahorn (1952).

Table 6.2 gives the canonical vectors, normalized to unity, with the corresponding roots. The first vector has all entries equal, as we expect for a symmetric matrix. The second vector specifies the major cleavage in the group:

TABLE 6.2. *Factorization of the Contact Frequency Matrix*

	Vector											
	1	2	3	4	5	6	7	8	9	10	11	12
Baldwin	0.289	0.335	0.071	−0.478	−0.007	−0.078	0.491	−0.541	0.128	−0.102	0.064	0.017
Fahey	0.289	0.406	0.024	−0.546	−0.040	0.122	−0.478	0.442	−0.056	−0.095	−0.023	−0.001
Rioux	0.289	0.432	−0.065	0.321	−0.016	0.000	−0.015	−0.032	−0.003	0.788	0.010	0.004
Murray	0.289	0.449	−0.091	0.588	0.010	−0.058	0.015	0.032	−0.008	−0.597	−0.009	−0.003
Doherty	0.289	−0.251	−0.361	−0.019	−0.804	−0.230	−0.019	0.031	0.144	−0.005	−0.023	0.001
Rafferty	0.289	−0.183	−0.047	0.026	−0.119	0.683	0.230	−0.019	−0.579	−0.019	−0.095	−0.039
Hall	0.289	−0.218	−0.460	−0.078	0.413	−0.398	−0.281	−0.268	−0.414	−0.002	0.018	−0.003
Donovan	0.289	−0.210	−0.419	−0.031	0.395	0.241	0.277	0.330	0.543	0.016	−0.003	0.034
Casey	0.289	−0.202	0.303	0.084	0.047	0.169	−0.396	−0.380	0.328	−0.017	−0.581	0.000
Carey	0.289	−0.204	0.297	0.071	0.023	0.043	−0.150	−0.058	0.118	−0.007	0.602	−0.615
O'Malley	0.289	−0.204	0.338	0.068	0.016	−0.038	−0.053	0.040	−0.005	−0.002	0.397	0.769
Lenihan	0.289	−0.151	0.410	−0.006	0.082	−0.455	0.373	0.422	−0.194	0.044	−0.358	−0.165
Root	0	−20	−51	−76	−109	−134	−149	−166	−181	−198	−208	−266
Decay	(none)	(slow)										(fast)

the Row I women vs. all others. Vector 3 pits the Row III women against the Row II women excluding Rafferty, who, in effect, mediates between Rows II and III. If we imagine the 12 women discussing a single issue with dyadic conversation rates proportional to those in the matrix $\mathbf{A}^*$, then, according to our simple model, the two major cleavages just mentioned will be the slowest to heal. At the other extreme, Vector 12, with the fastest decay rate (a half-life, as it were, only one-thirteenth as long as that of Vector 2) simply pits O'Malley against Carey. Intermediate vectors in general represent various within-row cleavages.

When we speak of these bipolar people factors as cleavages, we of course mean *potential* cleavages. To what extent there will actually be cleavage depends upon the vector $\mathbf{Y}_o$. For example, suppose there is some issue (say, whether or not the office windows should be kept open) on which initial opinions are sharply divided between the rows of women. Say,

$$\mathbf{X}'_o = [+1, +1, +1, +1, 0, 0, 0, 0, -1, -1, -1, -1]$$

Then, by Equation 6.17,

$$\mathbf{Y}'_o = [0 , 2.383, -1.409, -0.332, -0.221, 0.267, 0.239, -0.123, -0.186,$$
$$-0.024, -0.018, 0.028]$$

Ignoring the first value, which corresponds to the zero root, the absolute values of the y_o's are larger for the slow decay factors and smaller for the fast decay factors. This, then, is an issue aggravating the important cleavages. If, however, the x_o's happen to fall more randomly on the issue, the y_o's will not line up so neatly with the λ's and the issue may "cross-cut."

Applications of the model to other sociometric matrices will be described elsewhere. In this discussion, we have merely suggested that the mathematical model, simple though it may be, provides as a by-product a straightforward and powerful method for analyzing a sociomatrix in dynamic rather than static terms.[4]

EXTENSIONS OF THE SIMPLE MODEL

There are several ways to complicate the simple model and to explore implications. In particular, it is of interest to see whether a bimodal equilibrium distribution can be obtained for a compact network.

Returning to the basic assumption for the outcome of a single interaction between individuals i and j, a more sophisticated assumption might be that:

$$\Delta_j x_i = k_{ij}(x_j - x_i) \tag{6.18}$$

where k_{ij} is a nonnegative parameter which depends upon the pair of individuals involved instead of being constant over all pairs. One might perhaps specialize this by identifying

$$k_{ij} = c_i p_j \tag{6.19}$$

[4] The most advanced of previous methods was given by McRae (1960). Prior methods are summarized in Glanzer and Glaser (1959).

where c_i is the "persuasibility" of individual i and p_j is the "persuasiveness" of individual j, much as Cervin has done in this model of dyadic interaction (Cervin and Henderson, 1961). This specialization, however, is not necessary for our purposes.

Multiplying by the contact rate a_{ij} and passing to the differential equation form, we obtain

$$\frac{d_j x_i}{dt} = k_{ij} a_{ij}(x_j - x_i) = b_{ij}(x_j - x_i) \qquad (6.20)$$

where b_{ij}, the product of the effect parameter and the contact rate, might be called the "effect rate." Summing over j and forming the matrix $\mathbf{B}^*$ with elements:

$$\begin{cases} b_{ij}^* = b_{ij} \text{ for } i \neq j \\ b_{ii}^* = - \sum_j b_{ij} \end{cases} \qquad (6.21)$$

we arrive at the system

$$\dot{\mathbf{X}} = \mathbf{B}^* \mathbf{X} \qquad (6.22)$$

strictly comparable to the previous system Equation 6.8.

The row sums of $\mathbf{B}^*$ are, by definition, all zero and the off-diagonal elements cannot be negative. Therefore, the theorem of the previous section applies. If $\mathbf{B}^*$ is compact, attitudes converge toward universal agreement. The only thing that is essentially different is that there are additional ways in which a diffuse network can occur — if we allow k_{ij} ever to assume the value zero, there may sometimes be contact between individuals with no persuasive effect. For example, we may contemplate partisans whose attitude positions are not subject to alteration. If there be two such unmovable partisans with opposite positions, then universal agreement can obviously never be reached. In any event, with the reinterpretation of the network to refer to persuasive effect rather than mere contact, only a diffuse network avoids the mathematical inexorability of total loss of attitude entropy. It might be noted that the factor technique of the previous section can be applied to this more general model as well, except for the drawback that effect rates are much harder to ascertain empirically than sheer contact rates.

More drastic revision of the model can be introduced by making the system nonlinear. Indeed, there are good psychological reasons for so doing. It is intuitively reasonable and a matter of some evidence (Kelley and Thibaut, 1954; Tannenbaum, 1956; Sherif and Hovland, 1961, Chapter 7) that individuals with more extreme positions are more resistant to attitude change. Such an effect can be built into a revised model by assuming that the change in x_i under persuasive attempt is, for example:

(a) inversely proportional to $|x_i|$, or

(b) proportional to $(M^2 - x_i^2)$, where M is a bound on the possible extremity of attitude.

A version of the former assumption appears in Osgood and Tannenbaum's

(1955) attitude congruity model. The latter assumption is used in one of Cervin's (1957) models.

Another possible added consideration is that persuasion should be stronger when a more extreme position is advocated. One might achieve this by having the attitude change be proportional to $|x_j|$, for example. Both of the models mentioned above make such an assumption.

The dependence of $\Delta_j x_i$ upon both x_i and x_j may be expressed in a still more general way, namely,

$$\Delta_j x_i = k_{ij}(x_j - x_i)\, g(x_i, x_j) \tag{6.23}$$

For our immediate purposes, all we need assume about the function g is that it is everywhere positive. We shall see why shortly.

Weighting by contact rate, summing over all j, and using the differential representation we obtain

$$\frac{dx_i}{dt} = \sum_{j=1}^{n} b_{ij} x_j g(x_i, x_j) - x_i \sum_{j=1}^{n} b_{ij} g(x_i, x_j) \tag{6.24}$$

Let us now inquire about equilibrium points. At equilibrium, all time rates of change are zero. With the left-hand side of Equation 6.23 zero for all values of i, it would follow that the equilibrium values for the x's (denoted by the superscript $^\infty$) satisfy

$$x_i^\infty = \frac{\displaystyle\sum_{j=1}^{n} b_{ij} x_j^\infty g(x_i^\infty, x_j^\infty)}{\displaystyle\sum_{j=1}^{n} b_{ij} g(x_i^\infty, x_j^\infty)} \tag{6.25}$$

Inspection of Equation 6.25 discloses a simple interpretation. The value x_i^∞ is seen to be a *weighted average of all the x_j^∞* (including itself, since $j = i$ is a term in each summation). The respective weights are the fixed quantities $b_{ij} g(x_i^\infty, x_j^\infty)$. These by specification are nonnegative.

This interpretation leads at once to a neat theorem. It is obvious that the resultant of such a weighted average must lie somewhere in between the extreme values over which the average is taken. Thus, speaking informally, we infer that all of the x^∞ must lie in between each other. In other words, they are all equal, and the equilibrium point again corresponds to universal agreement.

There is one exception glossed over by this informal argument. If the matrix **B*** is *diffuse*, then zero coefficients will crop up in the weighted averages in such pattern as to allow a cleavage among the x^∞. Thus, the equilibrium of universal agreement applies only when the matrix **B*** is compact.

Summarizing and restating for the case of a compact group of individuals, we may assert the following:

Given a specification of attitude change in dyadic interaction as a function of the attitude positions of the two participants, if that function is such that the attitude position of each participant always moves toward the attitude position of the other, then any compact group of individuals engaged in mutual dyadic interactions at constant rates will asymptotically tend toward complete homogeneity of attitude positions.

This statement is based on the argument following Equation 6.23. It may not be totally obvious that the expression $(x_j - x_i)g(x_i,x_j)$ is a completely general way of expressing any arbitrary function that drives the attitude position of individual i *toward* the position of individual j. However, this is indeed the case. The term $(x_j - x_i)$ guarantees that the direction of change will be appropriate, provided that we require the function g to be everywhere positive. We might eliminate the false impression of nongenerality in Equation 6.23 by noting that

$$(x_j - x_i) = |x_j - x_i| \, sgn(x_j - x_i) \tag{6.26}$$

Then we can define

$$h(x_i,x_j) = |x_j - x_i| \, g(x_i,x_j) \tag{6.27}$$

and rewrite Equation 6.23 as

$$\Delta_j x_i = k_{ij}(x_j - x_i)g(x_i,x_j)$$

$$= k_{ij}h(x_i,x_j)sgn(x_j - x_i) \tag{6.28}$$

The function h is everywhere positive (except at the trivial point $x_i = x_j$), and Equation 6.28 is thus seen to embody the verbal statement of the key result of this section.

As an illustration of the generality of this formulation, consider the family of attitude change functions found in laboratory studies by Fisher and Lubin (1958); Aronson, Turner, and Carlsmith (1962); and others. Figure 6.1 illustrates such a function. The laboratory data has never been extensive enough to fit a precise function, but it will suffice to invent a function with the appropriate qualitative features, since our conclusion is general over all such invented functions.

If $|x_j - x_i|$ is zero, there is no attitude change; as $|x_j - x_i|$ increases, the amount of change monotonically increases up to some optimum; further in-

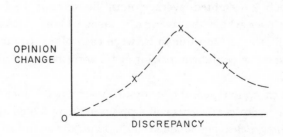

FIGURE 6.1. *Opinion change as a function of extent of communicator-communicatee opinion discrepancy. The dotted curve sketches one possible function fitting the three data points from the "mildly credible communicator" conditions — Aronson, Turner, and Carlsmith (1962)*

creases in $|x_j - x_i|$ result in monotonic decrease in amount of change, asymp-
totically approaching zero change; change in the direction opposite to that
intended by the persuasive communicator is not considered.

One possible choice of an attitude change function with these properties is

$$h(x_i,x_j) = (x_j - x_i)^2 e^{-c|x_j-x_i|} \tag{6.29}$$

where c is some positive constant. Now it is straightforward to write

$$g(x_i,x_j) = \frac{(x_j - x_i)^2}{x_j - x_i} e^{-c|x_j-x_i|} = |x_j - x_i| e^{-c|x_j-x_i|} \tag{6.30}$$

which is everywhere positive except when $x_j = x_i$, and the equilibrium derivation holds. Thus, the laboratory function of Figure 6.1 implies the eventual loss
of attitude entropy when applied to the field situation.

Since universal ultimate agreement is an ubiquitous outcome of a very broad
class of mathematical models, we are naturally led to inquire what on earth
one must assume in order to generate the bimodal outcome of community cleavage studies. Offhand, there are at least three potential ways of generating such
a bimodal outcome.

1. The contact network might indeed not be compact — it might be dis-
connected into two separate camps. This seems at first blush to be an im-
plausible case, for a single Joe Hatfield in occasional contact with a Mary
McCoy could readily convert a diffuse network into a compact network. However, if one allows for outside or impenetrable influences on community debate,
such as radio commentators, organized pressure groups, power elites, and the
like, diffuse networks are easy to imagine. Each such influence can be regarded
as a "person" who influences but is not influenced by prevailing attitudes.
Given two such exogenous "persons," the total network would be diffuse, and
if the initial positions of the two sources were different (as is common enough),
universal agreement would be impossible.

2. One might postulate that, under certain circumstances, the attitude position of at least one of the two participants in a dyadic interaction would move
away from the position of the other. For example, a "boomerang effect" might
occur if individuals with moderately partisan positions sufficiently irritated
one another to produce negative persuasive effects. Boomerang effects are
difficult to demonstrate for laboratory groups, but there is ample suggestion
that such effects can occur (Hovland, Harvey, and Sherif, 1957; Sherif and
Hovland, 1961, Chapter 7).

Another somewhat less obvious situation in which the respective attitude
positions might not move toward each other is that of mutual reinforcement
between moderate partisans on the *same* side of the issue. Both might then
move toward greater extremity. The originally less partisan of the pair would be
moving toward the other, but the originally more partisan of the pair would in
effect be moving away from the other. The mutual reinforcement effect is an
important feature of Cervin's (1957) model and of Rainio's (1962) stochastic

theory of social contacts, although no mass communication study germane to this effect seems to have been attempted.

3. We have assumed throughout that the contact rates a_{ij} and the effect parameters k_{ij} remain constant over time. This assumption is not in accord with common sense, with standard social psychological assumption, or with systematic field observations. One way of expressing the presumed variability of contact rates is that people tend to locomote into groups that share their attitudes and out of groups that do not agree with them. Simon (1957, Chapter 7), taking as a point of departure Festinger's (1950) theory of social communication, gives an extended mathematical discussion of the interplay between group cohesiveness and opinion discrepancy, among other variables. Observations of community controversy (Coleman, 1957a) suggest strongly that casual contact between opposing camps decreases as controversy between the camps intensifies.

One might imagine the present mathematical model extended to cover the case of variable effect rates. The mathematics is already difficult in the nonlinear model, and, in raising the number of variables from n to n^2, the dynamics of the model become gruesomely intractable. Nevertheless, some conclusions about equilibrium points are still possible.

Suppose that, whatever the postulated dependence of the effect rates b_{ij} on the positions x_i and x_j, there is at least one equilibrium point for the whole ensemble: $\{x_i^\infty; b_{ij}^\infty\}$. Referring to Equation 6.25, we may substitute the assumed equilibrium values for the b's:

$$x_i^\infty = \frac{\sum_{j=1}^{n} b_{ij}^\infty x_j^\infty g(x_i^\infty, x_j^\infty)}{\sum_{j=1}^{n} b_{ij}^\infty g(x_i^\infty, x_j^\infty)} \tag{6.31}$$

Then, by an argument strictly comparable to the previous one, it is apparent that *a compact equilibrium network implies universal agreement;* however, a diffuse equilibrium network in general implies a bimodal or multimodal equilibrium distribution of attitudes. Whether the network tends toward a compact or diffuse equilibrium depends upon further assumptions, and there is the interesting possibility that a single model could embody both possibilities, the final equilibrium depending upon the initial values of all the variables.

Figure 6.2 suggests in a rudimentary way how the attitude distribution might change over time for a variable contact rate model as contrasted with a constant contact rate model.

Three ways have been mentioned in which the original model might be elaborated or reinterpreted so as not necessarily to generate the homogeneous attitude outcome. There are other ways as well, but there are limitations to a completely mathematics-oriented approach to the problem. We have been asking, "What sort of a model with simple assumptions is needed to yield intuitively reasonable consequences?" This is probably the most common style of mathematical modeling. Nevertheless, there is an alternative approach, a

MODEL:

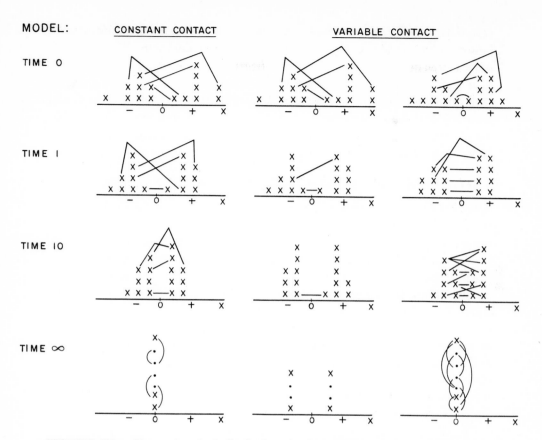

CONSTANT CONTACT   VARIABLE CONTACT

TIME 0

TIME 1

TIME 10

TIME ∞

FIGURE 6.2. *Changes in attitude distribution. In all distributions, crosses indicate people at various positions and lines indicate sociometric connections across the neutral point. In the first column, the four contacts across the neutral point serve to pull the two "camps" together, following the initial tendency toward greater within-camp homogeneity. In the second column, starting from the same situation, the initial pull in each camp toward its centroid breaks two of the between-camp contacts. The other two break later, permitting bimodal stability. In the third column, the camp centroids are closer together, and bonds across the neutral point tend to form rather than break. This then pulls both camps in toward the homogeneous equilibrium*

process-oriented approach. One may ask instead, "What are the important psychological variables and processes involved, and can one objectively specify their interrelations so that it is possible to carry out a simulation of the total system?"

This latter approach need not be inconsistent with the "traditional" mathematical models approach. Indeed, for circumscribed problem areas, the two approaches could be identical. For complex problems, however, the difference in orientation of the two approaches can make a real difference in research strategy and in the form of the models.

Perhaps what we mean by "process-oriented" is not clear. On other occasions (Abelson, 1958; Messick and Abelson, 1957), the author has twitted mathematical psychology for not being *psychological* psychology. Taking somewhat the same tack now, we shall try to make clear in detail what we mean by "process-oriented." One immediate point worth noting is that, of all the various possibilities so far considered for an attitude change function, none has been truly process-oriented. That is to say, in a conversation, discussion, or dispute about an issue, the participants do not simply line their attitude scale scores up against each other and bargain for a quantitative settlement. They exchange relevant verbal symbols and emotional signs. Such exchanges follow their own peculiar logic; their details are presumably amenable to psychological analysis. Without further ado, then, let us proceed to such an analysis.

A COMPUTER SIMULATION MODEL OF COMMUNITY CONTROVERSY

A slightly simplified version of part of the author's computer simulation model of community controversy will be presented here, the part dealing with social interaction. The other part deals with the effects of the mass communication media, omitted here in the interest of simplicity. The entire model has been programmed under the supervision of Alex Bernstein of the Simulmatics Corporation,[5] and is now running on the IBM 7090. Fuller details are given by Abelson and Bernstein (1963).

For each individual in the group under consideration, the computer carries in storage a quantitative representation of the individual's position on the issue and a record of the other particular individuals with whom he potentially may discuss the issue. In addition, a number of variables not previously discussed in this paper are included:

(a) *Interest* in the issue.
(b) *Attitude* toward each potential conversational *partner*.
(c) *Assertion-acceptances:* the particular assertions or arguments, pro or con on the issue, which are already known and accepted by the individual.
(d) *Assertion-predispositions:* the occasional predisposition to find certain assertions especially congenial or especially offensive, whether or not they are already known.

We are here presuming that the issue is one with fairly standard assertions on both sides, so that these assertions can be pre-coded and classified. Fluoridation of the community water supply is such an issue, for example.

The attitude positions, interests, attitudes toward partners, and assertion-acceptances are variables that may change in each time cycle. The assertion-predispositions and the network of conversational connections are taken to be constant throughout the simulation. There are several other variables that are employed to mediate conversational outcomes, and these will be described in context.

Each individual in turn is confronted with each of his potential conversational partners in turn, and there is a determination of whether or not a conversation is held. Denoting the individual by i and the potential partner by j, we obtain the following determination:

[5] Under a contract from the Social Studies Branch of the Dental Health Division of the United States Public Health Service.

1. The probability that *i might* talk to *j* about the issue is a direct function of *i*'s interest in the issue.

2. A conversation will be held unless *j*'s interest is below a certain threshold *and j*'s position is in the neutral range.

If a conversation is held, all the assertions accepted by *j* will be advanced toward *i*, whose general response will depend upon his "receptivity" to *j*. The following assumptions are made about receptivity:

3. Receptivity to *j* is an inverse function of the extremity of *i*'s attitude position.

4. Receptivity to *j* is a direct function of the extremity of *j*'s attitude position.

5. Receptivity to *j* is a direct function of *j*'s interest in the issue.

6. Receptivity to *j* is a direct function of the "assertion match" between *i* and *j*, which is positive when *j*'s assertions agree with those already accepted by *i* and negative when they disagree.

The central proposition involving receptivity is the following:

7. Individual *i* will be the more apt to accept assertions made by *j* the more favorable *i*'s attitude toward *j* and the higher *i*'s receptivity to *j*.

The response of *i* to each particular assertion made by *j* of course also depends upon whether *i* already accepts the particular assertion, already disagrees with it, or has not yet encountered it or made up his mind about it. These cases are distinguished in the following special rules, which also include other considerations:

8. If an assertion made by *j* has already been accepted by *i*, there cannot be a decrease in acceptance under any circumstances.

9. An assertion is more apt to become accepted by *i* if he has not previously encountered it than if he previously disagreed with it.

10. An assertion is especially apt to be accepted by *i* if it is consistent with his predisposition toward that assertion, and under no circumstances will be accepted if it runs counter to his predisposition.

11. An assertion is less apt to be accepted by *i* if it is inconsistent with his position on the issue.

12. When *i*'s attitude toward *j* is negative and his receptivity to *j* is very low, assertions made by *j* not previously encountered by *i* and not consistent with his position will tend to promote acceptance by *i* of converse assertions.

There are other consequences of conversational exchanges besides changes in assertion-acceptances. In particular, there may be a change in interest, according to the following rules:

13. Interest increases as a direct function of the "assertion match" between *i* and *j*.

14. Interest increases as a direct function of the number of assertions made by j that are relevant to i's predispositions.

15. Instances in which i accepts an assertion inconsistent with his position will result in a decrease of interest.

Other possible consequences of conversation are changes in attitude toward the issue and toward the conversational partner. These are assumed to be mediated by "conversational satisfaction." The satisfaction of i from conversation with j follows these rules:

16. Satisfaction varies as a direct function of the "assertion match" between i and j.

17. Satisfaction is the greater for each assertion by j consistent with i's predispositions, and the less for each assertion inconsistent with i's predispositions.

18. Satisfaction is the less for each assertion by j inconsistent with i's position on the issue.

The satisfaction variable now enters into one of the attitude change propositions:

19. As a result of conversation with j, the position of i on the issue will change if j's position was initially more extreme (in either direction) than i's.

20. The degree of such position change is a direct function of the degree of conversational satisfaction.

21. The direction of such position change is *toward* j if i's attitude toward j was initially positive, and *away* from j if i's attitude toward j was initially negative.

Attitude toward j itself may change according to the next proposition:

22. Attitude toward j changes as a direct function of conversational satisfaction, the direction of change corresponding to the sign of the satisfaction variable, which may be either positive or negative.

This completes the set of assumptions about the single dyadic interaction. After each individual i is exposed to *all* his potential partners, j, however, five more rules are applied. The first three deal with the probability that i will "forget" assertions previously accepted, that is, act in future interactions as though he had never encountered them. The fourth rule deals with review and adjustment of issue position so as to be more consistent with assertion-acceptances, and the fifth with over-all changes in interest.

23. The probability is greater that an assertion will be forgotten if it is inconsistent with i's position than if it is consistent.

24. Assertions are not subject to forgetting if they are consistent with predispositions.

25. If j makes an assertion that comes to be accepted by i, then j will not forget that assertion.

26. Attitude change on the issue is a direct function of the number of conversations held, and proceeds in the direction consistent with the majority of assertions accepted.

27. Interest in the issue increases as a direct function of the number of conversations held; if no conversations are held, there is a decrease in interest.

This list of 27 propositions describes the essence of the computer simulation model. Figure 6.3 schematically summarizes the couplings between variables.

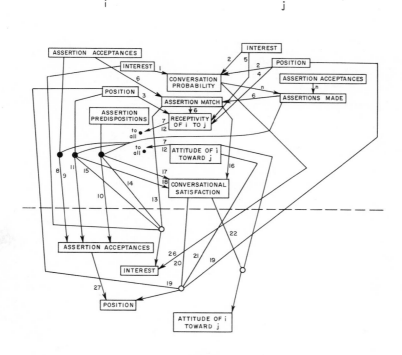

FIGURE 6.3. *Couplings between variables in computer simulation model. Numbers refer to propositions in text. The "forgetting" process (Propositions 23, 24, and 25) has been omitted. The symbol* n *means "no explicit numbering" of the proposition*

In order to effectuate the model, of course, it is necessary to quantify these propositions, inserting functional forms and assumed parameters. One advantage of the simulation approach over the mathematical models approach is that no restrictive simplicity considerations are imposed on the functional forms — linearity is not necessarily preferred. On the other hand, one apparent disadvantage is that so large a number of degrees of freedom are available to the model-builder that the model does not clearly stand or fall in any empirical test. When data is inconsistent with the model, there are many possible ways to make readjustments; when data is consistent with the model, it could be right for the wrong reasons. Although we do not wish here to discuss the metaphysics of computer simulation, it seems that some relaxation of the principle of parsimony might be required. Perhaps Occam's razor should be replaced by Occam's lawnmower.

The present model has thus far undergone only mock trials, using realistic albeit hypothetical data. Field trials are in prospect in the near future.

7

SOME NEW LOOKS
AT THE NATURE
OF CREATIVE PROCESSES

J. P. Guilford
University of Southern California

7 SOME NEW LOOKS AT THE NATURE OF CREATIVE PROCESSES

With all the concern about creativity these days, it is important that we do not lose sight of the fundamental psychological problems concerning the nature of creative thinking. As in most areas of psychological investigation, for every person who directs his energies to the solution of basic problems, there are dozens who find problems of application more appealing. This state of affairs reflects the pragmatic American temper, as expressed in the philosophies of William James and John Dewey. We are becoming increasingly aware, however, that if the wellsprings of basic knowledge are not kept flowing, the streams of knowledge deriving from those sources are in danger of drying up. In view of these considerations, we would like to emphasize in this paper the basic problems of creativity by giving full attention to the nature of creative processes.

A rough picture of the increasing interest in creativity can be obtained by comparing the rate of publication on the subject during the past decade with the rates of earlier decades. Using the collection of publications reviewed by M. I. Stein and S. J. Heinze (1960) (which is probably not complete) as a basis, we find that of approximately 330 titles reviewed, 155 of them (or nearly half) appeared during the 1950s. The curve of frequencies over the decades since the 1870s, when Galton published two titles, shows an exponential growth, with no signs of negative acceleration at this time.

As in the case of most psychological problems, early hypotheses concerning creative production were proposed by nonpsychologists. Such hypotheses have come from the introspections and anecdotes of highly creative people, such as Poincaré (1913) and Hadamard (1945). Other sources of such information are collectors of anecdotes who draw hypotheses from them, for example, Ghiselin (1955). The chief outcome from these sources has been in the form of four recognized stages or phases of what is commonly called "*the* creative process," often credited to Graham Wallas (1926). As is well known, those stages are: preparation, a period of information-gathering and of mulling over it; incubation, a period of general rest, during which it is believed that a lot of unconscious activity is going on; the electric stage of illumination when inspirations occur; and the follow-up period variously denoted as a time for verification, elaboration, or evaluation.

Hypotheses from professional psychological sources have been very rare until recent years. Psychoanalysts, beginning with Freud, have suggested hypotheses. These have naturally been couched in Freudian terminology and have emphasized emotional sources and involvements. As in most psychoanalytical theories, it is difficult to subject such hypotheses to empirical investigation by rigorous methods. In 1950, L. L. Thurstone proposed some hypotheses in his usual incisive manner and suggested how they could be investigated. In the same year this writer (Guilford, 1950) proposed some hypotheses especially to be investigated by the methods of factor analysis. The choice of this approach and the emphasis upon the intellectual aspects of creativity were in line with reinforcements received from investigating intellectual abilities in general. It was anticipated that from this approach we should not only realize the benefits of having instruments by which potential for creativity could be assessed for experimental and vocational purposes, but also that we should gain considerable understanding of creative processes themselves.

It is the main purpose of this paper to survey the results regarding traits of creativity derived from the factor-analytic approach, in order to obtain a better picture of where we stand with respect to a theory of creativity. What generalizations can be drawn from the results? What is the more general significance of the findings? Are new interpretations called for? What are some implications for general psychological theory? Can a theory of creativity be fitted into such a general theory?

After having considered the findings as indicated by these questions, we shall look again at older theories from this point of view. What are the relationships to the older theories? Do the older theories suggest problems not envisaged by the new theory? What are some of the important problems remaining to be investigated, by factor-analytic methods or by other methods?

MAJOR FINDINGS ON THE NATURE OF CREATIVITY

Factor Analysis as a Scientific Method

Thurstone sometimes remarked that the chief function of factor analysis is limited to the frontiers of a science. Certainly, in this idea he was entirely too modest. It appears that many who have used factor analysis for the discovery of basic traits have made lasting contributions to the conceptual framework of psychology. But, as Thurstone often warned, factor analysis must be used properly if we are to derive from it information of theoretical significance. The author and his associates have attempted to follow faithfully Thurstone's urging that in a factor-analytic study one should devote considerable time to hypothesis development and test development before the analysis and also much time to reflecting upon the outcomes after the analysis. It is in these stages that we function as psychologists. The psychologically important things that happen in a factor-analytic study take place in the heads of the psychologists themselves. The chief value of an analysis is to tell us whether we are probably right or wrong.

The factor analyses in the Aptitudes Project at the University of Southern California have observed these fundamental patterns, and the effort has been fruitful. It has expanded the list of primary intellectual abilities, as Thurstone called them, from approximately 30 when the Project was started about 15 years ago to more than 60 at this date. More important, the kinds of abilities that were discovered throw considerable light on such time-honored concepts as reasoning, induction, deduction, and problem-solving, and lead to a comprehensive theory of intelligence, known as the "structure of intellect," in which the creative-thinking abilities find logical places.

The Structure-of-Intellect Model

The structure of intellect is represented by a rectangular model of three dimensions. Imagine a block of space 4 × 5 × 6 inches divided into one-inch cubes or cells (see Figure 7.1). One dimension of the model represents four

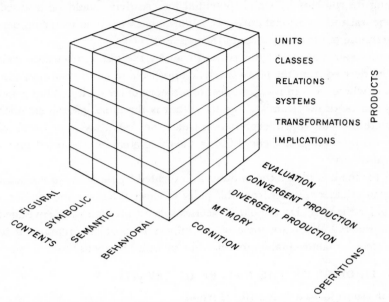

FIGURE 7.1. *The theoretical model of the structure of intellect*

broad, basic categories of information or *content:* figural (that is, perceived), symbolic (such as letters and numbers), semantic (verbal meaning), and behavioral (mental activities of which we can become aware, in others or in ourselves). A second dimension of the model represents five kinds of psychological *operations* that can be performed with any kind of information: cognition (knowing or being acquainted with), memory (storage), divergent production (generating a variety of items of information from an item or items of given information), convergent production (generating a fully determined item of information from items of given information), and evaluation (deciding on the "goodness" of information, whether cognized, recalled from memory, or produced divergently or convergently). The third dimension of the model pertains to kinds of *products* of information, from whatever category of information: units, classes, relations, systems, transformations (conversions, redefinitions, and so forth), and implications. Four times five times six yields 120 cells in the model, each one representing a unique ability, with a unique combination of a different operation applied to a different kind of content, yielding a different kind of product.

The chief heuristic value of the model in connection with research has been to predict undiscovered primary intellectual abilities. Besides finding logical places for the intellectual factors found previous to the construction of the model, we have found 13 new ones using hypotheses derived from the model. A number of studies are under way at this time, all of which are aimed toward determining whether factors suggested by the model will be found to exist as distinguishable traits. One study is aimed at the factors of evaluation dealing with the six products of semantic information, and a parallel study deals with factors of evaluation in the area of symbolic information and their relation to the learning of algebra, along with other symbolic abilities. Our first excursion in the area of behavioral information is aimed at the six hypothesized cognition factors. Some studies recently completed pertained to factors of divergent production in the figural and symbolic areas. At this time, the majority of the hypothesized factors of cognition and of divergent production have been demonstrated. None of the expected factors in the behavioral area has been discovered, for they have not been investigated from the point of view of this theory. Our initial efforts in this direction thus far look promising.

Because of the strong emphasis on information in the structure-of-intellect theory, in terms of categories of content and the products that we form within those categories, one can be easily led to an informational type of psychology in general. In recent informational psychology (Guilford, 1961), the principle of association, which has dominated psychology for centuries, is replaced by the six kinds of products, with correspondingly greater theoretical possibilities. The stimulus-response model, a special type of associational concept, is replaced by different kinds of dealings with information.

Information itself is defined as "that which the organism discriminates," a definition that is consistent with information theory. There is no necessary implication that discriminations must be conscious; in fact, many discriminations are unconscious. We have, then, an objective inferential psychology. It may be suggested, however, that the role of consciousness is that it enlarges tremendously the possibilities for making discriminations. This may be its chief biological function.

A new theory of learning follows from this general psychological theory (Guilford, 1960a). From the informational point of view, learning is the acquisition of new information. Its results are in the form of new cognitions, derived directly as a consequence of stimulation or indirectly through divergent or convergent production. Evaluation plays a decisive role in learning, since it is the informational interpretation of reinforcement. An organism is so constructed that its behavior is largely self-correcting. Feedback information is used as an indication that a response is successful or unsuccessful. Continual checking and rechecking serve to shape an appropriate action for coping with a particular kind of situation.

Incidentally, the structure-of-intellect model provides empirical concepts to take care of phenomena formerly called induction, deduction, and problem-solving (Guilford, 1960b). By "empirical concepts" we mean that the verbal concepts have referents in experience. In the factor-analytic context this means that terms point to certain types of intellectual tasks that are known in the form of tests.

Problem-solving cannot be precisely or univocally placed in the structure of intellect for the good reason that it is not an unvarying kind of mental activity. An organism has a problem whenever it cannot cope with a situation by means of previously learned strategies. Problems are of very numerous kinds, involving all kinds of information and requiring all kinds of products. Different operations also come into play as the problem-solver varies his attack upon the problem. For any particular kind of problem and any particular kind of population of organisms, a characteristic combination of intellectual abilities may be expected to contribute to individual differences. In fact, any psychological test presents problems of a unique kind, and factor analysis tells us what pattern of common factors contribute to individual differences in the scores.

I have given some attention to these general theories and issues for the reason that creative performance is to be largely accounted for in similar ways, as a significant part of the structure of intellect. The creation of a product is much like problem-solving. This is more obvious for the scientist, the inventor, the executive, and the business man than for an artist. Although it is not quite so obvious for creative artists, psychoanalysts point out that the artist is attempting to solve a *personal* problem (Patrick, 1941; Kris, 1953). At any rate, creative production in any form appears to rest most directly on certain areas of abilities within the structure of intellect and less directly on many others, the combination of abilities involved being determined, as in problem-solving, by the nature of the problem or of the need for expression.

Creativity and Divergent-Production Factors

From the beginning of our project research on creativity, it was thought that creative thinking depends upon abilities such as fluency, flexibility, originality, sensitivity to problems, and redefinition of objects. Factors of these kinds were found, most of which were recognized as belonging in the operation category of divergent production. We shall consider next some factors of fluency, flexibility, and originality and their properties as the nature of those factors became progressively clearer with succeeding analyses.

Fluency in the production of ideas has often been noted as a quality contributing to creativity. For example, the British statesman Winston Churchill was noted for his exceptional ideational fluency. Clement Attlee once said of him that in conferences, no matter what problem came up, Churchill always had about ten ideas on how to deal with it. Thurstone (1950) remarked that one of the most outstanding traits of Thomas A. Edison was his fluency of thinking. For every failing experiment, said Thurstone, Edison had several ideas for new experiments.

Our present conception of the nature of ideational fluency is indicated by its placement in the structure-of-intellect cell for the divergent production of semantic units. An idea (in the usual use of that term) is a semantic unit of information, communicable in verbal terms. In that location in the structure of intellect, it is parallel to the factor of *cognition* of semantic units, our old friend verbal comprehension, which is most purely measured by a vocabulary test. A vocabulary score informs us concerning the quantity of semantic units a person has in storage. A test of ideational fluency informs us concerning the facility or the efficiency with which he can get those units out of storage for use in some way.

It is rather interesting that we commonly find slight negative correlations between scores for the two factors, indicating that the more units of information we have in storage, the less easy, relatively, it is to get them out when needed. This fact may suggest that this is one way in which we are victims of proactive and retroactive inhibition. The more we have learned, the more interferences there are against revival for use. This is not necessarily an argument against possessing much learned information. Almost every writer on creativity stresses the importance of having information at one's disposal. The difficulty in retrieval suggests that we might find better ways of putting information in storage. The author strongly suspects that this step has a great deal to do with the ease of getting it out.

Associational fluency serves a word-finding function. Given a semantic unit and a relation, what different words are candidates for completing the relationship? If we give the item "What is the opposite of 'wet,' " the fully determined response for our culture is "dry." But if we give the item "How many words mean *almost* the opposite of 'wet,' " the responses might also be: "arid, desiccated, thirsty, uninteresting, sarcastic," and so on. We have found a slight relationship between scores for this factor and scores for the liking for risk-taking and tolerance of ambiguity, which suggests that the person who is willing to take chances and who does not set too high a standard of accuracy of meaning is likely to do better in tests of this ability.

Another fluency factor, known as expressional fluency, pertains to the construction of a variety of systems meeting certain requirements, for example, the construction of phrases or sentences. It was thought for some time that sentence-building was a matter of symbolic systems, in view of the rules of syntax involved, but it was found recently that a test calling for a variety of letter codes and a test calling for a variety of equations better qualify for representing a factor of divergent production of symbolic systems. Sentence-building emphasizes the production of semantic systems.

In tests of spontaneous flexibility, the examinee who keeps his responses restricted within the same class makes a lower score; the one who jumps from class to class makes a higher score. The ability is recognized as the divergent production of semantic classes (there are parallel abilities pertaining to figural and symbolic classes, also). Of course, one might say that the person who jumps from class to class may also be operating within a much broader class of classes.

There is a suggestion, therefore, that people in whom this ability is high have a preference for, or a habitual use of, higher-level abstractions. It is sometimes pointed out that creative production is more successful if the thinker begins at a high level of abstraction and works down to narrower classes as he progresses.

It can also be suggested that operating within broader classes permits the thinker to scan a broader range of logical possibilities in his memory storage. Sometimes a problem dealing with figural information, especially, is much more readily solved by making a translation into semantic information, where higher-level abstractions are possible, bringing within reach the needed information.

It can be said that spontaneous flexibility is a freedom from a kind of rigidity that can be called "perseveration." The flexible person will be less likely to keep his answers within limited areas in naming lists of objects (that is, there is clustering of responses), in inventing a list of dissyllables, and in giving a chain of associations (Frick, et al., 1959). So far as we know, this kind of perseveration is limited to tasks of these kinds and does not imply any more general trait of perseveration.

Adaptive flexibility involves variations in strategy or mental set, or in interpretation of goals. The examinee is forced to take some unusual approach to a problem in order to solve it. Tests that measure this ability often require a restructuring of problems before they can be solved; the most obvious interpretation will not do. Other tests require restructuring of the method of solution, for example, one in which each test item is to be solved in two or more ways. The kind of rigidity associated negatively with this ability should be described as a resistance against restructuring or a firmness of closure with regard to systems.

The factor of adaptive flexibility was first found in figural tests. It was later realized that a factor called "originality" is a parallel ability, an adaptive flexibility with semantic information. Three requirements were set up for original responses: (1) they are statistically infrequent in the population, (2) they are remotely connected with the given information, and (3) they are "clever" or ingenious. Such kinds of responses can be found in word-association tests, in tests calling for titles of story plots or captions for cartoons, in listing remote consequences to events, or in tests calling for symbols to represent words.

Adaptive flexibility with both figural information and semantic information has been placed in the transformation layer of the structure of intellect, since some kind of shift or redefinition is needed in doing the tests. The clever responses show this most clearly, and also show the relation of transformations to humor. A number of investigators have mentioned the close affiliation of semantic transformations with humor (Getzels and Jackson, 1962; Torrance, 1959). The following story will illustrate. Seven-year-old Mike was given an ice-cream cone by his grandmother. He asked for and received a cone with pistachio ice cream. A few moments later he was looking intently at the ice cream and mumbling something. His grandmother asked "Mike, what are you doing?" "I'm talking to the nuts in the ice cream," he replied. "And what are you saying?" asked the grandmother. Said Mike, "I said 'What is one and one,' and they said 'eleven,' I said 'What is two and two,' and they said '22,' and I said 'What is two and four,' and they said '24.' " "Mike, you know that isn't right," said the grandmother. "*I* know that," said Mike, "but *they* don't know it; they're nuts."

Some minor experiments throw some interesting light on the factor of originality (Christensen, Guilford, and Wilson, 1957). One hypothesis we tested was that, after a subject is given the stimulus information, his early responses in time will be less original and his later ones more original. With different kinds of items, we checked on possible changes in degrees of usualness, remoteness, and cleverness as functions of working time. The hypothesis was supported with respect to uncommonness and remoteness, but not with respect to cleverness. Over the working time of a limited number of minutes, the degree of cleverness remained constant. Another experiment compared the effects of change of instruction in a Plot Titles test. In one case, examinees were told to give clever titles and in the other no mention was made of cleverness. Under instructions to be clever, there was a reduction in the total number of responses, an increase in the number of responses rated clever, and an increase in the average degree of rated cleverness.

Not hypothesized at the beginning of our study of creativity, but hypothesized later in a study of planning abilities, was a factor of ability to elaborate. Starting with a kind of outline or a segment of some possible total, the examinee adds one element after another to produce an elaborate whole. Such an ability has been found in connection with figural, symbolic, and semantic information. Most older theories of creative performance have recognized a stage in which the creator elaborates his creation in some detail, usually in the later steps of creative production. In doing so, he is producing a variety of implications, one thing following another; hence we classify the elaboration abilities as divergent production of implications.

Creativity and Other Factors

Two important abilities recognized as having significance for creative individuals are outside the divergent-production category. Sensitivity to problems is one of them. This factor involves the recognition of errors, defects, or imperfections. Because of these characteristics, the factor is placed in the operation category of evaluation, having to do with implications. In connection with problem-solving, this ability makes us aware that a problem exists; thus it helps to initiate problem-solving. It also plays a role *during* problem-solving, as our factor-analytic study of problem-solving shows (Merrifield, et al., 1960). This role could be at the moment of deciding whether or not the problem is properly structured, but probably not, since a structured problem is a system. Consequently, this step is more likely to involve the ability to evaluate semantic *systems*. It could be at the moment of deciding whether or not a tentative solution is satisfactory. It could possibly operate anywhere the problem-solver realizes that he has a problem yet to be solved.

Factors coming under the general name of "redefinition" have been found in connection with figural, symbolic, and semantic information. A test of the Gottschaldt-figures type requires figural redefinition. This is Thurstone's Closure II factor. A test calling for the breaking up of a phrase in order to form a new one, such as the phrase "The red olive," which becomes "There do live," indicates the degree of *symbolic* redefinition. Using a familiar object or part of an object, such as using a bone from a fish for making a needle, indicates the degree of the ability of semantic redefinition. Since one right answer is called for in each instance, these redefinition abilities are classified under convergent production, in the product row of transformations.

It seems rather clear that these redefinition qualities are the opposite of a well-recognized quality of functional fixedness. A favorite problem for demonstrating this phenomenon is to hang two strings from the ceiling so far apart that the subject cannot reach one while holding the other; his task is to tie the lower ends together. By tying an object of some little weight to the end of one string and swinging it to produce a pendulum, the subject can solve the problem. His greatest hurdle is to decide on adapting some unusual object like pliers or a roller skate to serve as a weight. Birch and Rabinowitz (1951) demonstrated that if the subject has just used the object for some other purpose, he has more difficulty in redefining it as a weight. In their experiment, some subjects had just previously used a relay in doing some electric wiring for a circuit, and others had used a switch for a similar purpose. Given the string problem, all those who had previously used the relay chose the switch as a weight and seven of the nine who had used the switch chose the relay. In a control group, the choice was fifty-fifty.

The redefinition factors, then, represent a third type of freedom from rigidity: a rigidity of meaning or use. Because these factors are in the transformation layer, and because transformation as a general concept suggests some pliability of mind, we have reason to select the whole set of transformation abilities as rather direct resources for the creative thinker. Many a novel product is essentially a revision of an old one. During any sequence of steps in a creative episode, the creator makes numerous revisions, often against opposition. Freedom to make revolutionary reorganizations of information is another aid to creative production.

Considering the preceding discussion, we realize how much like problem-solving creative thinking is. This statement applies when we consider how many of the same abilities are involved and also how the major steps in problem-solving apply to the production of many creative results. On the route to a creative product, one becomes aware of the existence of a problem, either in the environment or in one's self, or at least aware of a need of some kind. We must structure the problem or achieve a better definition of the need in order to give some direction to our efforts. We think up possible solutions or possible things that will fulfill the need. We apply evaluative activity at steps along the way.

Sometimes the activity in problem-solving is described as trial-and-error behavior. Trial and error may occur at any point along the way. In terms of structure-of-intellect theory, trial-and-error behavior can be interpreted as an interplay of cognition, divergent or convergent production, and evaluation. We test ourselves as we go along. Feedback information indicates to us whether we want the information we have achieved or whether we do not.

RELATIONS TO OTHER CONCEPTIONS

The Wallas Stages of Creation

In considering the relations of the descriptions of creative processes presented from the standpoint of dimensions of intellect to other pictures, let us consider first the common stages of creation proposed by Wallas. It should be said first that investigators who have looked for such stages are by no means in agreement that they actually take place in one-two-three-four order. Patrick (1935; 1937; 1938), who has given considerable attention to the stages in her studies with poets, artists, and scientists, was willing to admit to much overlapping, particularly between neighboring stages. Vinacke (1952) found considerable overlapping, and Eindhoven and Vinacke (1952) found no separate stages in the production of paintings by artists. Even Wallas (1926) recognized that the stages do not describe consistent patterns.

Preparation for a creative episode involves the intellectual aptitudes that contribute to learning and remembering. Those writers who recognize the preparation phase seem to have in mind the special learning that is incident to the particular creative production. Actually, the creator's whole past life may contribute to preparation for any creative act. Patrick (1937; 1938) speaks of many "changes of ideas" during this stage, as if a number of false starts were made, or as if selections were being made from information retrieved from storage. This suggests trial-and-error behavior and whatever intellectual abilities may be involved in it, particularly those from the categories of divergent production and evaluation.

Little can be said about what actually happens during the stage of incubation. To say that there is mental activity but that it is unconscious is of no help. If activity does occur, whether conscious, unconscious, or half-conscious, we venture to suggest that information-processing is going on with much the same operations and products as can be inferred when individuals take different kinds of tests, and that much the same laws of thinking apply. Incubation is exhibited by the fact that an idea that appears to have been dropped suddenly recurs to the creator, or the person suddenly starts working again along a line discarded earlier.

The period of illumination, with its moments of inspiration, is of course the most spectacular part of a creative venture. Some writers, including Thurstone (1950), equate illumination to insight. It may well be that when we understand insight and its antecedents we shall also understand the phenomenon of inspiration. In the context of informational psychology, it can be said that an insight is a *sudden* achievement of a new product. We might, therefore, turn our attention to the conditions under which products develop, especially where this development takes some time preceding the climactic emergence, as in cases of insight. Behavioristic psychologists are inclined to dismiss the phenomenon of insight in an offhand manner by saying that it is due to past experience (McGeoch and Irion, 1952), without really facing the problem.

Observers of creators at work often report that the illumination involves an organized theme, motif, or total scheme, or what might be called a "system," one of the informational products. Some say that a scheme or motif is present when incubation begins, but that it is not as complete or as clear as at the moment of inspiration. There is sufficient striking change to lead to the hypothesis of unconscious work in the meantime. One can hypothesize, then, that a system can take shape in unconscious activity.

Theories proposed by psychologists to account for incubation and illumination are very reminiscent of theories of benefits from spaced practice. Indeed, there are a number of similarities between the conditions of incubation and of spaced practice. Incubation might well be studied from this point of view. Helmholtz proposed that incubation and illumination are matters of fatigue and recovery from fatigue (Patrick, 1935). Woodworth (1954) attributed those stages to the fading of interfering material that earlier had much recency value behind it, during incubation, and a freedom from this interference at the time of illumination. Woodworth discounts the hypothesis of unconscious activity during incubation, suggesting that the recurring "practice" on the problem is conscious and that the final inspiration may be merely an extremely rapid conscious activity. Others have talked of fresh starts and new strategy when the work is taken up again (Patrick, 1935) after a rest pause.

The stage of verification is more open to inspection. There is agreement that considerable elaboration and revision take place during this period. The operation of evaluation, in its many forms, obviously applies. To spoil the neat picture, some investigators find no such stage in painters (Eindhoven and Vinacke, 1952) and others find revisions, evaluations, and some elaborations in what are presumably earlier stages.

Creativity as High Intelligence

Spearman was probably responsible for starting the idea that the creativity of outstanding people can be accounted for in terms of high levels of intelligence, where intelligence was equated to his g factor. In his theory of cognition, Spearman proposed three levels or evidences of intelligence. We know our experience, we derive relations from it, and having relations and items of experience given we can deduce (his term was "educe") another item of information (he called an item a "fundament"). The eduction of correlates was regarded as the highest act of intelligence and the one that accounts for all creative production (Spearman, 1931).

From our present knowledge of intelligence, we know how very limited Spearman's conception was. The structure of intellect recognizes four possible factors for cognition of relations, three of them being known. It also recognizes four possible factors for eduction of correlates. Two of them have been demonstrated, and all are regarded as the convergent production of information to complete relationships. These abilities, and those having to do with cognition of relations, may contribute indirectly to certain creative performances, but many others, as we have seen, are much more likely to do so.

In their studies of "genius," Terman and his associates were evidently rather confident that high IQ accounts for the making of creative individuals. In these days, the question invariably comes up, "What is the relation between creativity and the IQ?" The reply should be another question, "*What* creativity and *what* IQ?" Unless the second question is answered, the first one cannot be answered. On an operational basis, the question would pertain to the correlations between selected tests. IQ tests have grown up with limited selection of abilities represented, mostly from the areas of cognition and convergent production. Creativity tests would be selected from the areas of divergent production and transformation. The answer to the main question would lie somewhere in the correlations between tests of the two kinds. As for the relation between mental age on a verbal IQ test and a composite of a few verbal tests of fluency and flexibility, recent findings suggest the hypothesis that the relationship is a curvilinear one. There may be a small correlation between IQ-test scores and creativity composite scores up to a limit on mental age, but above that level little or no correlation.

Psychoanalytical Theory

Although the author's acquaintance with the psychoanalytical literature dealing with creativity is limited, in examining some of that literature, overlooking many minor disagreements and inconsistencies, we find essentially unanimous agreement that creation involves much unconscious activity. But most writers attribute creative thinking to the preconscious or foreconscious, which is more accessible to the conscious part of the mind, and which is relatively free from the stereotypy of the unconscious, and in which there is release from repression.

There can be little quarrel with the idea that many of the steps in creative thinking are unconscious. But to scientific psychologists, we venture to say, the conception of the unconscious or the preconscious as an active agent represents one of animism's last stands in what pretends to be science. The same can be said of the concepts of "personality" and "self," as used by many psychologists.

Other suggestions from psychoanalytical sources are of interest. As one might expect, they have most to do with motivational and emotional sources of creative thinking. One suggestion is that problems giving rise to creative activity stem from personal conflicts. The solutions are in the form of symbolic representations. This description, of course, may fit creation in the arts but not in the sciences, unless the scientist fails to accept the compulsions of reality and resorts to some wishful thinking.

Some authors speak of creative activity as a regression to childhood levels (Hilgard, 1959; Maslow, 1959; and Rosen, 1953). The normal child shows his freedom from the restraints of reality because he does not possess so much accepted information regarding it. In appearance, there is something in common between the child's spontaneous imaginings and the thinking of the creative adult. Whether this is regression or a persistence of a child's inquiring attitude and playfulness with ideas would be difficult to decide on the basis of present information. The accumulation of knowledge and the pressures to conform and to grow up obviously depress this kind of thinking in most children.

The latter interpretation is in line with the suggestion (Kris, 1953) that the uncreative person represses his infantilism, whereas the creative person does not. A related idea is that the male artist, who shows on the average a stronger feminine tendency than other men, has some relief of repression of his feminism. Relief from repression, in general, makes possible the relaxed attitude that is favorable to creative thinking.

Finally, there is a common statement that the creative person is in good touch with his unconscious. As far as can be determined, this may be interpreted in two ways. In the language of informational psychology, the creative person has a more ready access to his memory storage. This interpretation was given earlier in describing the nature of ideational fluency. The other possible meaning is that the creative person knows more about his own motivations and can therefore more easily translate his needs into artistic products or other creative products. It can be suggested, in structure-of-intellect terminology, that such a person has relatively good behavioral cognition regarding his own desires and conflicts. He is also sensitive as to whether his product satisfies those desires; in other words, he has relatively good abilities to evaluate behavioral information.

Thurstone's Hypotheses regarding Creativity

Thurstone (1950) ties his theory of creativity to his theory of intelligence, which he had worked out years ago (1924). This linkage is consistent with the position we have taken in the Aptitudes Project, that creativity is a part of, or an aspect of, intelligence, as I have indicated much earlier in this paper. The key to Thurstone's theory of intelligence is that the intelligent person becomes focally aware of his mental activities at early stages of their development. To quote him, "The psychological act originates in the essentially affective and non-verbalized, nonfocal motivations and needs of the individual." Successive particularizations occur, involving successive decisions at choice points. As soon as any choice becomes focal in consciousness, the activity is under rational control. The earlier the person becomes conscious of the process, the more intelligent he is.

Creativity fits into the theory by virtue of the fact that there are different degrees to which the person has contact with unconscious phases of his mental act. The contacts are in the form of intuitions or hunches in which the creative person has relatively strong confidence. Thurstone cites the fact that we can classify objects even without a clear recognition of the nature of the classes. One can also cite the fact that we can use principles without realization of the nature of those principles. The clarification of either classes or principles may come later. Experiments along such lines were started under Thurstone's direction. They should be pertinent to the understanding of the moment of inspiration during the stage of illumination.

SOME NEGLECTED EXPERIMENTAL PROBLEMS

In addition to the kind of experiment just mentioned, other problems call for experimental attack in connection with both incubation and illumination. Concerning incubation, we would like to know why some persons tend to carry problems with them. Sensing a problem that has an appreciable degree of viability for the person leaves him with some degree of motivation to solve it. He may leave it, but he comes back to it; or it comes back to him. Are there individual differences in a trait of perseveration of motives? This is a problem for factor analysis. Also, do some persons have a trait of early closure to problems, while others display a lack of closure until a problem is either solved or proven to be insoluble? Perhaps curiosity plays a role. Perhaps some degree of anxiety is needed.

As indicated earlier, many of the features of incubation have resemblances to phenomena of spaced practice. It would be quite simple to study spaced practice in a task calling for divergent production or transformations when the task cannot be completed in one short practice period. As with ordinary experiments on spaced practice, control of the subject's behavior during longer rest periods would present a problem, probably more serious than in tasks not calling for creative solutions. One difference between incubation and ordinary distributed practice would be that in the former, that is, in a creative task, the subject is attempting to achieve an expressive goal, so to speak, whereas in the latter he is aiming toward a reproductive goal.

A new hypothesis of incubation to be investigated is suggested by typical performances in a fluency test. With an item for which we allow a few minutes, for example, "What would happen if we had eyes in the backs of our heads?" there is a tendency for responses to increase in quality. If the working time were made much longer, for example, a matter of hours, the responses would probably come at ever-increasing intervals, and possibly with the subject reaching way out for most unusual or original answers, the easier and more obvious ones having been given previously. In the intervals of waiting the subject cannot help his turning to something else, even perhaps forgetting his task. When he comes up with an "inspiration," it is much like an act of illumination. To our knowledge, such an experiment has not been tried, although some of Patrick's experiments come close. The hypothesis is that inspirations after long delays with intervening alien activity are due in part to the time it takes to fish out remotely connected information. That the fishing is unconscious is not unique; such scanning also occurs when we are trying to think of a name that does not come to mind immediately.

In connection with the phenomenon of illumination there are also many problems to be investigated. The observable emotional accompaniment is not difficult to understand, since it probably represents no more than the common elation that accompanies sudden success. There is the problem, however, as to how a total theme or motif develops. Since in structure-of-intellect terminology a theme or a motif is an example of the product of system, the problem is the more general one of how systems develop.

From the direction of the psychometric approach, we need further factor-analytic studies to determine whether the unknown but predicted abilities in the structure of intellect can be demonstrated. From the same approach we need studies to show to what extent each ability contributes to success in problem-solving and in creative production of various kinds, in each kind of population.

SUMMARY

In this paper, considerations have been given to some of the hypotheses concerning the nature of creative processes from nonpsychological sources and from psychological and psychoanalytic sources. Many of the findings from the psychometric approach of factor analysis during the past dozen years were reviewed, with interpretations.

From the point of view of abilities, the relation of creativity to intelligence was presented in terms of a theoretical model, the structure of intellect, with creative abilities in logical relation to other intellectual abilities. Similarities of creative production to problem-solving were pointed out, with the conclusion that both depend upon varying patterns of abilities, depending upon the kinds of information and the kinds of products involved.

An attempt was made to account for some of the historical theories and hypotheses concerning creativity in terms of the concepts of an informational psychology as represented by the structure of intellect. Certain areas of research on creativity that need concentrated attention were pointed out.

REFERENCES

Abelson, R. P. The Lack of Certain Mathematical Models in Psychology. Paper presented at the Western Psychological Association meetings, April 1958.

Abelson, R. P., and A. Bernstein. A Computer Simulation Model of Community Referendum Controversies. *Public Opinion Quarterly*, **27**, 1963, 93–122.

Aberle, D. F. Shared Values in Complex Societies. *American Sociological Review*, **15**, 1950, 495–502.

Aronson, E., Judy Turner, and J. M. Carlsmith. Communicator Credibility and Communication Discrepancy as Determinants of Opinion Change, 1962. (Mimeographed.)

Benoit-Smullyan, E. Status, Status Types, and Status Interrelations. *American Sociological Review*, **9**, 1944, 151–161.

Berge, C. *The Theory of Graphs*. New York: John Wiley & Sons, Inc., 1962.

Birch, H. G., and H. S. Rabinowitz. The Negative Effect of Previous Experience on Productive Thinking. *Journal of Experimental Psychology*, **41**, 1951, 121–125.

Bradley, R. A., and M. E. Terry. Rank Analysis of Incomplete Block Designs. I. The Method of Paired Comparisons. *Biometrika*, **39**, 1952, 324–345.

Campbell, D. T., and D. W. Fiske. Convergent and Discriminant Validation by the Multitrait-Multimethod Matrix. *Psychological Bulletin*, **56**, 1959, 81–105.

Cervin, V. B. Relationship of Ascendant-Submissive Behavior in Dyadic Groups of Human Subjects to Their Emotional Responsiveness. *Journal of Abnormal and Social Psychology*, **54**, 1957, 241–249.

Cervin, V. B., and G. P. Henderson. Statistical Theory of Persuasion. *Psychological Review*, **68**, 1961, 157–166.

Christensen, P. R., J. P. Guilford, and R. C. Wilson. Relations of Creative Responses to Working Time and Instructions. *Journal of Experimental Psychology*, **53**, 1957, 82–88.

Cliff, N. Adverbs as Multipliers. *Psychological Review*, **66**, 1959, 27–44.

Cliff, N. Adverb-Adjective Combination in Overseas Groups. *Research Memorandum* 60–16. Princeton, N. J.: Educational Testing Service, 1960. (Multilithed report.)

Cliff, N. Analytic Rotation to a Functional Relationship. *Psychometrika*, **27**, 1962, 283–295.

Cohen, A. R. Communication Discrepancy and Attitude Change. *Journal of Personality*, **27**, 1959, 386–396.

Coleman, J. S. *Community Conflict*. New York: The Free Press of Glencoe, 1957. (a)

Coleman, J. S. Multidimensional Scale Analysis. *American Journal of Sociology*, **63**, 1957, 253–263. (b)

Coombs, C. H. On the Use of Inconsistency of Preferences in Psychological Measurement. *Journal of Experimental Psychology*, **55**, 1958, 1–7.

Coombs, C. H. A Theory of Data. *Psychological Review*, **67**, 1960, 143–159.

Coombs, C. H. *Theory of Data*. New York: John Wiley & Sons, Inc., 1964. (In press.)

Davies, A. F. Prestige of Occupations. *British Journal of Sociology*, **3**, 1952, 134–147.

DuBois, P. H. An Analysis of Guttman's Simplex. *Psychometrika*, **25**, 1960, 173–182.

Dunkel, H. B. *General Education in the Humanities*. Washington, D. C.: American Council on Education, 1947.

Edwards, A. L. *The Social Desirability Variable in Personality Assessment and Research*. New York: Holt, Rinehart and Winston, Inc., 1957.

Eindhoven, J. E., and W. E. Vinacke. Creative Process in Painting. *Journal of General Psychology*, **47**, 1952, 139–164.

Fagen, R. R. Some Contributions of Mathematical Reasoning to the Study of Politics. *American Political Science Review*, **55,** 1961, 888–899.

Ferguson, G. A. The Factorial Interpretation of Test Difficulty. *Psychometrika*, **6,** 1941, 323–329.

Festinger, L. Informal Social Communication. *Psychological Review*, **57,** 1950, 271–282.

Fisher, S., and A. Lubin. Distance as a Determinant of Influence in a Two-Person Serial Interaction Situation. *Journal of Abnormal and Social Psychology*, **56,** 1958, 230–238.

French, J. R. P., Jr. A Formal Theory of Social Power. *Psychological Review*, **63,** 1956, 181–194.

Frick, J. W., J. P. Guilford, P. R. Christensen, and P. R. Merrifield. A Factor-Analytic Study of Flexibility in Thinking. *Educational and Psychological Measurement*, **19,** 1959, 469–496.

Galanter, E. H. An Axiomatic and Experimental Study of Sensory Order and Measure. *Psychological Review*, **63,** 1956, 16–28.

Getzels, J. W., and P. W. Jackson. *Creativity and Intelligence*. New York: John Wiley & Sons, Inc., 1962.

Ghiselin, B. *The Creative Process*. New York: Mentor Books, 1955.

Glanzer, M., and R. Glaser. Techniques for the Study of Group Structure and Behavior. I. Analysis of Structure. *Psychological Bulletin*, **56,** 1959, 317–332.

Goldberg, S. C. Three Situational Determinants of Conformity to Social Norms. *Journal of Abnormal and Social Psychology*, **49,** 1954, 325–329.

Goodman, N. *The Structure of Appearance*. Cambridge, Mass.: Harvard University Press, 1951.

Guilford, J. P. Creativity. *American Psychologist*, **5,** 1950, 444–454.

Guilford, J. P. An Emerging View of Learning Theory. In *Intelligence, Creativity, and Learning*. Bellingham, Wash.: Western Washington College, 1960. (a)

Guilford, J. P. Basic Conceptual Problems in the Psychology of Thinking. *Annals of the New York Academy of Sciences*, **91,** 1960, 6–21. (b)

Guilford, J. P. Factorial Angles to Psychology. *Psychological Review*, **68,** 1961, 1–20.

Gullahorn, J. T. Distance and Friendship as Factors in the Gross Interaction Matrix. *Sociometry*, **15,** 1952, 123–134.

Gulliksen, H. Measurement of Subjective Values. *Psychometrika*, **21,** 1956, 229–244.

Gulliksen, H. Linear and Multidimensional Scaling. *Psychometrika*, **26,** 1961, 9–25.

Gulliksen, H. The Structure of Individual Differences in Optimality Judgments. *Research Memorandum* 62–7. Princeton, N. J.: Educational Testing Service, 1962. (Also to appear in Bryan, G., and M. Shelly, *Human Judgments and Optimality*. New York: John Wiley & Sons, Inc., 1963, in press.)

Gulliksen, H., and L. R Tucker. A General Procedure for Obtaining Paired Comparisons from Multiple Rank Orders. *Psychometrika*, **26,** 1961, 173–183.

Guttman, L. A Generalized Simplex for Factor Analysis. *Psychometrika*, **20,** 1955, 173–192.

Hadamard, J. *An Essay on the Psychology of Invention in the Mathematical Field*. Princeton, N. J.: Princeton University Press, 1945.

Hall, J., and D. C. Jones. Social Grading of Occupations. *British Journal of Sociology*, **1,** 1950, 31–55.

Harary, F. A Criterion for Unanimity in French's Theory of Social Power. In Cartwright, D., ed., *Studies in Social Power*. Ann Arbor: University of Michigan, 1959.

Hatt, P. K. Occupation and Social Stratification. *American Journal of Sociology*, **55,** 1950, 533–543.

Hays, W. L., and J. F. Bennett. Multidimensional Unfolding: Determining Configuration from Complete Rank Order Preference Data. *Psychometrika*, **26,** 1961, 221–238.

Hefner, R. A. *Extension of the Law of Comparative Judgment to Discriminable and Multidimensional Stimuli*. Unpublished doctoral dissertation, University of Michigan, 1958.

Hilgard, E. R. Creativity and Problem Solving. In Anderson, H. H., ed., *Creativity and Its Cultivation*. New York: Harper & Row, Publishers, 1959.

Hovland, C. I., O. J. Harvey, and M. Sherif. Assimilation and Contrast Effects in Reactions to Communication and Attitude Change. *Journal of Abnormal and Social Psychology*, **55,** 1957, 244–252.

Hovland, C. I., and H. A. Pritzker. Extent of Opinion Change as a Function of Amount of Change Advocated. *Journal of Abnormal and Social Psychology*, **54,** 1957, 257–261.

Hyman, H. H. The Psychology of Status. *Archives of Psychology*, No. 269, 1942, 94.

Kelley, H. H., and J. W. Thibaut. Experimental Studies of Group Problem Solving and Process. In Lindzey, G., ed., *Handbook of Social Psychology*. Reading, Mass.: Addison-Wesley Publishing Company, Inc., 1954.

Kendall, M. G. *Rank Correlation Methods*. London: Charles Griffin & Co., Ltd., 1948. (2d ed., New York: Hafner Publishing Company, 1955.)

Klingberg, F. L. Studies in Measurement of the Relations among Sovereign States. *Psychometrika*, **6,** 1941, 335–352.

Kris, E. Psychoanalysis and the Study of Creative Imagination. *Bulletin of the New York Academy of Medicine*, 1953, 334–351.

Luce, R. D. *Individual Choice Behavior*. New York: John Wiley & Sons, Inc., 1959.

Maslow, A. H. Creativity in Self-actualizing People. In Anderson, H. H., ed., *Creativity and Its Cultivation*. New York: Harper & Row, Publishers, 1959.

McGeoch, J. A., and A. L. Irion. *The Psychology of Human Learning*. New York: David McKay Company, Inc., 1952.

McKenzie, L. Matrices with Dominant Diagonals and Economic Theory. In Arrow, K. J., S. Karlin, and P. Suppes, eds., *Mathematical Methods in the Social Sciences*. Stanford, California: Stanford University Press, 1960.

McRae, D. Direct Factor Analysis of Sociometric Data. *Sociometry*, **23,** 1960, 360–371.

Merrifield, P. R., J. P. Guilford, P. R. Christensen, and J. W. Frick. A Factor-Analytic Study of Problem-Solving Abilities. *Report of the Psychological Laboratory*, No. 22. Los Angeles: University of Southern California, 1960.

Messick, S. The Perception of Social Attitudes. *Journal of Abnormal and Social Psychology*, **52,** 1956, 57–66.

Messick, S., and R. P. Abelson. Research Tools: Scaling and Measurement Theory. *Review of Educational Research*, **27,** 1957, 487–497.

Michigan, University of, Detroit Area Study. *A Social Profile of Detroit: 1955*. Ann Arbor, Michigan: Author, 1956.

Morris, R. T., and R. J. Murphy. The Situs Dimension in Occupational Structure. *American Sociological Review*, **24,** 1959, 231–239.

North, C. C., and P. K. Hatt. Jobs and Occupations: A Popular Evaluation. *Opinion News*, **9,** 1947, 3–13.

Osgood, C. E., G. J. Suci, and P. H. Tannenbaum. *The Measurement of Meaning.* Urbana: University of Illinois Press, 1957.

Osgood, C. E., and P. H. Tannenbaum. The Principle of Congruity in the Prediction of Attitude Change. *Psychological Review*, **62,** 1955, 42–55.

Palmer, Gladys L. Attitudes toward Work in an Industrial Community. *American Journal of Sociology*, **63,** 1957, 17–26.

Paterson, D. G. The Conservation of Human Talent. *American Psychologist*, **12,** 1957, 134–144.

Patrick, Catharine. Creative Thought in Poets. *Archives of Psychology*, **26,** 1935, 1–74.

Patrick, Catharine. Creative Thought in Artists. *Journal of Psychology*, **4,** 1937, 35–73.

Patrick, Catharine. Scientific Thought. *Journal of Psychology*, **5,** 1938, 55–83.

Patrick, Catharine. Whole and Part Relationship in Creative Thought. *American Journal of Psychology*, **54,** 1941, 128–131.

Peterson, Ruth C., and L. L. Thurstone. *Motion Pictures and the Social Attitudes of Children.* New York: The Macmillan Company, 1933.

Poincaré, H. *The Foundations of Science.* New York: Science Press, 1913.

Rainio, K. A Stochastic Theory of Social Contacts. *Transactions of the Westermarck Society*, Vol. VIII. Munksgaard, 1962.

Rasch, G. *Studies in Mathematical Psychology. I. Probabilistic Models for Some Intelligence and Attainment Tests.* Copenhagen, Denmark: Nielsen and Lydiche, 1960.

Richardson, L. F. *Arms and Insecurity.* Pittsburgh: Boxwood Press, 1960.

Richardson, M. W. Multidimensional Psychophysics. *Psychological Bulletin*, **35,** 1938, 659–660.

Rosen, V. H. On Mathematical Illumination and the Mathematical Thought Process. In *The Psychoanalytic Study of the Child*, **8,** 1953, 127–154. New York: International Universities Press, Inc.

Schiffman, H. *A Mathematical Model for Interpersonal Communication.* Doctoral dissertation, unpublished, Psychology Department, Princeton University, June 1960.

Shepard, R. N. The Analysis of Proximities: Multidimensional Scaling with an Unknown Distance Function. I. *Psychometrika*, **27,** 1962, 125–140. (a)

Shepard, R. N. The Analysis of Proximities: Multidimensional Scaling with an Unknown Distance Function. II. *Psychometrika*, **27,** 1962, 219–246. (b)

Sherif, M., and C. I. Hovland. *Social Judgment.* New Haven: Yale University Press, 1961.

Simon, H. A. *Models of Man.* New York: John Wiley & Sons, Inc., 1957.

Spearman, C. E. *Creative Mind.* London: Cambridge University Press. New York: Appleton-Century-Crofts, 1931.

Stein, M. I., and Shirley J. Heinze. *Creativity and the Individual.* New York: The Free Press of Glencoe, 1960.

Tannenbaum, P. H. Initial Attitude toward Source and Concept as Factors in Attitude Change through Communication. *Public Opinion Quarterly*, **20,** 1956, 413–425.

Thurstone, L. L. *The Nature of Intelligence.* New York: Harcourt, Brace & World, Inc., 1924.

Thurstone, L. L. A Law of Comparative Judgment. *Psychological Review*, **34,** 1927, 273–286.

Thurstone, L. L. An Experimental Study of Nationality Preferences. *Journal of General Psychology*, **1,** 1928, 405–425. (a)

Thurstone, L. L. Attitudes Can Be Measured. *American Journal of Sociology*, **33,** 1928, 529–554. (b)

Thurstone, L. L. Theory of Attitude Measurement. *Psychological Review*, **36,** 1929, 222–241.

Thurstone, L. L. The Measurement of Social Attitudes. *Journal of Abnormal and Social Psychology*, **26,** 1931, 249–269. (a)

Thurstone, L. L. Multiple Factor Analysis. *Psychological Review*, **38,** 1931, 406–427. (b)

Thurstone, L. L. *A Simplified Multiple Factor Method and an Outline of the Computations.* Chicago: University of Chicago Bookstore, 1933. (a)

Thurstone, L. L. *The Theory of Multiple Factors.* Chicago: Author, 1933. (b)

Thurstone, L. L. *The Vectors of Mind.* Chicago: University of Chicago Press, 1935.

Thurstone, L. L. *Multiple-Factor Analysis.* Chicago: University of Chicago Press, 1947.

Thurstone, L. L. Creative Talent. *Proceedings of the Invitational Conference on Testing Problems.* Princeton, N. J.: Educational Testing Service, 1950.

Thurstone, L. L. *The Measurement of Values.* Chicago: University of Chicago Press, 1959.

Thurstone, L. L., and E. J. Chave. *The Measurement of Attitude.* Chicago: University of Chicago Press, 1929.

Thurstone, L. L., and L. V. Jones. The Rational Origin for Measuring Subjective Values. In Thurstone, L. L., ed., *The Measurement of Values.* Chicago: University of Chicago Press, 1959.

Torgerson, W. S. Multidimensional Scaling: I. Theory and Method. *Psychometrika*, **17,** 1952, 401–419.

Torgerson, W. S. *Theory and Methods of Scaling.* New York: John Wiley & Sons, Inc., 1958.

Torrance, E. P. Explorations in Creative Thinking in the Early School Years: A Progress Report. In Taylor, C. W., ed., *The Third (1959) University of Utah Research Conference on the Identification of Creative Scientific Talent.* Salt Lake City: University of Utah Press, 1959.

Tucker, L. R. Description of Paired Comparison Preference Judgments by a Multidimensional Vector Model. *Research Memorandum* 55–7. Princeton, N. J.: Educational Testing Service, 1955. (Multilithed report.)

Tucker, L. R. Factor Analysis of Double Centered Score Matrices. *Research Memorandum* 56–3. Princeton, N. J.: Educational Testing Service, 1956. (Multilithed report.)

Tucker, L. R. Determination of a Functional Relationship by Factor Analysis. *Psychometrika*, **23,** 1958, 19–23.

Tucker, L. R. Dimensions of Preference. *Research Memorandum* 60–7. Princeton, N. J.: Educational Testing Service, 1960. (Multilithed report.) (a)

Tucker, L. R. Intra-Individual and Inter-Individual Multidimensionality. In Gulliksen, H., and S. Messick, eds., *Psychological Scaling: Theory and Applications.* New York: John Wiley & Sons, Inc., 1960. (b)

Tucker, L. R. Systematic Differences between Individuals in Perceptual Judgments. (To appear in Bryan, G., and M. Shelly, *Human Judgments and Optimality.* New York: John Wiley & Sons, Inc., 1963, in press.)

Vinacke, W. E. *The Psychology of Thinking*, 1st ed. New York: McGraw-Hill Book Company, Inc., 1952.

Wallas, G. *The Art of Thought*. New York: Harcourt, Brace & World, Inc., 1926.

Woodworth, R. S., and H. Schlosberg. *Experimental Psychology*, 2d ed. New York: Holt, Rinehart and Winston, Inc., 1954.

Young, G., and A. S. Householder. Discussion of a Set of Points in Terms of Their Mutual Distances. *Psychometrika*, **3,** 1938, 19–22.

Zimbardo, P. G. Involvement and Communication Discrepancy as Determinants of Opinion Conformity. *Journal of Abnormal and Social Psychology*, **60,** 1960, 86–94.

INDEX

Closure II factor, 170
Coefficient of reproducibility, 130
Coefficients, derived, 112, 123; derived transformed, 123; transformed derived, 112
Cognition, factor of, 166; theory of, 172
Cognition of relations, 173
Cohen, A. R., 142, 143
Cohesiveness, group, 154
Coleman, J. S., 67, 144, 154
Communication, mass, 142, 154, 156
Communicator, persuasive, 153
Community controversy, 143, 154, 156
Compact matrix, 145, 150, 151
Compact network, 145, 146, 149, 153, 154
Comparative judgment, model for, 44, 45, 47
Compatible transformation, 116
Complex roots, 145
Comprehension, verbal, 167
Computer simulation, 156, 159
Concept formation experiment, 49
Conditional proximity data, 48
Conditional proximity matrix, 43, 48, 49, 51, 52, 59; analysis of, 49–58
Conjoint distances, 46
Contact frequency, 147
Contact frequency matrix, 147
Contact network, 153
Contact, social, 143
Controversy, attitude, 142; community, 143, 154, 156
Conversational connections, network of, 156
Coombs, Clyde H., 42, 47, 54
Coombs' theory of data, 42, 58
Core matrix, 115–117, 122
Cornell University, 5
Correlates, eduction of, 172, 173
Correlation matrix, 49, 59
Covariance matrix, 59
Creation, stages of, 171
Creative thinking, 173; motivational and emotional sources of, 173
Creativity, and high intelligence, 172, 173; illumination stage of, 171, 172, 175; incubation stage of, 171, 172, 175; and IQ test scores, 173; preparation stage of, 171; and problem-solving, 166; stages of, 162; tests, 173; theory of, 162; Thurstone's theory of, 172, 174; verification stage of, 172
Cross-classification, three-way, 110; two-way, 110
Curiosity, 175
Data, conditional proximity, 48; observed, 110, 112, 113, 122; preferential choice, 46, 55; similarities, 45, 46; single stimulus, 45; stimulus comparison, 45; symmetric proximity, 48; theory of, 42, 58; three-way classification, 110; three-way cross-classification, 110; two-way classification, 110; two-way cross-classification, 110
Data matrix, binary, 132; three-dimensional, 110
Davies, A. F., 67

Deduction, 165
DeMontpellier, Gerard, 72
Depth mode, transformation in, 117
Derivational mode, 115, 116, 122–124; original, 116; transformed, 116
Derivational mode elements, 113
Derived coefficients, 112, 123
Derived transformed coefficients, 123
Detroit Area Study, 84
Dewey, John, 162
Diagonal matrix, 134, 137
Diagonal matrix of roots, 117, 146
Differential, semantic, 110
Differential equation, 143, 150
Difficulty, item, 130
Diffuse matrix, 145, 151
Diffuse network, 145, 150, 153, 154
Dimension, 110, 112
Directed graph, 145
Discrepancy, opinion, 154
Disjoint distances, 46
Distances, conjoint, 46; disjoint, 46; interpoint, 46, 47, 58, 63
Distribution of attitude positions, 48, 144
Distribution, equilibrium, 149, 154
Divergent-production, of semantic classes, 167; of symbolic systems, 167
Divergent-production factor, 166
Dominance matrix, 43–47, 49, 59
Double-centered matrix, 70
Double-mode matrix, 113, 115, 116, 119, 123
DuBois, P. H., 131
Dunkel, H. B., 71
Dyadic interaction, 152, 153, 158
Edison, Thomas A., 5, 166
Educational Testing Service, 62
Eduction of correlates, 172, 173
Edwards, Allen L., 20, 130
Eindhoven, J. E., 171, 172
Elaboration, 172
Entities, idealized, 115, 122; observed, 115, 122
Entropy, attitude, 146, 150, 153
Equation, differential, 143, 150; linear differential, 144–145
Equilibrium, 151, 154; attitude position, 147; distribution, 149, 154; distributions of attitudes, 145; network, 154; point, 144, 151, 154; stable, 145; unstable, 145
Evaluation, 165, 169
Expressional fluency, 167
Factor, ability to elaborate, 169; bipolar, 146, 149; circular triads, 81; Closure II, 170; divergent production, 166; g, 172; of cognition, 166; originality, 168, 169; redefinition, 169, 170; sensitivity to problems, 169
Factor analysis, 36–42, 55, 62, 63, 70, 110–129, 163; nonmetric, 59
Factor analytic model, three-mode, 115
Fagen, R. R., 145
Fatigue, 172
Fechner, Gustav Theodor, 11